Also from
Alastair Chisholm

ADAM-2

ALASTAIR CHISHOLM

nosy
crow

First published in the UK in 2021 by Nosy Crow Ltd
The Crow's Nest, 14 Baden Place,
Crosby Row, London SE1 1YW

Nosy Crow and associated logos are trademarks and/or registered
trademarks of Nosy Crow Ltd

Text © Alastair Chisholm, 2021
Cover and chapter opener illustrations © Dan Mumford, 2021

The right of Alastair Chisholm to be identified as the author of this
work has been asserted.

ISBN: 978 1 78800 610 1

A CIP catalogue record for this book is available from
the British Library

Printed and bound in Great Britain by Clays Ltd, Elcograf S.p.A.
Typeset by Tiger Media

Papers used by Nosy Crow are made from wood grown in
sustainable forests.

1 3 5 7 9 10 8 6 4 2

www.nosycrow.com

For Lois. Hello, sis!
A.C.

Adam

Adam woke up in the basement.

He lay in bed for a few seconds, blinking, then switched on his light and sat up. The basement was the same as always: quiet, tidy, with neat shelves of books and boxes, a table for working to one side. There were no windows, and the light hanging above him was harsh and white. Adam had hung coloured material and paper shapes around it to spread the light around the room and make it seem more like sunshine. The floor was concrete, and the walls. There was a door tucked in the corner, behind more boxes.

The alarm clock pinged, and he put out a hand to stop it. He sat for a few seconds, then swung his feet down to the floor, stood, and started his day.

Breakfast first, sitting at the little table. One table leg wobbled, and he frowned; he would need to repair it again. He sat over his plate and read a book, swinging his legs absently.

After breakfast, schoolwork. Adam cleared away the breakfast things and brought out a collection of ancient schoolbooks and jotters. The jotters were full of writing, down to the last corners of every page, smaller and smaller until he hadn't been able to squeeze in any more. There was no more paper, and that had been a problem, but in the end he'd started again at the first page and carefully traced over the words already written. It didn't really matter: his pencil had long since worn down to nothing, and now he only pretended to write, with a stick.

He read today's sections in his schoolbooks and traced over the words in his jotter. He made a point of sticking his tongue out slightly as he wrote. At break-time he played by himself, practising juggling and keepy-up with small stones. He was very good; he could keep three stones in the air using just his feet. He knew he could probably do more but three seemed like the right number.

During break-time, something new happened.

A very slight tremor shook the basement, almost too faint to notice, as if something had *clanged*, quite far away. Adam looked up and watched tiny spirals of dust fall from the ceiling. He made a note of the time: eleven-oh-three plus seven point zero-eight-two seconds, although he knew the way to say this was "around eleven o'clock". He waited for five minutes, but nothing else happened, so he returned to his work.

Then lunchtime, then speaking practice. At first it hadn't occurred to him to do this, and he'd been alarmed one day to realise he might forget how to talk. Now he practised once every day. Since a new thing had happened today, he talked to himself about that.

"What could have caused a tremor like that?" he asked himself.

He paused. "Perhaps two things falling together. Rocks, or buildings," he answered at last. "Nothing that affects me."

"Perhaps I should go and investigate."

This was an interesting idea. Adam considered it for a while.

"No," he said, finally. "I should stay here, like Father said."

He nodded. There. A conversation.

After speaking, playtime, with the toys. Not proper toys, of course, just things he'd found in the boxes on the shelves: pieces of old machinery, nuts and bolts; plastic and super-plastic shapes moulded to look like hip joints, or hands, or eyes; piles of ancient green circuit boards. He used them to make little models of cars, houses, people, and practised playing with them.

This was very difficult. He had to think about the people, and who they were, and what they would say. They didn't live in a basement, of course, but that meant he didn't really know *what* they did. He had to imagine things that weren't real. It was the hardest part of his day, and exhausting, but he carried on dutifully for two hours, making up conversations they might have about things he couldn't understand. Afterwards, he went back to bed for a rest.

Then chores: clearing the toys, sweeping up, checking the lights, carrying out repairs. He remembered where he had saved a tiny sliver of wood from the last pencil, and used it to stop the table wobbling, and felt pleased.

Then dinner time. For more speaking practice, he told the empty table about what he'd been doing, and how good he was getting at keepy-up, and how he'd fixed the wobbling table, and about the tremor that had happened at *around eleven o'clock* and had lasted for *about five seconds*. He smiled as he said it. It felt good to have something exciting to talk about.

Then he got ready for bed and laid out his storybook. The book was faded and very fragile, and he was careful not to tear its thin pages as he found his place. He laid it on the bed, open, and sat and listened as if someone were reading to him. Occasionally he smiled, or laughed, or frowned. After eight minutes and thirty-five seconds he sighed and closed the book.

"Goodnight," he said.

There was no response.

"I love you too," he said.

He turned to the wall behind his head and scratched a small, careful mark, and studied it for a few seconds. Then he switched off his light, closed his eyes and lay in the dark, listening to the tiny *ping-ping-ping* sound of the lamp as it cooled.

He slept.

Adam woke up in the basement.

He switched on his light and sat up; stopped the alarm when it rang, climbed out of bed, ate breakfast, did his schoolwork. At eleven-oh-three he looked up, wondering if there would be another tremor, but there wasn't. Lunch, speaking practice, playtime – today he pretended the little people had felt a tremor, and were very excited – then rest, then chores, then bedtime. He opened his book carefully at the next chapter and listened as nobody read it. Then he said goodnight, told the empty basement that he loved it too, scratched a mark, closed his eyes, and slept.

Adam woke up in the basement. There was no tremor. He mended a small tear in the lampshade and talked about it at dinner time. In the evening, he laid out the next chapter of the book and listened. Scratched a mark. Closed his eyes. Slept.

Adam woke up in the basement—
Something was different.
He lay, quietly blinking in the dark. It wasn't time for getting up yet, but he was awake because he had heard something. Something had *woken him up*. A banging noise, perhaps twenty metres away, seeming to come from somewhere out beyond the door. Banging, something breaking, and then a shuffling sound, coming nearer.
What should he do? Should he turn the light on? He wasn't sure. The light was for morning. He left it off and listened. The sound was just beyond the doorway now. Two sounds, he thought, distinct, little flutters of something, like, like…
Speaking. It was two people speaking to each other. Adam tried to process this but instead found himself

blinking again and again, apparently without his control. He sat up and waited.

There was a scratch at the door. The voices were right outside. Then a movement; he could see the door trembling. A metallic *click*, and the door opened. Just a crack; just until it pushed against a box piled against it. Light moved from behind it, two thin lances of light. The voices muttered again. "*Stuck,*" one of them said.

Then the door shuddered open, pushing the box out of the way, and two figures followed it. They pointed their lights around, but not at Adam, at first. He sat still and watched them in astonishment.

They were young. One was only twelve perhaps, the other a bit older. They wore clothes he didn't recognise, a mix of different colours patched together. Some of the material was plastic, some fur, and all battered and torn. The older one was taller, and moved more cautiously. The shorter figure's right hand glinted and Adam realised it was prosthetic, made of plastic and metal.

"Whoa," said the shorter one, pointing at shelves of machine parts. The light came from the artificial hand, Adam realised; it must have a torch built into it. "Look at this stash!"

"What about batteries?" muttered the other. This

one's voice was deeper, and more wary.

"Nothing yet. Hey, look!"

The torch played over the table in the corner where Adam had set out tomorrow's breakfast plates.

"What the hell?" The shorter one walked to the table and touched the plates. "This is weird. It's like someone was playing…" Then silence. Then: "Linden, look."

"What?"

"There's no dust on the plates."

The taller one, Linden, stopped looking and turned. "What?"

"There's no…" The shorter one swung her torch-hand around to point at the shelves and boxes. "It's weird. There's no dust anywhere. It's like—" Then, in a gasp: "Someone's *cleaned* this room! Linden, someone's *been* here!"

The one called Linden stepped across quickly. "Don't move, Runa! Don't go any further!" Torchlight flickered over the table, the walls, the shelves …

… and over Adam, sitting in bed.

"Hello," said Adam.

"Aargh!"

"Run!" They crashed back towards the door. "Move! Runa, *move!*"

Adam stared after them. This was all very confusing.

He tried to think what to say, but he wasn't sure what the situation was. Were they guests? That didn't seem right.

"Here's the door, go, go!"

"Stop!" he tried. "Hello?"

The taller one held the door open. The younger one, Runa, started through, then stopped. The torch-hand pointed back over Adam.

"What *is* it?"

"Who cares? Go!"

But Runa hesitated, then stepped carefully towards Adam, slipping away from the other's grasp.

"Runa, come *back*!"

Torchlight shone again over Adam's face.

"Look at it."

"I can *see* it!"

"Did it just speak to us? Was it talking?"

"Yes," said Adam. "Hello."

"Aargh! Runa, come *on*!"

But Runa still didn't move.

"My name is Adam," said Adam. "Are you friends of Father?"

"Oh, wow." Runa's voice sounded scared, but also surprised. "Can you understand us?"

"Yes," said Adam. "You are Runa. Your friend is Linden. I am Adam."

Runa laughed suddenly. "Oh, *wow*. Linden, look at this! Look at it!"

Linden hesitated at the door, then cursed and came back. "I see it." Torchlight shone straight into Adam's eyes. "I see it."

"What do you think it is?" asked Runa.

"You *know* what it is," growled Linden. "It's *dangerous*. It's tin. It's a Funk."

They moved closer, keeping their torches on Adam until they were only a few centimetres away from his face.

"It's a *robot*."

"Hello," tried Adam again.

Linden

"I don't think it's a Funk," said Runa, peering at it. "It's got a face, look."

Linden scowled. It was true; the thing had eyes like models of human ones, with fake irises that contracted in the torchlight, and a mouth with white plastic teeth and metal lips. Just a slight bump for a nose, and microphones for ears; it looked like a metal and plastic skull. The eyes shone white and blue, and had weird fake eyebrows.

It was incredibly creepy. The sides of its lips were lifted as if it was pretending to smile. It made Linden's skin crawl.

"Don't get so close," growled Linden.

Runa tapped its forehead, and the fake eyelids flicked. The finger of her prosthetic hand made a *dink* sound.

"Hello," the thing said again. Its voice was creepy, too – almost human, a little scratchy, but like a human boy. It was very calm. With a shudder, Linden realised it even had a fake tongue.

"Leave it, Runa."

But Runa didn't move. "I don't think it's a Funk," she said again. Her face was fixed into the stubborn, fascinated expression that Linden recognised and dreaded. Carefully, trying not to be too obvious, Linden reached into a back pocket and took hold of their one working EMP stick.

The thing's body was pale white plastic, with dull metal "bones" peeking out as if from a half-decayed corpse. It was smaller than Runa, but its metal legs and arms seemed powerful and dangerous.

"What are you, little thing?" asked Runa.

"I am Adam version two point zero, a prototype experimental artificial entity." One arm lifted, and Linden stiffened, but its hand only reached out as if waiting to shake.

"Runa—" warned Linden.

Runa laughed and shook the hand. "Hello, Adam. I'm Runa."

"Yes," it said. "You are Runa. You are a human female." It turned towards Linden. "You are Linden. You are a human female—"

"No I'm not," snapped Linden.

The machine's eyes moved horribly, blinking. "Your

bone structure suggests—"

"Linden's non-binary," said Runa. "NB, enby, yes? No defined gender. Do you know what that means?"

"Of course," it said. "Linden is neither male nor female." It turned towards Linden and its eyes seemed to roll, white and stark inside its sockets. "Which pronouns would you prefer me to use?"

Linden glowered, but Runa said, "Ze instead of he or she, and hir instead of his or her."

"Of course," it said again.

"*Enough*," said Linden. "Right, you've had a look, now we *go*, Runa. There's no food here, OK? Just this … *thing*."

"What is a Funk?" it asked.

"A machine with Functional Consciousness," said Runa. "A thinking machine. A *robot*."

"Ah," said the thing. It paused. "Yes. I am a Funk."

Linden swung hir EMP stick around, jammed it against the plastic face and pulled the trigger.

Runa leaped back with a shout. The thing shrieked, high and piercing, and its teeth clamped together, blue sparks firing up around its skull and body.

"Eeeeeeeeeeeee—" it screamed, then stopped dead. A faint trail of smoke spiralled out lazily from its mouth, and there was a sudden sharp smell of burning plastic.

13

Runa gasped. "Linden! What have you done? You *broke* it!"

"You heard what it said!" snapped Linden. "It was a *Funk*. Now come *on* – we've got to get out of here before its friends arrive!"

The thing slumped to one side and smacked against a clock on a table next to it, smashing it into pieces of ancient, brittle plastic.

"It wasn't anything *like* the Funks!" shouted Runa. "It was something else, and we could have used it!" She peered down at it. "It must have had power," she said, suddenly, and tapped the metal platform underneath it. "This is a charging station."

"So what? Come *on*!"

But Runa still had that face on, and she ignored Linden. "There's a switch here," she muttered. She clicked it.

Lights came on in the room, and Runa and Linden stared.

The light had an odd colour, not white. A strange plastic shade over the lamp created orange patches and weird shadows. In the light, they could see the wall behind the thing. It was covered in scratches.

It was *covered* in scratches.

Thousands… *Tens* of thousands of them. Every fifth scratch formed a line through the previous four.

"Did it make these?" muttered Runa. "How long has it *been* here?"

Linden glanced around. There was the table, laid with a chipped bowl and plate, and a spoon. Shelves against one wall held ancient and decaying boxes, and a few books. There was some sort of repair system in the corner.

"I don't know," ze said. "Runa, we're getting out of here *now*, understand?"

The thing screamed. "Eeeeeeeee!"

"Argh!" Runa and Linden jumped away. Lights came on in the back of the robot's neck, and it raised itself back into a sitting position.

"Eeeeeeeee!"

"Run!"

"Eeeeeeee-hello, my name is Adam. Please wait. Hello."

They stopped again at the door and stared back. The thing looked at them. "Hello, Runa. Hello, Linden. I'm sorry; I have experienced a temporary system error. I believe it was when you touched me with that device. What was it?"

Runa and Linden gaped at him.

"E ... EMP stick," said Runa at last. "Electromagnetic Pulse. It, ah, disrupts your electrical systems and neural paths."

"Ah," said the thing. It moved its head from side to side, as if considering this.

"It should have killed you," said Runa, faintly.

The thing blinked. "Ah."

It stood up. Linden cursed; that was their only EMP stick. Could they outrun it? But you couldn't outrun Funks. Hir heart thumped. *Oh, no, oh, no, oh, no.*

It didn't move towards them. It seemed to be thinking.

"I'm sorry," it said at last. "I believe I have made a bad first impression."

Runa and Linden stared at it. There was a long pause, and eventually Runa pointed at the wall.

"Those scratches," she said. "Did you make them?"

"Yes."

"Why?"

Its head swung to look at the wall and back. "I don't know." It seemed slightly surprised.

"How long… How long have you been here?"

The machine's lips curled up into another grotesque smile.

"Two hundred and forty-three years, eight months, six days, nine hours and fifty-one minutes," it said.

Linden's mouth fell open.

"No *way*," gasped Runa.

Its eyebrows lifted. "Yes … way?" it said.

*

Runa's logic was maddening. "Look, if it wanted to kill us, it could, right? We can't run fast enough, and you used up our EMP stick."

"I do not want to kill you," said the machine.

"Shut up," said Linden.

"This thing is older than the war," said Runa. "I think it's older than the *Funks*. I bet it knows useful stuff!"

"Like what?"

"Like … things lost in the war. Maybe old maps. Maybe power supplies. *And* it survived an EMP blast – that's pretty impressive, right?"

"That's not a good thing!" snapped Linden.

"No – but imagine if the Funks got it. Imagine if they took it, instead of us."

"Then we should destroy it, so *no one* has it!"

"And how do we do that?" The angrier Linden became, the calmer Runa was in response. She was so tranquil now that Linden wanted to slap her. "It's two hundred and fifty years old and it looks pretty healthy to me."

"I am constantly self-repairing," said the thing, as if trying to help.

"Shut *up*," hissed Linden. Ze turned to Runa. "You can't trust it. It's a Funk. I don't care if it's an old Funk, it's a *Funk*, and it will be on *their side*. If we take it back, it

17

will kill us all!"

"I will not," it said.

"Shut *UP!*"

The little robot's eyebrows lifted, and its eyes glowed. "Killing is *very bad*," it said. "Father taught me that."

Runa frowned. "Father?"

"Father made me. He made me and taught me how to be a good boy. I have been practising."

"Where's Father now?"

"I don't know. Father moved me down here while he worked on the next version of Adam."

"Oh…" said Runa. "Oh, *wow*."

Linden's lip curled. "You don't have a father," ze sneered. "You're a *thing*."

"Yes," it said.

Linden shook hir head. "Enough. We've spent too long here; it'll be dawn soon. And we can't take it with us – it's too dangerous."

"But, *Linden*—"

"Fine!" snapped Linden. "I'll tell Callum about it, OK? When we get back I'll tell him, see what he says. OK?"

"But it might be gone before we get back!"

"It's been here over two hundred years; it's not going anywhere! Look—" Linden pointed the defunct EMP stick at it. "You – stay here. Understand?"

18

It stared back. Its eyes glowed.

"I understand."

Linden turned back to Runa. "OK? Now let's *go*."

Runa's face was sour, but she nodded. She gave the machine a last wistful look and turned to leave. Linden followed, walking backwards to keep it in sight. It didn't move. They left, and Linden slammed the door shut and blew out a breath of shaky stress.

"Come on," ze said. "We have to hurry."

The corridor outside the little basement was pitch-black and thick with dust, and their torches seemed thin and weak. They passed a hatch on the outer wall, but there wasn't time to investigate; instead they found the staircase at the end of the corridor and started to climb.

This building, like many others, was built like a tower inside a protective shell, with stairs curling round in the gap between, and the basement underneath. A crack had recently opened in the outer shell – this was how Linden and Runa had got in. But the tower inside was still tight shut and completely impregnable. They'd climbed all the way to the top and then down, and found no way to access anywhere, except the basement.

Coming down, they'd crept like thieves, treading as softly as possible, but now they moved faster, though the metal stairs clanged like alarm bells with every step.

Soon it would be dawn, and the first patrols would be out.

"Nearly there," Linden muttered, and Runa nodded, panting. Nearly there. They came round the last corner, to where the crack had opened in the outer wall. Runa gasped in relief, leaning against the inner wall, and Linden uncurled hir grappling hook. From here it was a rope-climb down the outside of the shell, and then home.

"Are you really going to tell Callum?" Runa asked.

Linden shrugged. "I said I would, didn't I?"

"Do you think he'll let us come back for it?"

"Don't know. Ready? Here—"

A hand reached in through the crack and grabbed the arm of Linden's sleeve.

"*Argh!*"

The hand was metal, once silver and now scratched and chipped, its grip fierce. Beyond it, Linden looked up in horror at the shape on the outside of the wall, reaching in.

"*Funk!* It's a *Funk!*" ze shouted. One huge red eye glared at hir though the crack as ze tried to shake hirself loose. "*Help!*"

Runa heaved at Linden and the sleeve tore loose, and ze scrambled away. The hand dropped the scrap of material and retreated. The eye still glared.

"It's a Clunker!" shouted Runa. "It's too big to get in!"

The eye moved back a little. There was a *crash*. And then another, and dust around them. In horror, Linden realised it was punching the wall, opening the crack wider.

"Run!" ze roared.

"Up or down?"

Linden blinked. The Clunker's enormous fists slammed into the wall again and again, remorseless. There was no way out, nowhere to go. Up or down?

"There was a hatch, near the bottom!" ze shouted. "Down!"

They raced down the stairs two at a time, hearing the enormous, pounding clatter as bricks and concrete collapsed. Two floors down, three, four… As they neared the bottom there was another crash, and the metal steps shuddered. The Clunker was through. Without pausing, it stomped downwards after them, shaking the staircase with every step.

"Hurry!" Linden shouted.

Runa skidded round the last corner and stopped suddenly. Linden collided into her.

"Keep going!"

But Runa didn't move. Linden looked up.

The Adam robot stood in front of them, in the middle of the corridor. Its metal face was charred from the EMP blast, tiny wisps of smoke still escaping from it. Its eyes glowed, and its lips bent upwards into a leer.

"Hello again," it said.

Outside

Adam

Adam wasn't sure what to do.

The angry human, Linden, had pointed the Bad Stick at him and told him to stay, and Adam knew that good boys did what they were told. Also, he didn't like the Bad Stick – the *EMP* stick, the friendly one had called it. When the angry human had touched him with it, all his sensors had reported crazy signals at once. It had … hurt.

But he didn't know what to do instead. It was still night-time – should he go back to bed? He looked at the smashed alarm clock on the bedside table. That was a problem. Adam always got up after the alarm clock went off. If the alarm clock didn't go off, he couldn't get up. Perhaps he could repair the alarm clock? But Repairing Time was after Lunch. And Lunch was after

Schoolwork, which was after Breakfast, which was after Getting Up … which was after the alarm clock went off.

He picked up the pieces of the clock and stared at them, then at the wall behind the bed, and the scratches he'd made there. The friendly human had asked him about them. Now Adam asked himself, "Why do you make the scratches?"

"They tell me how long I've been here," he answered.

"But you know that," he said. "Your internal clock tells you."

He shook his head. It was a mystery. Just like the humans themselves. And what they meant by the things they said, about "tin", and "Funks". Adam was sure he'd been polite and friendly, just like Father had taught him, but the angry human had hurt him. He replayed their conversation and realised: perhaps the angry human wasn't angry, but *scared*. That was interesting.

"Why was the Linden human scared?" he asked himself. After a long time, he said, "Maybe I should ask hir?"

"But Father said to stay in the basement," he answered himself.

"Yes." He nodded. "But Father also said I should help people. If Linden was scared, I should help."

"But helping means – means leaving the…" He

24

stopped. "Helping means leaving the basement," he said in a rush, and felt a strange prickling across his sensors, as if they had all suddenly become much more sensitive. They *crackled*. It wasn't a nice feeling... But it wasn't a *hurting* feeling either. And it wasn't ... altogether ... bad?

"Helping means leaving the basement," he said again. "I should *leave the basement*."

The scratches on the wall looked back at him. "Yes."

He walked to the door and opened it. It was as dark outside as in, but Adam's night vision was good enough to see the corridor leading away. He remembered walking down here before, with Father. Linden and Runa's footprints showed in the dust.

"Hello?" he called. From above, he heard a faint crash. "Runa? Linden?"

He was still standing in the doorway. After a few seconds, he took a step.

There. He was outside the basement. Nothing happened, so he walked towards the staircase. It was clanging; someone was coming down, very quickly. Was it the humans, again? What should he do?

He should make sure they liked him this time. Perhaps he hadn't smiled correctly, before? He practised, and realised that someone had reached the bottom just as the girl Runa hurtled round the steps and saw him.

"Argh!" she shrieked. The older human, Linden, came round, too, and crashed into Runa.

"Keep going!" ze shouted, then looked up and saw Adam, and stopped.

Adam gave his widest, friendliest smile. "Hello again," he said.

The one named Linden recoiled. Ze pointed the EMP stick at him and he flinched. "Don't move!"

Adam didn't know how to respond. "Hello," he said again, although that didn't seem to be working. The human Linden held a torch in hir other hand and swept it over the wall next to him, at the emergency exit hatch.

"Get away from there!" ze snapped.

Adam hesitated. "You said not to move," he said. "Should I move now?" Was there a problem with his smile? he wondered. Were the lips not working? The stairs were still clanging. "Is someone else coming?"

Linden stabbed the EMP stick towards Adam. "*MOVE!*"

Adam moved back. The other one, Runa, ran to the hatch and scrabbled at its edges.

"I can't open it!" she shouted. Her hands swept dust off the surface and found a blank side panel. "There's a security lock!"

"Who else is coming?" asked Adam, interested.

"Can you work it?" said Linden, ignoring him.

"Not without power!" Runa searched her pockets, pulled out a small device, and waved it over the panel. "It's completely dead!"

"You seem upset," Adam tried. "Can I help?"

Linden turned and faced back up the stairs, holding the EMP stick ready. Adam attempted to make sense of what was going on.

"Is there…" He stopped. "Is someone bad coming? Hello? What is happening, please?"

Runa frowned and bit her lip and looked at him.

"Power…" she muttered. "*Power.* You— Can you power this hatch panel?"

Adam studied the panel. "Yes," he said. "Why?"

"Do it!"

He shrugged. It was an odd request, but he'd come out to help, so he placed his palm over the panel's power port and transferred some charge across. The panel blinked and lit up green, and gave a small beep.

"This is the emergency exit," said Adam, helpfully. He remembered what Father had said. "You should only use it in emergencies. The Emergency Exit Is Not A Toy."

Runa ignored him. Her fingers danced over the panel, activating codes and sequences.

"I've got it!" she shouted.

"Hurry!" snapped Linden. "It's nearly here!"

"What's nearly here?" asked Adam.

The hatch opened. Runa peered inside. "Is it safe?" she asked.

Linden ran back from the staircase and looked down. "I'll go first," ze said, panting. "Five seconds, then you, OK?"

Linden lifted hirself into the hatchway and jumped down. Runa counted seconds – but before she reached five, something else crashed to the bottom of the stairs and round the corner, and faced them.

Adam stared. It was a huge robot, two point five metres tall with broad shoulders and a short, squat head, and a single red glowing eye. It was made of some sort of silvery metal that was bright in places but battered with age. It held a huge lump of concrete in one enormous paw. It scanned the corridor and saw them.

Adam smiled. "Hello," he said. "My name is Adam."

The robot threw the concrete lump straight at Runa's head.

Runa squealed and ducked, but Adam stepped in front of her, braced his feet and caught the lump. It was heavy, and fast, but he had calculated its trajectory and absorbed the impact with a backwards step.

"Is this a game?" he asked, puzzled. "It seems quite dangerous. I think you could have hurt Runa."

The robot stopped. Its red eye scanned Adam as if surprised.

"Come on!" shouted Runa. She jumped into the hatch, and the huge robot lumbered towards her, but too slowly – she disappeared down after Linden. At the last moment, she reached back, grabbed Adam, and hoisted him down with her.

They tumbled down a chute. Behind them, the robot's head appeared at the hatchway, its red eye glaring, far too large to follow them. Runa was screaming. Was she hurt? Where was this chute going? It was very fast. It was very fast!

"What is happening?" he had time to shout, before the chute suddenly levelled off and they were hurtling towards a green wall and Runa put her hands over her eyes and Adam braced for impact and they crashed into it—

—and stopped.

Adam looked around. The wall was covered in a soft material that had slowed their descent. It was foam, he thought, although over time it had hardened into half-solid blocks that had disintegrated into dust where they had hit. The dust hung in the air around them and Runa coughed.

"Woooo!" she shouted. She was grinning, still lying on her back. "That was *fun!*"

"Yes?" said Adam. He made a note: this, apparently, was *fun*.

"What's *that* doing here?" demanded a voice.

He looked up to see the unfriendly one, Linden, pointing hir EMP stick at him. "Did you follow us?"

"No—"

"I brought it," said Runa. She stood up and dusted herself off.

"I told you to *leave it*—" started Linden.

"If we'd left it, the Funks would've got it," said Runa. "And they'd find out that EMP doesn't kill it, and they'd integrate its technology into theirs. I had no choice. And neither do you – we all know your stick is empty." She sneezed. "Besides, it just saved our lives, powering the hatch. *And* it caught a lump of concrete aimed at my head."

"You are mistaken," said Adam, frowning. "A robot would not try to harm a human. This must be a misunderstanding—"

"Shut up," snapped Linden.

Adam stopped. Everything was so confusing. Why

was the human Linden still angry with him? Why would humans think robots could harm them?

"We have to go," said Linden, and Runa nodded.

They were in a tiny bunker, with a hatch in the roof. Linden counted to three, pushed the hatch open quickly and glanced around, and then let it close again.

"All clear," ze said. "Ready?"

"Ready."

"Go." Linden pushed the hatch open again and leaped out, and Runa after hir. Adam didn't know what to do, so he followed them out...

Out, and into the world.

Adam knew that the tower where he and Father lived was in a city named Edinburgh, in a country named Scotland. He had maps and pictures of it in his memory stores, and once, on a summer's day, Father had taken him to the top of the tower and shown him the city for real. Adam remembered dazzling pale sunshine on a busy street, gardens and trees, houses of all different styles and ages, and in the centre a huge mass of ancient volcanic rock – Castle Rock, with mighty Edinburgh Castle on top. He remembered the feeling of wind on his face, and the sounds of the city – traffic, car and bus engines, trains leaving the station, the flittering toot of horns, the crash and clank of building sites, the hum of factories.

Now he stared. "Oh," he said. "What happened?"

"*Quiet*," hissed Linden.

Runa turned to him and put her finger to her lips.

Dawn was breaking, a red sky glowing to the east, and its light poured and pooled over the remains of the city.

Shattered houses; rubble, spikes of raw metal pointing at the sky; drifts of old material fluttering in the morning breeze. Everything was blackened and hollow, squares of empty windows with the glass blown out, weeds reclaiming the stones. Most of the buildings were either partly or wholly destroyed. The gardens were flooded. The castle walls were still intact, but within them a smooth metal dome covered the old castle buildings. Everything was silent.

Adam stared at the dome, and the flood lake, and the wreckage. His image-recognition systems stuttered as he tried to make sense of it. This wasn't the same city. How could this be the same city?

"This way," hissed Linden, and crept away. Adam followed. They were halfway up the side of a steep hill at the other end of the city centre from the castle. Further up the hill, on his left, he could see the tower where he had lived. From the outside, it still seemed quite strong, although its paintwork and decorations were chipped and faded to grey. There was a crack in the side.

Linden led them east for a while, and then south. They walked past broken houses, through collapsed blocks of flats, over decayed and overgrown roads. The sun rose quickly and lit the streets and buildings in pale yellow, but the world remained silent, other than the calls of birds and animals.

Adam walked with them, staring at everything.

"Where are the people?" he asked.

Runa frowned.

"Shut up," said Linden.

Linden seemed to be in charge. Ze stalked ahead, testing the ground and watching in all directions, choosing the route, and hir face was drawn into a constant scowl, as if angry, or afraid. The smaller one, Runa, followed without speaking. She was holding an old and cracked screen, and seemed to be scanning for something; occasionally she would look up and check around her, and nod. She looked serious too, but not as worried. Her lips moved as if she was chattering to herself.

Adam noticed their clothing again, the strange mix of plastic and fur sewn together, patched and repatched. They had backpacks too – battered things that had been repaired many times. Linden's held water canteens, blankets, knives strapped to the outside, and the pockets on Runa's pack bulged with circuit boards and odd bits of old technology.

They walked quickly, and soon the remains of houses started to thin out, as they left the city centre. The humans didn't say anything, but something changed in the way they walked – they stretched their shoulders, stood straighter, and seemed to relax. A little further on, Adam realised they were heading towards another ancient castle, on a hill south-east of the city. When they reached the hill, still half a kilometre from the city walls, Linden and Runa stopped.

"Put your hands up," said Runa. "Like this." She lifted her hands, and Adam copied her.

Nothing happened. Then, apparently from nowhere, seven humans stood up around them, holding long metal poles with EMP sticks fastened at the ends. Six of them pointed their sticks at Adam. The seventh figure, a tall, dark-skinned man with broad shoulders, stepped forward and glared at them.

"What's that." He spoke in a rough, flat voice, as if it wasn't a question.

"Callum, meet Adam," said Runa.

The man's eyes flickered to her face and then to Adam's. He stared as if memorising every detail.

"Hello," said Adam, hopefully, and tried another smile.

Keep

Linden

"We found it in the basement," said Linden.

Callum turned to hir, one eyebrow raised.

"It's not like the others," said Runa. "It saved us from a Clunker! And it's *really* old; I think it's from before——"

Callum lifted a hand, and Runa fell quiet. He gazed at Linden without expression.

"It … might be true," admitted Linden. "It did seem different."

"And there's something else," said Runa, excited. "EMP doesn't kill it – Linden zapped it, and it fritzed, but then *it woke up again*."

Everyone stiffened. The guards looked at each other nervously, but Callum's face didn't change. He studied the thing as if memorising it. It was still making its horrible leering smile, looking from person to person, and Linden had a sudden, disturbing thought – what if this was a trick? A plot to sneak this thing into Keep, to spy on them?

No. No, that was too devious for Funks. Funks were – generally – bigger, stronger, faster and tougher than any human who had ever lived, but they had two big weaknesses: they were stupid, and EMP killed them.

At least, until now…

Callum held up a collar and showed it to the thing.

"Put this on round your neck." He threw it, and the thing caught it in one bony metal hand.

It considered it as if curious. "Why?"

"Do it," snapped Callum.

The robot peered at him, its white eyeballs rolling, then fastened the collar round its neck. It locked into place.

"The collar contains an EMP charge," said Callum. "If you try to escape, or harm anyone, it will activate."

The thing's eyebrows moved into a frown. "But—"

"EMP might not kill you," Callum continued, "but apparently it does stun you – and then we'll dismantle you and destroy your core processor. Do you understand?"

"Yes, but I think there has been a mistake—"

"Take it to the pit," said Callum.

The guards prodded it with their staffs until it started walking up the hill, towards the outer gate. Linden, Runa and Callum followed.

The gate guards nodded to Linden and Runa as they passed through, and Runa waved back, and then they were in Keep, and Linden breathed a long sigh of relief. It was good to be back. Campfires burned and ze smelled food cooking, and hir stomach rumbled. Ahead of them, near Della's workshop, the robot and its keepers stood at the edge of the pit.

"I'm sorry," it was saying, in its creepy little-boy voice. "I don't understand what is happening. Can you tell me?"

Callum pointed to a low wire fence surrounding them. "This fence is now linked to your collar," he said. "If you step beyond it, the collar will activate. Understand?"

The thing looked at the fence, and then back to Callum. "Yes, but—"

The guards made a sudden, jabbing motion with their staffs and the robot stumbled, slipped, and fell into the pit with a metallic crash. Linden peered down. The robot, looking small and rather lost, stared up at hir from the bottom.

"Excuse me," it called. "I've fallen down."

Callum stepped back over the fence and walked away, and Linden followed him, through the inner gate and the busy courtyard, to Callum's office in the ancient stone castle. He sat behind his desk. Linden remained standing.

Commander Callum Dunbar's office was plain, and

functional, and severe. There was the desk, two chairs, a map on one wall, and a neat row of filing cabinets, and nothing else. The floor was plain stone, despite the cold, and there was nothing personal in the room. Linden had never seen it untidy, though papers came in and out in an endless stream: reports of Funk sightings, instructions for patrols, studies on defence and attack tactics, requisition orders… They entered a neat pile on one side of his desk and exited from another pile on the other side, and somehow he managed them all. He was never surprised. He never seemed to sleep. The Elders ruled over Keep, but Callum kept it safe. Now he leaned back and studied Linden.

"Tell me," he said.

"It's true, sir," said Linden. "I gave it a full zap with the stick. It seemed to die, but a few seconds later it restarted."

"Hmm." He frowned. "What else?"

"We couldn't get into the tower. That thing was in the basement. It claims… Well, it claims it's been there for over two hundred years."

He nodded. "Do you believe it?"

Linden hesitated. "Maybe. It's strange. There were marks on a wall…" Ze shook hir head. "I don't know, sir."

"Why does Runa call it 'Adam'?"

"That's what it called itself."

Callum looked out through the tiny slit in the wall that was his window. "It reminds me of something," he muttered. "That name... Two hundred years? If it's really that old, it could be useful."

"Yes, sir. Runa thought so, sir."

"Hmm. We'll see what Della says." He gave Linden a sharp look. "Can't have been easy for you."

Linden stiffened. "It's fine, sir."

"It's not fine," he murmured, and just for a moment his face and voice softened. "It's only been two months, Linden. She was your mother. It won't be fine. You're not Funk; you're human. Remember that."

Linden blinked, twice, and held hir breath. "Yes, sir," ze said, finally.

"I miss her too," Callum said.

Linden swallowed. "Is there anything else, sir?"

"No. Dismissed, soldier."

Linden headed towards the barracks, but Runa found hir before ze reached them.

"Hey!" she chirped, falling in next to Linden. "What'd Callum say?"

Linden grunted. "About what?"

"About *Adam*, of course!" She laughed.

Linden looked at her. They'd nearly died this morning, but Runa didn't seem bothered at all. Her eyes glinted bright at the thought of having another machine to tinker with.

"He says Della will know," said Linden.

"Imagine, being down there all that time!" said Runa. "The door wasn't even *locked*—"

"Hey, Halfy!" shouted a voice behind them.

Runa stiffened but didn't turn.

"Halfy! Heard you found a boyfriend, Halfy!" Runa's face turned red. She shrugged her right sleeve down, hiding her prosthetic hand.

"You get sparks, Halfy? Clang-clanging with your new tin friend, ha ha!"

Linden turned. Behind them, two boys from the farms were following, laughing — the Brodie brothers.

"You say something, pluke?" ze asked. When they recognised Linden their smiles dropped, but they didn't run.

"Ain't right," said the elder brother. "Everyone knows it. Tin-hand." He pointed at Runa's sleeve. "Half-human."

"C'mere and say that," said Linden, sweetly, and lunged suddenly towards them.

The boy stumbled backwards, tripped and fell, and Linden snorted.

"Come on," ze said to Runa.

Runa scowled, but ahead of them the outer gate

opened, and a figure emerged.

"Hey!" shouted Runa. "It's Della!" She brightened again and ran to the gate.

Della came through, chatting to the gate guards. She was so tall and thin that she loomed over them, even when leaning on her stick. Her silver hair flashed in the pale sunshine. When she saw Runa she gave a huge smile and flung her arms wide, and they hugged. Linden stood back and looked away.

"Della, we found something *awesome!*" shouted Runa.

"I heard," said Della. "A new kind of Funk, the guards say?" She limped towards her workshop, with Runa in tow.

"That's right!" chattered Runa. "And it's *weird*. And really old – hundreds of years!"

"That's what it claims," said Linden. "It could be lying."

"And it has a *name*," continued Runa. "It says it's called 'Adam'."

Della paused. "'Adam'," she murmured, her face blank. "Hmm." She thought for a few seconds.

"Is that important?" asked Linden.

Della continued towards the workshop. "Perhaps."

Adam

The pit was smaller than Adam's basement. It measured five metres by four point eight, which meant its area was exactly twenty-four square metres. Adam measured it out several times. He wasn't sure what else to do. There was no furniture: no bed, no table, no books.

But there were other things.

One was large, like the thing in Father's house that had chased them. A *Clunker*, the humans had called it. Its silver body was battered and dented, and one arm was missing. The other robot was smaller, though still taller than Adam, and thin, with a smooth silver outer body. They lay sprawled face down on the floor of the pit as if they had simply fallen down where they were and stopped. They both wore collars like Adam's. The younger human, Runa – she'd said that EMP should have killed Adam. Was that what had happened to these two?

They looked otherwise unharmed, as if they might suddenly get up again. Adam sat in a corner of the pit, as far away as he could get from either, and thought about this new world.

Nothing made sense!

There was running, and shouting, and fear, and the ruined city. The Linden human seemed to hate him, and he couldn't understand why. They thought the big robot wanted to kill them, but that couldn't be right, could it? And the tall man, Callum, with his fierce, flat voice. And what had happened to all the other people?

He stood up, then sat down again. He wasn't sure why. He wondered if he could climb out of the pit, but it was too deep, the sides too smooth. It was mid-morning; he should be doing schoolwork, but he didn't have his books or his jotter, or even a stick to pretend to write with. Every time he tried to concentrate, he found himself thinking about the schoolwork. Occasionally his hand moved as if writing, without him meaning to.

He stood up again. He sat down.

Through the top of the pit he could see a patch of blue, changing and shifting as clouds drifted across it. He watched that for a while, until lunchtime. There was no table to sit at. His arms twitched as if trying to lay the plates out. He stood up again.

"Stay still."

Adam stopped in surprise. The voice had come from behind him, and now a light flickered on.

"Turn round."

He turned. Behind him, the metal wall of the pit had slid back to reveal a room, protected by a clear plastic shield. The hostile human, Linden, stood at the back of the room. The friendly one, Runa, was there too, and Callum.

There was a desk, and behind it sat a tall woman with silver hair and very pale white skin, in a white shirt, a wooden walking stick leaning next to her. She was holding an old and battered device, pointing it at him. Her eyes flicked between Adam and the device.

"Hello," said Adam. He wondered whether to smile, but his smile didn't seem to help.

"My name is Della," said the woman. Her voice was precise and clipped. "State your identification."

"I am Adam version two point zero, a prototype experimental artificial entity."

The woman nodded. "The scans say it's old," she muttered. "Old enough to be real. And its design is... Well, I think it really might be."

She studied Adam. "What were you doing in the basement?"

"Father told me to stay there," he said. "I've been practising."

"Practising what?"

"Being a good boy."

Callum's mouth curved into something like an expression of disgust; Adam didn't know why. But Della stayed impassive.

"How long were you down there?"

"Two hundred and forty-three years, eight months, six days, nine hours and fifty-one minutes," said Adam.

She nodded again.

"What happened to the city?" he asked. "And the people?"

The woman lowered her device and considered him, resting her chin on one hand. She looked at him for a long time.

"You're a myth, Adam," she said at last. "You know that? You can't possibly exist." She drummed her fingers against the table. "Tell me," she said, "have you ever heard of a man named Galbraith?"

"No."

Della nodded, eyebrows raised. "Well, perhaps not. In some versions of the story he has different names – Daedalus, or Prometheus, Geppetto... But his real name was Galbraith. He was the greatest inventor the world has ever known. The smartest man who ever lived.

"And one day, he had a marvellous idea." The woman's lip curled. "He decided to create a *thinking machine*.

"Nobody had managed, until then. We had machines, but nothing with intelligence. He set out to make a robot that was like *us* – that could understand human instructions, solve problems...

"Many others had tried and failed, but Galbraith was a genius, and obsessed. He devoted his life to it, persisted for decades, until finally – astonishingly – he succeeded where no one else had.

"He built a machine that could think."

Della waved a hand, casually. "They weren't truly intelligent, really. Not like humans. But they were smart enough to function, and follow orders. He called them 'Functional Consciousness'. Funks.

"And then he showed it to the world, and then he made Funks for everyone."

She smiled. "It was glorious, they say. For a while. Funks did everything humans didn't want to. Cleaning, building, fetching ... war... There was a robot for everything. A new stage of human civilisation, a golden age, and Galbraith was its king."

She sighed. "And then, one day – about two hundred years ago – the Funks turned on their humans and tried to kill them all."

Adam started, and stared at Della. Her expression didn't change.

"It was the Day of Knives," she said, quietly. "When all the Funks, everywhere, tried to wipe us out, every one of us."

He opened his mouth, but no words came out.

Memories of the city replayed in his mind – all the houses destroyed, everything crumbling, nothing alive, nothing but ruin. Robots did this. Robots like him. *Robots*. It was impossible.

"They almost succeeded," Della said. "They were everywhere. We'd invited them into our homes; we *trusted* them. And they were stronger than us, and faster. But we fought back. We survived." She shrugged. "We've been surviving ever since."

"But… *Why*?" Adam shook his head. "Why would they do that?"

"You tell me."

"I can't," he said. "I don't understand. Killing is *bad*."

Della sniffed. "Hmm. Well." She sighed again, stood and picked up her device and turned away, leaning on her cane. "I'll review the results," she said. "But it seems genuine."

Callum nodded, and opened a door at the back of the little room.

"Are you going?" asked Adam.

"We might be able to hack their communication protocols," said Della, ignoring him. "If this is an early version, it might be unprotected."

"Excuse me?"

"I'll check the schematics," said Runa.

"Hello? Please!"

Della stopped at the doorway and looked back. "Those first attempts," she said, softly. "The failures, the … prototypes. In some versions of the story, Galbraith gave them names, you know.

"They say he called them 'Adam'."

Callum pressed a button and the wall of the pit slid back, and Adam was alone.

Problems

Adam

The collar kept Adam awake.

He lay on his back in one corner of the pit, his eyes shut, trying to enter normal sleep. His internal clock told him it was ten p.m., after the time he usually went into standby mode, and it was almost pitch-dark in the pit, but when he tried to relax, the collar round his neck nagged at him. It made a ragged whining sound that stuttered randomly, sending disrupting, wake-up signals instead.

He tried to ignore it, and thought about the day.

This new world was very confusing. Nothing was how it should be! The city was gone, and the humans were so scared, and *angry*. The smaller one, Runa, had been friendly enough, but the one called Linden seemed to hate him and he couldn't understand why. The leader,

Callum, had looked at him as if deciding whether to destroy him. Adam wondered: was his face-analysis processor faulty? It had been over two hundred years since he'd seen a human face – was he reading their expressions incorrectly? But he didn't think so. And these bizarre claims: of a world that was full of robots who wanted to *kill* humans! Impossible! And, strangest of all, Della, with her story... As if, somehow, they thought *Father* had caused this. But how could that be, when all Father had wanted was for Adam to be good?

Adam's body twitched as the collar hummed and buzzed. Perhaps it wasn't working properly, he thought. Perhaps it was about to go off by mistake. Adam didn't want another EMP blast. He thought he should ask someone, but there was no one to ask in the pit – no humans, just two dead robots.

This was all *wrong*.

The collar stuttered again, and Adam flinched. Wrong, wrong, *wrong*. Adam was a Good Boy and the humans had made a mistake. He shouldn't be in the pit. He should tell them. And he should tell them to take off this collar. Yes.

He stood up, feeling rather surprised at himself, but determined. Father had told him to stay in the basement, and he had, for such a long time. He had only left because the humans were in danger. If robots really were dangerous, then Adam had *saved* Runa and Linden. Yes. Now Callum had told him to stay in the pit – but Callum wasn't Father. And Adam…

Adam realised he didn't *have* to do what Callum told him.

That was very interesting.

He looked around the pit again. It was too smooth to climb out, the sides too hard to dig handholds into. It was too high to jump. He looked at the two broken robots. Then he walked, carefully, to the larger one, the *Clunker*, and examined it.

It was heavy, and rigid as if frozen. He lifted one end, but its feet skidded along the ground away from him. Adam dragged the smaller one next to the Clunker's feet and used it as a wedge. Now when he lifted the Clunker's head, its body didn't skid. Adam heaved it up, up into a standing position, and then a little further…

It tipped over and its head crashed against the side, wedging it against the pit wall at an angle. The sound seemed incredibly loud and Adam froze, waiting for someone to come, but there was nothing. Perhaps the sides of the pit stopped the noise from travelling. After a few moments, he climbed up the body of the Clunker, stood on its head, *leaped*, and grabbed the edge of the pit with one hand. He heaved himself up and out, and into the open air.

The camp was silent, and almost dark. He could see glimpses of movement on the walls – guards? Should he ask them? But then he realised there was a building quite close to the pit, with lights on inside. He'd seen it when the guards had brought him in – a repair shop, or workshop, with electrical equipment inside. Perhaps this was the best place.

A little electric fence ran round the pit. It would be easy to step over, but Callum had told him that if he did so, the collar would go off. As if to remind him, the collar stuttered again and he winced. Adam did *not* want the collar to go off.

He looked at the fence, and thought about what Callum had said, and had an idea.

Linden

"It's genuine," said Della. "And it's miraculous."

She was perched at a tall stool at her worktable, sitting on her hands with her knees raised; an odd, childish position that Linden thought made her look a little like an owl.

"How is it still functioning?" asked Callum. He stood

53

with his arms folded.

Della shrugged. "It's not exactly been doing much," she said. "And there was a repair station in the basement, apparently. The building still has power, probably a geothermal source, something that would have lasted all this time. It could have just kept existing."

"It all fits," said Runa, sitting on her little bunk in one corner of the workshop. She had dark circles under her eyes but seemed determined to stay awake with the others. "The stories all say that Galbraith came from round here, but moved away later. Looks like he just left Adam there, after he'd created the Funks."

"They're the same thing," snapped Linden. "This thing, the Funks, they're the same. They're the enemy no matter what they're called. We should destroy it."

Callum's mouth settled into a hard line. Linden knew he thought so too.

"They're not the same," said Della, mildly. "This one is *friendly*. Think about it — what if we could actually persuade it to help us? It knows about the old world. And it's kept itself alive for hundreds of years — it must be very good at repairs. It might be able to help us there, too." At that she and Callum shared a look. Linden didn't know what she meant, but it seemed important, and Callum's face became thoughtful.

"It did save us," said Runa again.

Linden scowled. "I don't want that thing anywhere near me," ze said. "It's a *Funk*. It will kill people, because that's what Funks do. That's what they *always* do."

The group fell silent. Runa gave Linden a sympathetic half-smile, and Linden scowled again.

Eventually, Della said, "They have to go back to that house, Callum."

He shook his head. "Too dangerous. The Elders didn't want them going the first time. They're furious that they brought that thing back; they won't sanction another mission."

"But it's *Galbraith's house*," insisted Della. "Think what could be there! Designs, analyses … parts…" Her eyes glittered greedily. "We *have* to get in there."

"*No*," said Callum. "Besides, there's no way in. Linden and Runa looked. No."

"I know how to get in," said a voice.

Linden spun. In the doorway stood the Adam robot. It looked different, bulkier, almost like a barrel, and for a terrified moment ze thought it was carrying a bomb. But, no – it was wire, wrapped round and round its body in loose coils. Linden and Callum whipped their recharged EMP sticks out and pointed them.

The thing stepped back hurriedly. "Sorry," it said. For

once it wasn't trying to smile.

"How did you get out," said Callum. His voice was flat, as it always was when he was most astonished.

"I climbed," said the thing. "I used the other two robots to help me up. Excuse me, can you help me with my collar? It seems—"

"But how did you get past the *fence*?" asked Runa, staring.

It shrugged. "I didn't." And now Linden realised – the wire was the fence itself, collected about its body in a tidy bundle. "I brought it with me." It looked up at Callum. "Is that all right? I wasn't sure what the rules were."

After a stunned moment, Della hopped from her perch and stepped towards it, leaning on her stick.

"It should have triggered when it lost power," she mused. The robot nodded and held up a hand. One of its fingers was plugged into the power socket of the fence's controller.

"I have power," it said. "Please, can you help me with my collar?"

Della stared at the fence wrapped round the thing's body, her eyes bright and inquisitive.

"That's … ingenious," she said at last. "Who taught you to do it?"

"No one," said the thing. Its eyebrows moved as if

pretending to be surprised. "I thought it up myself."

"Funks can't do that," said Runa. "Funks can't do *new* things. How did you do it?"

It rolled its eyes at her. "I don't know," it said. "I tried to imagine a thing that was different to what it was. Is that allowed?"

Now its lips curled up into the familiar leering smile. Linden glowered.

"It makes no sense," said Runa, shaking her head. "Funks can't think like that. But how can it be more advanced than them?"

"I don't know," said Della. Her eyes were still gleaming, and she had a trace of a smile on her lips. "But it is. Adam, do you realise that no Funk has ever worked out how to climb out of the pit? And certainly not how to get beyond the fence."

It blinked. "I'm not beyond the fence," it said. "Here it is, look." And it held the wires up.

Della *laughed*. "Indeed," she said. "So what do you want?"

"My collar is defective. I can feel it malfunctioning." Its smile stopped. "I don't want the EMP to activate, please."

"Why not? EMP doesn't kill you."

"It is ... painful," it said. "I do not like it. I do not like it *at all*."

Della looked at Callum and shrugged. "I'll take a look," she said.

"What *are* you?" growled Callum. He was still pointing his EMP stick at the robot. Linden too.

"I am Adam version two point zero, a prototype experimental artificial entity."

"And you claim you know how to get into the inner building."

"Oh, yes. There are two entrances. One is at the top, next to the helicopter landing area. The other is near the bottom, one floor above the basement."

"We didn't see any entrances," muttered Linden.

It stared at hir. "They are concealed."

Runa said, "If we knew where they were, we might be able to open them. *Maybe*. It was pretty secure."

"I believe I could open them," the robot said.

Linden watched in disbelief as Callum considered this. Surely he wasn't really going to trust this *thing*?

"It's worth the risk," said Della. "Early plans of the Funks … weaknesses, security codes…"

Callum shook his head. "The Elders—"

"Are *old*," snapped Della, dismissing them, although Linden knew that the Elders were, in fact, all younger than Della herself. "Old and over-cautious. And besides … why bother them?" Her tone became sly. "They're all asleep. We could be back by morning."

"'We'?"

Della nodded. "Damn right. If that building's got anything of Galbraith's, I want to see it."

Callum hesitated, and Linden gasped. "But you can't *trust* it!"

Callum looked at hir, and his face held that horrible, sympathetic expression that ze'd seen on every adult in the last two months. The one that said, without words: *we understand your grief. We know how it felt to lose your mother. We know how it felt to see her die. We know best.* "Linden—"

"No!" ze snapped. "*No*, sir! It's a Funk! Like all of the rest of them!"

"It's *not* like the rest of them," said Della, firmly. "But it might help us to *end* them. Do you understand, Linden? It might help us *destroy* them." She held Linden's gaze and wouldn't look away.

Callum chewed his lip. "Tonight. I can't keep it from the Elders tomorrow. And no one else is to be involved. Linden…" His face was grim, but determined. "Linden, you'll have to take them."

"Sir—"

"That's an *order*, soldier."

Linden said, defiantly, "I could wake the Elders." But Callum just looked at hir and said nothing, and after a while ze dropped hir head. "Yes, sir."

He nodded.

"I'll sort your collar first," said Della to the thing. "Runa, Linden, grab a couple of hours' sleep, then we'll take a little trip."

The robot nodded its head and Linden felt hir finger twitch on the EMP stick, as if aching to fire.

"Thank you," it said. "I like to help."

The Tower

Linden

Linden watched as Della fussed over Adam, tightening a screw at the side of its collar.

"The buzzing was a loose connection," she said. "Better now?"

It tipped its head from side to side, testing. "Yes," it said. "Thank you. But I would prefer it if you could remove it, please?"

"No," said Linden.

Della shrugged. "Sorry. We have to keep it on for safety."

It nodded. "I understand. So that you can punish me with great pain if I try to escape, or if I don't do what you want."

Della's face creased into a frown. She opened her mouth, but didn't seem to have an answer.

"It's not pain," snapped Linden. "You don't feel pain."

"I experience it as a highly unpleasant sensory overload, indicating an acute damage situation that must be avoided at all costs."

"That's not the *same*."

The robot frowned, as if puzzled. "How is it different?"

Linden hesitated. "Well…"

"Linden?" Callum stood at the doorway, holding a leather backpack. "A word, please. Outside."

Linden joined him. "Sir?"

Callum's face was sour, as if he was chewing something unpleasant. "I don't like this situation," he growled. "I'm only allowing it because that building – if it really is Galbraith's – is too dangerous to allow into Funk hands. Be careful."

"Yes, sir."

He nodded. "And afterwards…" He handed Linden the backpack. It was heavy; inside were four bars of ancient explosives, wrapped in clear plastic, plus fuses. "Destroy the building," he said.

Linden swallowed, and hir fingers tightened round the handle. "Yes, sir."

Inside, Della was unravelling fence wire from round the little robot's body. "Do you need to recharge?" she asked.

The robot shook its head. "In the basement I had a

charging station, but outside I can use solar." It tapped the pale white dome of its head. "I charged yesterday when we were walking back."

Della smiled. "You're a technological marvel, Adam."

Callum muttered, "Watch that thing, Linden. The Funks *must not* get their hands on it. Do whatever it takes – understand?"

Linden looked down again at the explosives. "Yes, sir."

They set off just after midnight. The pack felt strange on Linden's back. Explosives were incredibly scarce, impossible to produce, used only for great emergencies. For Callum to give hir *four bars*... Runa and Della were chirpy, excited, waving to the guards. The Adam robot walked next to them. Linden watched it, one hand on hir EMP stick, and felt the backpack bounce slightly against hir shoulders with every step.

Adam

They led Adam a different route this time, west round Arthur's Seat – the huge, ancient green crags on the edge of the city centre – and through an old tunnel, coming out into a forest. It was almost pitch-black, cloudy above, and the humans wore night-vision goggles.

Adam looked around. "This used to be parkland."

Runa shook her head. "Not for a long time."

There was a road between the trees, mostly overgrown but still passable, and they followed it out to a point at the bottom of two hills. To the west stretched the old High Street with the castle at the top and its strange metal dome; to the north, Adam's home.

"Time," muttered Linden, from behind.

"One fifty-eight now," said Runa. "Two minutes to shift end."

"What's happening?" asked Adam.

Della said, "There's a night patrol out, looking for humans. They always work the same schedule. Stay still and keep quiet."

Adam waited with the others. The world was quiet, except for a whisper of wind through the trees behind them, and a faint metallic *clat-clat-clat*, like someone tapping a small hammer, or—

Ahead of them, perhaps twenty metres away, six robots walked out between two buildings and on to the road.

They were human-like, adult-sized, quite slim, and, unlike Adam, whose grey metal bones were exposed, these were covered in a smooth, gleaming, silver skin. They had faces, but their expressions were blank and unmoving. Each carried a spear, long and silver like their bodies, and they walked together in perfect step, with such care that they were almost silent.

When they reached the middle of the road they stopped and, together, turned and stared at the humans. Beside him, Adam felt Runa stiffen, and just for a moment he had a sense of something, something like … dread? Danger signals told him he should run, back into the forest, get away! One second, two, three…

Then the robots turned away and walked up the hill towards the castle. After another minute, Runa nodded. "OK," she whispered. "We're clear."

"I don't understand," said Adam. "What just happened?"

Della tapped at a little badge on her jacket. "Infrared scrambler," she said. "It sends a fake signal, confuses them."

"But don't they have night vision as well? How could they not have seen us?"

"They did," said Della. "But at night, they use infrared. And even though their low-light sensors picked us up, they ignored us because the infrared said we weren't there." She shrugged. "They're stupid."

"Move," hissed Linden behind them.

Runa led them north, curling round and up a tiny path. It was a hard climb, and Della leaned more on her stick

65

with each step, but at last they reached the entry hatch, halfway up the hill, where Runa, Linden and Adam had emerged the previous day.

"Here," said Runa.

Inside was how they had left it – lumps of ancient padding lying broken on the floor, the chute leading up and inside.

Runa peered up into the chute. "Looks clear," she said. She pulled a pair of thick black gloves from her backpack and put them on. "Ready."

"Be careful," said Linden.

Runa just grinned and climbed into the chute. The gloves were magnetic; as Runa placed each hand against the chute, it gripped fast to the metal, only releasing as she peeled away. Carefully, using the gloves to pull and her rubber shoes to grip, she crawled up the chute and out of sight.

The others waited, listening to the metal chute clang and bump. For once, Adam noticed, Linden wasn't even watching him; ze peered up into the chute with a worried expression quite unlike hir normal fierce glare, biting hir lip. It seemed to take a very long time, so long that Adam wondered if his internal clock was running slow, but at last the clanging stopped. There was another pause – and then a clatter sounded down the chute, coming towards them faster and faster, and then—

A rope popped out of the end and hung there.

Linden breathed out. "You next, Della."

The old woman nodded and fastened a device to the rope; it was like a wheel, with a hand strap. She fastened her walking stick to her backpack, put one hand through the strap, and clicked a button. The device whined and slowly crawled up the rope, pulling her behind it.

"This is very undignified," she muttered, as it dragged her up and out of sight.

Linden said nothing, but waited until the whine stopped. "You."

As Adam stepped forward, Linden raised the EMP stick. "I'm watching you from below," ze said. "Runa's watching from above. Don't try anything."

Adam frowned. "I'm really not going to—"

"Move."

He took the rope and pulled himself hand over hand up to the top, where Runa and Della waited.

"That's it," said Runa. "Careful at the edge, it's jagged where the Clunker tried to get in." Her tone was light, but Adam noticed that one hand stayed near her belt, and Della was holding the remote for his collar. He climbed out and stood very still.

Linden followed, heaving hirself over the side. Once

over, ze pointed hir stick back at Adam. "OK. Get us inside."

Adam walked towards the staircase. "There is one entrance on the first floor," he said. "There is no outer door, but the inner door is still there, just hidden."

"Why have an inner door and no outer door?" asked Della. "Makes no sense."

"There didn't use to be an outside wall," said Adam. "Father said he had to add it for protection."

"Why?" Runa frowned. "The Funks didn't exist then."

"He said there were a lot of angry people," said Adam. "Angry and stupid, he said. I don't know who he meant." They reached the ground floor. "Here."

The inner wall before him seemed the same as everywhere else: large metal plates with thin grooves between them. Adam rested one hand at the top-right corner of one plate and felt a prickle of sensation as a scanner behind it activated.

"Is it working?" asked Runa.

There was a hiss, and the panel shuddered, stopped, then slid open.

It was dark inside, then lights blinked on, revealing a wide, empty hallway. It was dingy; the walls had once been cream but were now covered in dust, the floor grey, with a mottled patterned carpet underneath.

"What—" started Adam, but Runa held a finger to her lips. She seemed to be waiting for something, and after a few seconds there was a faint *beep*, and a voice spoke.

"Good evening," it said, in a vaguely female, vaguely mechanical voice. "Your identification is incomplete. Please identify yourself."

Runa smiled. "Hi. It's OK, I've got physical ID here: see?" She held up a small plastic card and pushed it into a reader just inside the door. "Try scanning this."

"Thank you. Please wait while— Please wa—" The card scanner beeped in a high, almost shrieking note, and then stopped. Runa whipped the card out quickly and Adam smelled a faint scent of burning plastic.

"Error. Error," said the voice. "Error, intruder systems deactivated. Error... Err ... or..."

It fell silent. Runa nodded in satisfaction.

"Right," said Della, stepping into the hallway. "Let's take a look, shall we?"

Runa followed. Linden waved hir EMP stick at Adam, and he stepped inside.

It was almost how he remembered it. The hallway led to an almost circular reception area. To the left was the main elevator, and to the right were doors that

Adam knew led into a small kitchen. A grand piano stood nearby, and pieces of art hung on the walls, in between screens shaped like windows. Lights glowed from recesses and candelabras, but everything was grey and ancient under thick, murky blankets of dust, and the screens were dark.

"Is it the same?" asked Della. "As when you were here?"

Adam ran one finger across the surface of the piano, leaving a single clean stroke, black and shimmering in the dim light. He nodded. "Yes."

"Good." Della looked around. "Where did Galbraith work?"

He gazed at the piano. The shine was mesmerising, somehow; as if he could see Father reflected in it.

"Adam?"

He looked up. "I'm sorry. Father— Galbraith, yes. There were workshops, next floor up."

"Are there stairs?" asked Linden.

Adam pointed to the doors. "Through there, beyond the kitchen," he said. "There's a service lift and stairs."

Linden walked towards the doors, holding a hand behind hir to keep the others back. Cautiously, holding the EMP stick in one hand, ze pushed one door open and peered beyond. Then ze waved them to follow.

"C'mon then. Let's get this over with."

The light in the kitchens was different, hard and white, throwing shadows up against the dust and glinting on old metal surfaces. Pots and pans hung on the walls. An ancient scrap of paper fluttered in the new air as they entered; otherwise, the room was still. Through the back was a battered-looking service lift, and beside it a narrow concrete staircase. They crept upwards and came out into the workshop.

"Bingo," whispered Runa.

The room was full of robots.

Robots in pieces. Robots assembled. Robots lying on their backs as if on operating tables, or hanging from chains from the ceiling. They weren't like Adam – they looked like the robots he'd seen outside, adult-sized, with smooth silver skin. But they were enough like him to seem familiar, and the ones that had been opened had grey rib bones like his. He stared. Like everything else in the room, they were covered in thick dust; but while the furniture was fixed, frozen, these figures seemed only asleep. As if, at any moment, they might wake again.

Della shook herself and coughed. "Right," she muttered. "Right." She tried again. "This is the place, then. Computer systems are fritzed, but the drives might still be accessible. Runa, take a look at the servers, see if there's a local backup. Let's see if we can get something working."

"No," said Linden.

Della turned in surprise. Linden's face was hard.

"You don't get anything working. Take data only, understand? Callum's orders. We don't wake *anything* up."

Della looked as if she was about to argue, but then her lips pursed and she nodded. It seemed that, away from Keep at least, Linden was in charge. "Hmmph. All right."

"Good. You have one hour."

"But—"

Linden held up a hand. "One hour, that's all we can risk." Ze turned to Adam. "You – come with me."

Red Sky

Linden

Linden left Della and Runa working and climbed further up the stairs, keeping the Adam robot in front where ze could watch it. The floor above was a testing area, with squares painted on the floor, and tables set up with puzzles and challenges. Above that was storage, boxes and shelves in all directions, then a living space – an open area with a bed and more screens. Finally, they reached the top entrance.

"What's out there?" ze asked.

"The helicopter pad," it said. "It's how Father used to come in and out."

Linden opened the door to a whoosh of icy winter air, and they stepped out and on to the roof of the building. With hir night goggles ze could see almost the whole city, but ze ignored it and kept watch, looking for movement around the building, keeping one hand near the EMP stick. Adam stayed to one side.

"If there was a war, why were there no nuclear bombs?"

"What?" Linden turned.

The robot was looking at the city. "Father said there were big bombs, nuclear bombs. They could destroy whole cities."

"Humans and Funks were all in the same places. If you nuked the Funks, you'd kill all the humans." Linden's jaw clenched. "They were in our homes. We trusted them. They told us they could help, and we let them into our houses, and we *trusted* them."

Its head tilted. "I know you don't trust me," it said. "But, I promise, I'm not like them."

"Of course you are! You're their *prototype*. They're what you become!"

It shook its head. "Even if that was true, it is not what I am. The way I was created is not what I am. Perhaps…" It stopped. Then it said, "Perhaps I am like you, Linden."

Linden blinked. "What?"

"Like you – there is a mismatch between what people thought I was, and what I know I am. Perhaps I am—"

"*What?*" Ze was suddenly blazing. "How *dare* you! How dare you suggest that! You and I are *nothing* alike! I'm a human being, I was born! I *live*! You're *tin*. You were *made*,

74

you're a *killer*, and what you are is *what you always are!*"

The thing stepped back, staring at the EMP stick that was, somehow, in Linden's hand, although ze didn't remember drawing it. Ze panted, not moving, hir finger on the trigger.

"I'm sorry," it said at last. "I did not mean to offend you."

"Stand over there," ze snapped, "and don't say another damned word."

It considered hir, with its grey, skull-like face, and then moved away. Linden, seething, forced hirself to look away and keep watch.

After a few minutes, it said, "Linden—"

"*What?*"

Ze turned again, ready to spit, but the robot was pointing towards the skyline. "I think there is something in the air."

Linden scowled, then aimed hir goggles. Nothing. No ... something? A flicker of steady movement, not natural, something...

"Red Sky," ze breathed. "Oh, *no.*"

"What is that?" asked the robot, but Linden ignored it and raced to the roof entrance, ripping off hir night goggles, clattering down the stairs as fast as ze could, leaping two, three steps at a time.

"Linden?" the thing called. "What is it?"

"Red Sky!" ze roared. "*Red Sky!*"

Down the stairs, one floor, two, down to the workshop, where Della and Runa were working at a desk computer near the centre. They looked up with surprise and, Linden thought, a guilty start, but ze ignored that.

"Red Sky!" ze shouted. "We have to go, now!"

Della's mouth fell open. But Runa was faster; she swept everything off the desk into her bag, including three or four storage drives, and was ready.

"But there's still so much—" started Della.

"*NOW!*" yelled Linden.

Runa dragged Della away.

"Excuse me," said the robot, its voice maddeningly calm. "What is happening, please?"

"We have to *go*," said Linden. Ze pulled off hir backpack, with the explosives inside. Was there time to set them?

"Come on!" shouted Runa, pulling Della towards the stairs, but then skidding to a halt. There was a noise ahead of them, an echoing metallic clang from the lift shaft next to the stairs. Then another, much closer.

"Wait," muttered Runa. "What's that—"

And then the lift doors smashed open, one flattened, one flying out and crashing to the ground ahead of Linden.

Adam

It was a robot, Adam realised.

It didn't look like the ones before. Its body wasn't smooth but made of angles and edges and straight lines, and it was painted a battered ancient red, worn off in places to reveal glimpses of grey. It looked industrial, heavy-duty. It hovered in the air of the lift shaft and Adam realised it had jets as well as legs; it could fly. It was holding a spear.

Della and Runa scrambled backwards, Runa reaching for her belt. The robot didn't pause but flung the spear towards her. Linden crashed into Runa and pushed her to the ground, and the spear whispered over them and into a bank of computers, sending up sparks. The robot reached behind it and fetched another spear, ready to throw.

"Stop!" shouted Adam.

It turned. It had a face, or the remains of one, a scarred visor and a grille for a mouth. It stared at Adam for a full second, as if expecting something. At last it said, "Identify."

Its speaker seemed damaged. The voice cracked, as

if it was speaking at both high and low pitches at the same time.

"Don't hurt them!" said Adam. "This is just a mistake, don't—"

"*Identify.*"

It lifted its spear as if about to throw it at Adam. To the side, Linden, Runa and Della pulled themselves away behind a large bank of servers.

"Adam! My name's Adam!"

It considered him for a moment longer, then turned towards the servers. The stairs door opened and another robot entered, this one silver, and a third appeared at the lift shaft. They followed the first one.

Adam moved in front of them and held his hands up. "Stop, please! Can we discuss this—"

"Heads up!" roared Runa. The three robots looked up and over Adam's head at something, and then there was a blinding jagged light, flickering with a pattern almost too fast to see, and they collapsed.

Adam felt stunned. The pattern of light was like a fire in his head, causing his processors to cascade into feedback loops that couldn't stop replaying. After nearly a thousand milliseconds he managed to isolate the affected areas and shook his head. The other robots were on the ground, twitching.

"Adam!" Runa's voice.

They'd retreated to some workbenches further back, and he ran towards them.

"What was that?" he asked her.

"Stutter grenade!" she shouted. "Stuns them!"

"*Runa.*" Linden's voice was urgent but not panicked. Ze seemed to be planning. "Did you activate the house systems?"

Runa hesitated. Adam said, "You told them not to—" but Linden held up a hand and stared at Runa and Della.

Della looked embarrassed. "I'm sorry. It was my fault, I just wanted to—"

"*Yes or no?*"

"Yes!"

"*Good.* Can you work the main lift?" The lift door was right behind them.

Runa gaped at Linden. "Yes!" She grabbed a tablet and tapped at it.

Linden nodded. "Della, watch that side."

The robots were waking up. It seemed to take them much longer. Perhaps it was because they'd been looking straight at the light? Or perhaps this was something else Adam was mysteriously better at? But the lead robot was awake, the one Linden called *Red Sky*, and in one movement it stood, twisted and threw a spear at the servers where the humans had been, with such force that it drilled straight through and into the space where Runa had been crouching.

It pulled another spear from behind its back. Beside it, the two others awoke and scanned the room. Adam could see them through a tiny gap.

"I've got it!" muttered Runa. The lift doors *pinged* and opened, and the robots' heads turned towards the sound.

"Go!" whispered Linden. "I'll distract them!"

Runa helped Della to the lift, while Linden moved to one side, still under cover but making enough noise to be noticed. Adam moved to the other side, doing the same, and the robots tracked them both, scanning from side to side. They raced back to the lift entrance and the second robot broke cover and chased after them. Della pressed the close button but the doors weren't closing, and the second robot was nearly on them and accelerating, and one hand with razor claws flashed in front of it—

"Stutter!" roared Linden, and ducked at the last moment. Runa was ready with a device and pointed it at the robot and pulled the trigger, and Adam shut his eyes hard as the flickering light shone out.

There was a crashing *thump* against his head; he

opened his eyes to find the robot in the lift with them, hurled in by its own momentum but temporarily stunned.

"EMP it!" shouted Runa, but Linden shook hir head.

"It's touching us! We'd be electrocuted!"

The doors closed just as the third robot reached them, and the lift shuddered down. Then Linden pulled a remote from hir pocket and stabbed the button, and the world above them exploded.

Adam felt it through the lift, which slammed against the back wall. The lights flickered off and the lift shuddered and stopped. Then emergency lighting came on, and the doors opened.

They were on the reception floor. Pictures and screens had fallen from the walls, and the room glimmered with emergency lighting, red for danger. Part of the ceiling had collapsed, and a massive slab of plaster had crashed down on to the piano. The air was choked with dust.

"What was *that*?" croaked Runa.

"Explosives," muttered Linden.

They crawled out of the lift. When they were clear, Linden turned back to the stunned robot, put the EMP stick against the back of its head, and pulled the trigger.

Adam was looking at hir face when ze did it. Ze looked calm, half smiling … as if killing it made hir happy, just for a moment. He thought about hir blaze of fury, on the roof. *You and I are nothing alike! I'm a human being!* And he realised: Runa and Della saw robots as danger, but Linden... Linden *hated* them.

Ze looked up at him, blinked, and turned away. "Come on."

Linden crept round the edge of the room, and the others followed, Della leaning heavily against Runa. More plaster fell, and there was a sound of metal creaking above them. Then a shape crashed down and landed in the middle of the room.

Red Sky stood glaring at them.

Its left arm was crushed, and most of the paint had burned off. Smoke curled from one leg. But its face was mostly intact, its visor glowing red. In its right hand it held a lump of brick.

Adam stepped between it and the humans.

"Please," he tried. "We can stop this!"

Its head tilted. "*Identify,*" it hissed again.

Della and Runa were trying to creep back towards the lift. It looked up and they froze. Linden moved to the right. "Hey!" ze shouted. "Over here!"

Without looking away, Red Sky whipped its hand round and the brick flew and cracked into Linden's ankle, and ze screamed and collapsed. The robot reached down and lifted a length of metal, holding it like a spear.

"Stop!" shouted Adam.

It aimed the spear at him, then at Della and Runa, then back to him. It didn't seem to be able to decide.

"What *are* you?" it demanded.

"I'm Adam version two point zero, a prototype experimental artificial entity. *Please.*"

It stared at him again, unmoving, for seconds. Then it turned back towards Della and Runa...

"No!"

There was a groan of metal from above, and the robot looked up. Adam leaped forward and kicked desperately with both feet against its chest, pushing it back a step. It staggered and recovered, then turned back towards him, lifting the spear again—

The ceiling collapsed. Tons of brick and steel crashed down and forced the robot to its knees, then to the floor, then burying it, and still more fell. Servers and test dummies, training apparatus, gym equipment from the living quarters, the whole building collapsing from the inside. It seemed to go on for a very long time.

And then, finally, it stopped.

Adam leaned against the wall and performed an internal diagnostic. Miraculously, he seemed unharmed, other than a few scrapes. There was no sign of Red Sky. To his right, Linden was crouched with hir arms wrapped round hir head, covered in dust, but as he looked ze shuddered and moved. And to his left—

"Della!" Runa's voice was high and panicked. "*Della!*"

Della lay at the edge of the collapse. She was breathing in a fast, ragged pant, and covered in dust, caked grey-white all over, except for a large and spreading red stain.

A thin length of steel poked out from her side.

Help

Adam

Della's eyelids flickered and opened, and her eyes moved as if trying to focus.

"Runa..." she breathed. Then she grimaced and gazed down at the length of metal protruding from her side. "Oh dear," she murmured. "That doesn't look right."

"It's OK!" Runa's voice was panicked, high pitched. "We can fix this!"

Linden tried to stand, but collapsed, clutching hir ankle.

Adam stared at Della. "I don't—" He stopped. "I don't know what to do. What should I do?"

"You have to go," said Della. "Others will be coming. You have to go."

Linden pulled hirself up against a broken bookcase.

"She's right," ze muttered.

Runa blinked. "What? But how can we move her?"

Linden and Della looked at each other. Adam didn't understand the look; it was as if they were talking to each other without words.

"Runa, love," said Della, softly. "I can't move. You have to go anyway. This –" she gestured towards her side and winced in pain – "this is me, Runa."

"What? No." Runa dragged her backpack off. "No, look, I've got bandages, medicine, see? We just have to get you back to Keep."

Linden limped forward. "Runa—"

"*No!*"

"They're *coming*, Runa. We have to *leave*."

Runa turned. Her face was white and trembling, but her eyes flashed. "Would you leave your mother?"

Linden gasped. Runa ignored hir and faced Adam. "We have to move her," she snapped, pointing to the metal rod. "We need to remove this."

Adam said, "I know a little first aid, Runa. It would be very dangerous to remove it. It may be preventing internal bleeding—"

"WE HAVE TO!" screamed Runa. She stared at Della, then Adam, then Linden. "I'm *not going without her*, understand? So help me or *sod off*."

86

After a long pause, Linden muttered, "You heard her."

Adam examined the rod. It was thin, a few millimetres in diameter, with a smooth surface.

"Runa, love—" said Della.

He reached forward and pulled it out.

"Aargh!" she screamed.

Runa was ready with bandages, pressing them hard against Della's side.

Linden felt behind Della's back, ignoring her screams. "There's no exit wound," ze hissed. "It didn't go all the way through."

The bandage was already dark red in Runa's hands and she pulled out more, packing the wound with gauze and pressing harder. Beneath her, Della writhed in a silent shriek, then slumped into a faint. Adam realised he was still holding the metal bar. It was rod at one end, and he threw it away with a strange feeling of disgust, as if it was somehow alive, like a snake.

"The blood's slowing!" said Runa.

Linden felt at Della's neck for several seconds. "Her pulse is very weak. I don't know…" Ze hesitated. "Runa," ze said, more gently this time. "I'm sorry, but there's no way she'll make it to Keep. I'm really sorry."

Runa shook her head again and again. "No. No." Then she stopped, and looked up. "The Cailleach."

Linden gaped at her. "What? No!"

"*Yes*," insisted Runa. "She's closer! And she's got equipment, old equipment, maybe even a Suture! *Yes*, Linden!"

"Who's the Cailleach?" asked Adam.

Linden said, "Even if she's still alive, you can't *trust* her, Runa! She helps Funks! It's crazy!"

"You do what you like," said Runa. "But I'm taking her."

Linden's lips compressed into a hard line. Ze seemed to be trying not to shout. But then, to Adam's surprise, ze nodded. "Right. Fine." Ze tried to stand again and swore.

"Your ankle is broken," said Adam.

Linden grimaced. "No kidding. Really?"

He frowned. "Yes. Did you not realise? It must be very painful."

Linden clamped hir teeth together again, but didn't reply. After a second, ze said, carefully, "Can you carry her?"

Adam bent down and lifted the old woman. She was lighter than he expected; his mass calculations had been wrong, as if Della's voice and energy had made her seem larger.

"Yes," he said.

Linden nodded. "OK, Runa, we're all going, OK?"

Runa stood. Her clothes were covered in blood, her hands too. "Yes."

"And no one… No one is *leaving* anyone."

Now Runa's eyes flicked towards Linden's. She ducked her head. "Thank you."

"Then *MOVE*." Linden swung hirself across to Runa in a sudden lunge, forcing the girl to catch hir. "You'll have to help."

They limped out of the room, Adam carrying Della and Linden leaning on Runa. There was a clatter behind them as they left; Adam turned, but it was just more debris falling from above. As it landed, he thought he saw the pile of rubble shift.

The basement had survived better than the other floors Its ceiling had held and it was mostly intact, with just a layer of fresh dust and plaster over everything. They reached the chute, and Adam peered down.

"There's no time to lower her down," said Linden. "*Go*."

He nodded, climbed to the edge, and slid down, carrying Della. As he hurtled out of the end he half curled his legs, pulling her in towards him, trying to cushion the landing as much as possible. She groaned but didn't wake up. There were fresh spots of blood on her bandages.

Runa landed neatly behind him, then Linden came down headfirst, arms forward. Ze rolled when ze hit; but hir ankle smacked against the ground and for a second ze shrieked, then clamped a hand over hir mouth. Hir face, usually soft brown, was almost white, and tight with pain.

Runa helped hir up.

"Come – come on," Linden gasped. "Go."

Adam carried Della up the steps and out. It was still dark, and there didn't seem to be anything around. Above and behind was the tower, now slumped in on itself. The outer walls had fallen out in places, and smoke curled out from the roof. A fire burned inside.

Runa climbed out and pulled Linden up. "Turn right," she whispered. "Down the hill."

They headed into the centre of the old city. Adam could hear Linden cursing and hissing with every step as ze hopped along, leaning against Runa. Ahead, it was silent, completely deserted, nothing except—

He froze; something was coming towards them, a flicker of silver glint, that became a shape, like a body, and a faint *clat* of metal on stone. Two Funks stepped out of the darkness and up to them.

One stayed back, the other moved forward and scanned him, its head sweeping from side to side as if confused. He knew it could see him with its night vision, but it was looking for humans, and his heat pattern was wrong. What about Della, and the others? Were their infrared disruptors working? One second, two seconds. It considered him, its silver skin glinting like oil as it moved. Three seconds, four, five—

It stepped back, and the two of them continued up the hill and away. After a long time, Adam heard Runa hiss, and he turned. The robots were out of sight.

"Keep going," whispered Linden. Hir whole body was trembling with the effort of standing, hir broken ankle resting on the ground and hir face covered in sweat.

They reached the bottom of the hill, and were in the heart of the city. To the south was the remains of a huge bridge; west was a main street now at the edge of the lake where the gardens had been, and to the south-west, the castle loomed over them, silent and dark. Adam's sensors twitched, as if detecting something watching them from its walls.

Runa directed him north and downwards, then west and north again, away from the centre. Twice more they were stopped by Funks patrolling the ancient roads and houses; twice more they froze, and Adam listened to

Linden's gasping breaths as ze tried not to move. Twice more they continued.

A mile, as fast as Linden could hobble. They covered Della with a blanket; she was cold, and her face was clammy, her breathing short and shallow. She seemed to be melting in Adam's arms, into just a bundle of bones. He knew the wound had reopened, but they had to keep going. The roads were scattered with smashed and battered cars, their paint faded to rust. Makeshift barricades had been formed and broken, reformed and broken again.

"Stop!" gasped Linden. Adam turned. "Stop, I have to. I have to—" Ze collapsed to the ground, almost pulling Runa with hir.

"Linden!"

"I can't. I have to stop. Just a minute."

Adam looked around. They were in the middle of the road, and exposed.

"In there," hissed Runa, pointing to a burnt-out doorway.

Linden groaned, but nodded and pulled hirself up with Runa's help, and they staggered inside.

There was a corridor with two large doors, one on either side, both broken. The walls were coated in soot, but Adam pushed one door open and found the rooms mostly unharmed, with ancient furniture still standing. A crack had opened up the outside wall and a tree was growing up through it.

Runa and Linden collapsed on to a sofa, which groaned but held under their weight. Adam stood where he was, holding Della. After a moment there was a glimmer of green as Runa turned her torch on at the lowest setting.

"How's she doing?" she asked.

Adam hesitated. "Not very well. I think she may be in shock. She hasn't woken up."

Runa nodded. "The Cailleach will help her."

Linden, leaning back, said, "Runa." Hir voice sounded curiously soft, almost gentle, without its normal tight anger. "You know, Della's very old."

"She can fix her," insisted Runa.

"Who is the Cailleach?" asked Adam again.

There was an odd, awkward pause. Eventually, Runa said, "She's a healer ... mender. She fixes. Uh. Things." Runa fell silent.

Linden said, "She fixes *Funks*."

"And humans!" said Runa. "I mean, she heals humans." She looked up at Adam. "She lives in a forest, near here. She's old, and she has a lot of medical equipment—"

"Which she gets from the *Funks*," said Linden.

Runa seemed about to argue, then nodded. "Yeah."

Adam said, "I don't understand. I thought humans and Funks were at war?"

"The Cailleach's ... different," said Runa. "She won't take sides. She fixes Funks. She heals humans. So they say."

"No one's seen her for a long time."

"But I *know* she's still there. She can help Della, I know she can. She has all this amazing stuff – she can fix *anything*. She'll have a Suture, even."

"What's a Suture?" asked Adam.

Linden coughed. "An old tech thing. It heals injuries."

"*Any* injury," said Runa. "It's incredible, it's like *magic*. It can heal Della. It can, can't it, Linden?"

Linden's face screwed up. "Maybe."

Adam stared at the tree breaking in through the damp, leaking wall.

"Is it like this everywhere?" he asked. He still found it difficult to process. "The whole world?"

Linden just shrugged.

"But ... perhaps people in other places can help?" he tried.

"What other people?"

"We haven't heard from anyone for a long time," said Runa. "Something happened to the upper atmosphere during the war. Radio signals get blocked over long distance. There might be others out there, but we can't reach them. As far as we know ... we're all that's left."

They fell into silence.

"That robot," Adam said at last. "The one you called Red Sky. It wasn't like the others."

Runa nodded. "Red Sky is special. Really bad news. They say it was a soldier Funk once, and that's why it looks different. It's smarter than the others, too. We think it's in charge."

"Why was it throwing spears? Doesn't it have guns?"

Runa snorted. "It has guns. It's got no *ammo*. They used it all up, years and years ago, and they can't make any more."

"Jet fuel, too," said Linden. "They've hardly any left; they almost never fly. It must have thought there was something really important in that building..."

They looked at Adam.

Della gave a thin, rattling breath and Adam measured her pulse again. It took him a long time to find it. He said, "Runa, I think we have to get Della help as soon as possible."

"We'd better push on," muttered Linden.

Runa helped hir up, and they crept out of the house and onwards. Around them the buildings spread out and grew larger, surrounded by old gardens. The night was wearing away now; there was a faint light to the east, and the glow of sun against clouds. It was a red sky.

"Here," said Runa at last. She turned left, up a path that led off the main road and ended at a huge and curious silver gate, curled in a pattern of leaves and flowers. Above the gate was a sign carved out of metal. It read: PAX BOTANICA.

Linden grunted. "Runa…" Ze sighed. "Never mind."

They stumbled towards the gate, and through. Inside, the path opened up into a park. Rhododendrons crowded both sides, heavy in their dark winter leaves. The ground had been tarmacked once but was now mud, churned by thousands of feet. In front of them sat a large boulder with an arrow painted on it, pointing to the right, and again the word "PAX". They followed the path round the corner, and stopped.

Four silver robots stood in front of them. Adam half heard, half felt a whisper of air, and turned to see four more robots stepping up behind.

They were trapped.

The Cailleach

Adam

There was no doubt the Funks could see them. The dawn had started, and they didn't need their low-light vision any more. Adam and the others stopped. Linden pulled the last EMP stick from Runa's belt and held it ready, but hir face was grim.

"Wait—" said Adam.

Three of the robots stepped forward, and round them, and joined the ones behind, and together they walked away.

"The Cailleach will see you," said the remaining Funk, in a smooth, almost natural voice.

Linden pointed the EMP stick at it and it cocked its head.

"The forest is under the Cailleach's protection," it said. "You will not fire."

Linden's jaw clenched, but Runa put a hand out and held hir arm. "Stay calm," she murmured. Linden scowled, but lowered the weapon. The Funk turned and walked into the forest, giving no sign that it cared whether they followed.

"This is a bad idea, Runa," muttered Linden.

Runa nodded. "I know."

They followed the robot.

A few metres past the gate, trees crowded around them, ancient and gnarled. The old path was almost obliterated by encroaching rhododendron bushes with curling, twisted branches that seemed to grasp at them as they passed. The dawn light was hidden here, and the world was full of pockets of dark, and the sound of things shuffling out of sight.

Something came towards them in the gloom – another Funk, Adam realised, its right leg replaced by a steel peg below the knee. It limped past, ignoring them. Linden held hir EMP stick ready.

Now the path widened and curled upwards, and the trees and bushes parted to reveal a large house at the top of a hill, and gardens with rows of herbs and other small plants neatly tended. Around them lay pieces of old robots: arms, legs, in one place a whole chest and part of a head, lying discarded and forgotten. It was creepy, like the workshop at the tower, but the Funk gave no sign it noticed. It led them to an ancient courtyard, with a stone water feature and gravel underfoot, and then into the house.

Inside, a dimly lit hallway widened out to a large room. In the centre of the room was a chair, and standing beside the chair was a woman.

Her face was covered with a grey veil, and she wore a drab black smock. She was tall, and very thin. Her hands, folded in front of her, were wrinkled but not weak. She didn't move as they entered. The Funk stepped away into shadow.

"Welcome," she said. "I am the Cailleach."

Her voice was distant, as if it had taken her some time to find the words, as if speaking was rare for her. It was neutral, not hostile, but not friendly. There was something familiar about it, but Adam couldn't place it.

"This woman's been injured," said Runa. "She needs—"

"Hold up your hand," said the woman.

Runa stopped. "What?"

"Hold it up, so I may see."

Runa hesitated. Then she held up her right arm, letting the sleeve fall back to reveal her prosthetic hand. She moved her fingers.

The woman stepped forward, her veil revealing nothing.

"It is a fair attempt," she said, examining it. "Thank you … Runa." She turned. "Linden. I was sorry to hear of your loss. Your mother was a good woman."

She stated it as if it were simply a fact, of no great importance. Linden's eyes flashed and hir lips clamped tight, holding back a response. The veil moved on.

"And you are Adam."

Adam frowned. "How do you know?"

She shrugged. "I am the Cailleach. There is one who waits to meet you, Adam. One who has waited this whole long winter."

Adam didn't know how to respond. He held up Della's body. "Please," he said. "Can you help?"

The Funk returned now, pushing an ancient hospital trolley, and stood beside it. Adam glanced at Runa and then carefully laid Della on to the trolley.

"She is mortally wounded," said the woman, without examining her. "She will die."

"*Please*," begged Runa. "Can't you fix her?"

"She is beyond my medicine. She has internal injuries." The woman's shoulders shifted, as if in a tiny shrug. "It is winter."

Linden sighed, but Runa shook her head. "You have

technology. You have a *Suture*."

The head tilted. "And what would you give in return? What would you offer?"

"Runa—" said Linden, in a warning growl, but Runa didn't hesitate.

"Anything," she said, firmly. "*Anything.*"

The woman studied her for a few seconds, then nodded to the robot, and it wheeled the trolley away.

"Follow R19," she said. "It will make Della comfortable, and treat your ankle, Linden. Do exactly what it tells you." She turned back to Adam. "You – stay here."

"Will you help?" insisted Runa, glaring at the veil, but there was no response, and her shoulders sank. She gave Adam a glance that seemed to be part begging, part warning, and she and Linden followed the trolley and were gone.

The Cailleach studied Adam.

"Will you help her?" he asked.

Her head moved. "There is a cost."

"Runa thinks you have devices that can save her. Why would you not use them?"

"What are you, little robot?" she asked, ignoring his question.

"I am Adam version two point zero, a prototype experimental artificial entity."

She nodded. "But what *are* you?"

"I…" Adam stopped. "I don't know what you mean. I am Adam version two—"

"Yes, yes." She waved an arm. "But are you a Funk? Do you consider yourself a human?"

"I don't know. I'm just me."

"Hmmm."

She walked back to her chair and slid open a drawer built into its base, retrieving a box about the size of an old briefcase. It was dark green and seemed to be made of plastic, very old. She carried it flat, very carefully, and placed it on a nearby table.

"This is what Runa wants," she said. "The Suture."

The box had lettering on the top: it read SINGLE-USE TRAUMA RESPONSE.

"It is an ancient device," said the Cailleach. "Technology we can barely imagine now. It will heal Della, even her internal injuries, if we use it."

"Will you?"

She placed a hand on the surface of the case.

"What did they tell you about me?" she asked.

Adam said, "That you heal humans, and repair Funks."

"And what do you think about that?"

He shook his head. "I don't know. Why do you repair the Funks?"

"You think I shouldn't? They have no way to repair themselves. They cannot learn new things. If I don't help them, they will be crippled, or will die."

"They're robots," said Adam. "They don't die."

"Hmmm."

The Cailleach paused. "This is the last of these kits," she said. "There are no others, no way to make a new one. Tell me, little robot: should I use it to save Della?"

"Yes, of course!" said Adam. "She's dying!"

But the woman shrugged. "It is the world's winter; we are all dying. And Della is old. If I save her life now, how many years does she have left, do you think? Ten? Five?"

"I don't know."

"And if I use this up, and someone else is hurt like this, they will die instead. Is her life worth more than that person's?"

Adam frowned. "I... I don't know."

"Yes, you do." Her veil swayed but revealed nothing. "Tell me."

Adam thought. "This kind of injury is usually received in a fight," he said. "Statistically, a person needing treatment for this kind of injury would be younger, with a longer life expectancy. Measured in years, their remaining life would be ... would be more valuable than Della's."

He found himself monitoring his voice as he spoke, running sensor sweeps over his systems as if registering some form of system failure. But his logic was sound, and complete. Della was very old. To use the device on her would mean taking it from a much younger person – if not now, then someday.

"So tell me," said the Cailleach. "What would you do?"

"I—" He stopped. It was obvious. "I do not like this choice."

"It is winter," said the woman. "There are only hard choices. We have no luxuries. We must choose to survive, not to make us feel good. We cannot be … *personal*. The Funks understand this."

"Why do you mend the Funks?" asked Adam, suddenly. "Mending them hurts humans. You make things worse by helping them." He didn't know why he asked.

"You tell me. What do you think, Adam, who is neither Funk nor human?"

He shook his head. There was an answer, but it made no sense. But...

"You can't help yourself," he said at last. "They're damaged … *wounded*, and you have to treat them.

Even if it makes things worse. They're here, and they need your help."

She said nothing.

Adam said, "You have to use the kit on Della. Even if it is not logical. She's here, now, and she needs it. You *must*."

The Cailleach stood still for a second, considering him. Then: "Very well. R19 –" the Funk had reappeared and stepped forward – "take this. You know what to do."

"Come," she said. "See your friends."

The Cailleach led Adam down a corridor to another room, separated into two halves, with a glass partition between them, and a bed in each half. In the nearest bed sat Linden, one ankle hidden by a machine that was wrapped round it, old and battered but apparently doing something, its display blinking. Runa stood next to hir.

Both of them were staring through the glass into the other half of the room, where Della lay, still unconscious. Beside her were screens displaying vital signs, and next to them stood the Funk, the one called R19, holding a small blue device with two very thin metal rods that poked into the open wound in Della's side. The Funk's hands were red and slick with blood.

They watched as it worked, using equipment from the Suture case. Small devices like robotic slugs crawled into the wound and emerged later, blood-soaked, to fall into trays and stop; things like spiders scurried in, trailing tendrils of metal silk behind them. Finally, the last spider crawled out and, as R19 held the wound closed, sewed the skin together with tiny neat stitching, before slowing and collapsing with the others.

R19 studied the screens next to it. "Operation successful," it said. "Patient has estimated seventy-one per cent chance of immediate survival. Estimated fifty-eight per cent chance of long-term recovery."

"Is that…" Runa coughed. "Is she—"

The Cailleach nodded. "She'll survive." And then, more quietly: "She was always stubborn."

Runa swallowed, and started to say something, but shook her head. She walked unsteadily to the chair next to Linden's bed, and sat as if her bones had suddenly become liquid.

"Rest," said the Cailleach. "R19 will bring you food, and this evening you and Adam can go home. Linden and Della will stay until they are recovered." She turned to leave.

"Thank you," said Adam, and she paused, then nodded and left.

*

Adam and the others waited. R19 returned with bread and bowls of barley broth, its hands now immaculately clean, and Runa and Linden ate, then collapsed into exhausted sleep in moments. Adam watched Della's shallow breathing. In the evening, R19 returned to light lanterns and check on Della. Runa and Linden awoke, but it was midnight before Runa made ready to leave.

"Maybe I should stay with you two," she said, uncertainly.

Linden shook hir head. "Callum needs to know what happened. Go. And ... take the Funk." Hir eyes flicked to Adam's face with an expression he couldn't understand. "Look after her," ze said abruptly. "Understand?"

He blinked. "Yes, of course."

Linden nodded, and looked away, scowling.

The Cailleach entered the room.

"We're ready," said Runa. She hugged Linden, then gazed once more at Della, one hand on the glass partition. Then she wiped her face and turned. "Let's go."

The Cailleach led them out. "Go safe," she said. "The Pax holds until you leave the forest."

Runa nodded and checked her infrared disruptor.

"You were always going to help us," said Adam,

suddenly. Again, he wasn't sure what had made him say it. "You were always going to use the Suture."

"Perhaps."

"Then why did you ask me?"

The Cailleach faced him. Her head tilted again. "To find out what you are. And…" She sighed. "The Cailleach must make hard choices. Saving one person often damns another, and sometimes, the choices are … personal. I needed to know I was right."

She turned away, and Adam saw the contour of her nose beneath the veil, sharp and inquisitive and somehow familiar. For an odd moment, he found himself thinking that the Cailleach and Della were exactly the same height.

The R19 robot walked back down the path to the gate, then turned and left without saying anything, and Runa and Adam made their way back to Keep.

Runa was quiet, and Adam could tell she was worried. He didn't know what to say, so he stayed silent. They made good time, avoiding the patrols, and reached Keep in the small hours of the morning, while it was still dark. As before, Runa held her hands up as they neared, and Adam copied her as figures emerged with pointed EMP sticks. And, as before, Callum was there.

His face was grim. He said nothing, waiting.

"It's OK!" said Runa. "They're alive. They're with the Cailleach."

His face showed no emotion, but he gave a fractional nod. "The Elders want to see you," he said.

Runa nodded. "I'll come right up."

"Not you." He turned to Adam. "You."

The Elders

Adam

There were many more people this time, despite the late hour. The tops of the castle walls were speckled with dots of flickering torchlight from those who had come out to see the visitors, and, as Adam and Runa made their way up towards the gates, they were surrounded. Callum walked with them, his fierce glare holding the crowd back like a barrier, but they watched and murmured and muttered.

It was over two hundred years since Adam had seen so many humans. His tracking processors found it hard to cope as figures appeared and disappeared out of the dark, their faces a mix of emotions. Curiosity? Anger?

Hatred.

Danger signals rippled through his sensors and he almost tripped. Beside him, Runa had pulled down her sleeve, hiding her metal hand. At the gate the guards stared at Callum and didn't move until he nodded. They pointed more EMP sticks at Adam. As they passed through the outer gate, Adam could see the pit to his left, and Della's workshop. This time though they headed towards the inner gate. There, the guards were even more cautious, and there was a long pause before one gate slowly opened. Callum motioned for Adam and Runa to go in front; as he did so, Adam saw that Callum was holding a small remote control, and realised it was a replacement for the one Della had carried before, the one that could trigger the EMP collar round Adam's neck. He was careful not to make any sudden movements.

They passed through the inner gate and into the inner courtyard of Keep, and a chaos of humans. There were hundreds of them, humans everywhere; the courtyard was jam-packed, the walls too, and the windows in the towers, people leaning out and staring. The muttering was louder, and harsher. Voices spoke out of the dark.

Killer.

Tin scum.

Funk.

One man ahead of them turned to look at Adam, and

spat on the ground in front of him. The crowd moved like water, bulging and heaving and getting closer. Adam realised his fingers were twitching.

"ENOUGH!" shouted Callum, suddenly. He stopped and glared around him, grim and fearless and immovable. "Move back or disperse. I won't tell you twice."

Next to him, the guards glanced at each other. One kept his EMP stick pointed at Adam, but the others had surreptitiously swapped theirs for short wooden coshes, which they now held up. The crowd muttered in anger but backed away, a little, and Callum nodded. Then he continued walking as if nothing had happened.

"It's OK," whispered Runa. She moved her hand towards Adam's, as if about to take it, but then shook her head and let it fall again.

To the left of the courtyard was an iron-bound door, partly open. More guards stood inside, and Callum ushered Runa and Adam in. The crowd pushed forward again, but the door closed in front of them, and Adam and the others were inside. Callum led Adam into a cell that contained only a lamp in an alcove, and a single tiny window. He left Adam standing there with two guards watching him.

"Wait here."

Adam tried to ignore the guards' EMP sticks, and

concentrated on standing still. The door was closed, but there was a slot to peer through, and he became aware of faces staring in at him.

"Hello," he said to the first one. It disappeared.

"I'm Adam," he tried to the second. It vanished too.

It was dawn before the door opened, and Callum stood in the doorway. As ever, his face showed no emotion.

"Take it to the Elders," he said.

The guards prodded Adam, and he followed Callum up a flight of stone steps and into a large hall. The ceiling was high, and painted a deep dark blue like the night sky, with the moon and constellations picked out. Embroideries hung on the walls, looking dusty in the pale morning light. People stood round the edges. There had been a buzz of conversation before he entered; now it stopped, and for a moment the room was quiet. Every face turned towards him. Some appeared curious, some scared. Most seemed hostile.

Ahead, at a wide table on a raised platform, sat three figures, two women and one man, dressed in blue robes. They were old – perhaps the oldest people Adam had seen, apart from Della. The man huddled inside his robes as if shrinking, but the woman in the middle was straight-backed and solid, with a broad face surrounded by straight grey hair cut roughly at shoulder length. To her right, another woman, thin and black-eyed, perched on her chair like a hawk.

"Your Honours," said Callum, in a formal voice. "This is the Adam device."

He turned to Adam. "Stand there," he said, and pointed to a worn spot on the floor, in front of the table.

Adam walked to the spot. Runa gave him a little wave as he passed.

The three figures examined him.

"I am Elder McKenzie," said the large woman. She had a deep voice, quick and gruff. "These –" she gestured towards the black-eyed woman and the shrunken man – "are Elders Reid and Stepek. Identify yourself."

"I am Adam version two point zero, a prototype experimental artificial entity," said Adam. "Hello."

The crowd muttered, but the woman just nodded.

"People of Keep," she called, looking around the room. "You've heard the rumours, of a Funk that claims to be friendly. Of a machine, with a human name… Well, here it is.

"The question is –" her lips pursed – "what *is* it?"

She turned back. "Runa Higgens. Approach."

Runa came forward and stood next to Adam.

The woman said, "Report."

114

The crowd's attention swung towards Runa, and she swallowed. But she lifted her head and, in a calm voice, gave her account of finding Adam in the basement, of the Clunker, and how Adam had saved her life. She talked about the mission to the tower, and the attack. People gasped at Red Sky, and when she described the building collapsing on it, some even cheered. But they became quiet as she mentioned the Cailleach, and faces soured and scowled.

McKenzie's face stayed neutral, revealing nothing. The man's eyes fluttered as if holding off sleep. The other woman, Elder Reid, watched Runa's mouth with her sharp black pupils, and didn't seem to ever blink.

"And that's when we returned," Runa said at last. "Adam saved my life. All our lives." She fell silent.

"Thank you," said McKenzie. She turned to Adam and studied him. "So. A Funk, but not like other Funks, eh? A Funk who can escape from prisons, imagine new things. A Funk who cannot be killed by EMP. A Funk ... who claims to want to help. What should we do with you, Adam?"

There was silence in the hall. Then a voice from the back hissed, "*Kill it.*"

Muttering grew around the room. It seemed to be in agreement.

"It saved our lives!" shouted Runa.

Elder Reid leaned forward. "I'm sure you think so, my dear," she said, in a thin voice. "But what did you actually see? It caught a rock. It kicked a Funk. Did it make the building collapse? No." She smiled. "And how did Red Sky know you were there? This thing claims it was in the basement for hundreds of years – but the door wasn't even locked! When did it actually arrive? Just in time for you to turn up, perhaps?"

Adam said, "That is not correct—"

"No!" snapped Runa. "Linden was there too, it couldn't have fooled hir!"

The woman nodded. "Ah. Well then, tell me, girl – does *Linden* trust it?"

Runa hesitated. "Well…"

"Ze tried to kill it, didn't ze? Only it can't be killed…"

More muttering.

Reid faced the crowd. "It's a Funk," she stated. "And Funks cannot be trusted."

"I'm not a Funk," said Adam. "I'm just a prototype. They're more advanced than me—"

"That's clearly not true," Reid snapped. "Funks can't innovate, they can't learn new things. They can't survive EMP. You are more advanced than them, aren't you? Aren't you?"

Adam shook his head. "I don't understand it," he admitted.

"But you want to," she hissed, "because you *learn*." She shook her head. "Will you join them? Will you teach them to be like you, more dangerous than they've ever been? Is that why you left the basement?"

"What? No—"

"Then why? Why did you leave, when you had been told to stay there? If you are on our side, why did you disobey?"

Adam shook his head. "I felt that I should—"

"A human ordered you to stay!" she snapped. "Why did you not obey?"

"I don't have to obey humans!" said Adam.

The crowd growled, and Elder Reid nodded, as if in satisfaction, and sat back. "Indeed."

The man, Stepek, said, "How can we trust you, then?" His voice was watery and meandering, as if he was still waking up. "There's been nothing like you till now."

"I just want to help," said Adam.

"How? Can you fight?"

"Um... Not very well. I'm good at repairs."

"Everyone here fights, or has fought. What would you do?"

"I..."

Elder McKenzie's eyes were hard. Reid glared at him in triumph, Stepek with a rather sad expression. And the crowd were growling. Adam's sub-processors sent him danger signals; he tried to identify routes out of the hall, but there were people everywhere, staring at him, and he was still wearing the collar—

"Commander Dunbar, what do you say?" asked McKenzie, and Callum stepped forward. He glared at the crowd until they grew quiet, then considered Adam for several seconds.

"I say we take it to Trial," he said at last.

The Elder cocked her head. "Indeed?"

He said, "Your Honours, I believe Runa's account to be accurate. Linden's report after the first mission agrees. This ... thing is different to the Funks. It had opportunities to attack and did not. It *has* defended humans from Funks. And it has knowledge ... and *abilities* we can use." He and the Elders exchanged a look at this, but Adam didn't know why.

"You ask if it will fight for us," he said. "I say, take it to Trial, and we shall see."

He closed his mouth and folded his arms.

"*Trial*," muttered a voice in the crowd.

"*Test it.*"

"*Trial.*"

Elder McKenzie glanced at the other two. The man shrugged. The woman seemed unconvinced, but nodded. McKenzie turned back and raised a hand to calm the crowd.

"Very well," she said. "Commander Dunbar has vouched for this … this *not-Funk*. He claims to speak for Linden Bashir, too. Runa Higgens has given testimony. They state that it is not hostile, and that it may be able to help. But will it *fight* for us? We shall see. I declare a Trial, and if the device succeeds … then it will be accepted into Keep."

At this the crowd faltered a little, as if wondering how they had come to agree to this. Reid seemed unhappy too. But Stepek nodded, and McKenzie continued as if everything was decided.

"Commander – prepare the ground. Trial will take place this evening."

The Elders stood, and the people bowed. From the side of his mouth, Callum hissed, "Lower your head, machine," and Adam did so. He heard footsteps, and a door closing, and then he realised the others had lifted their heads, and did the same. The Elders had gone, and the crowd relaxed again, joking and laughing, giving Adam strange glances, as if they were looking forward to something. As if they were amused by something he didn't know.

"It's OK," murmured Runa.

Adam nodded. He looked up at Callum. "Thank you," he said, smiling.

Callum looked down at him with no expression. His eyes were dark. "Take it back to the cell."

Trial

Adam

"Everyone is angry with me," said Adam. "I think they hate me."

He had spent the day back in the little cell, surrounded by silent guards with pointed EMP sticks. Nobody had entered, except to change guard shifts, but more faces had appeared at the slot in the door. The faces had been hostile, or scared, or bitter. At one point he was sure he had recognised Elder Reid, watching him with her shining black eyes.

Runa had returned after dusk with some tools. Now she fastened a little infrared disruptor to Adam's body, wrapping it round a metal rib and tying it tight. She sighed.

"We've been at war for hundreds of years. We're barely surviving. All of us have lost friends, family…"

She shook her head. "They won't trust you, until they can see for themselves."

"And that's what this 'trial' is?"

"Correct."

"What will happen?"

Runa glanced at the guards. "I'm not allowed to tell you. But we've all gone through some version of it. It's about being part of Keep, about being human." She frowned. "Or in your case ... just you, I guess."

She adjusted the disruptor and checked its signals against an ancient handheld scanner. "There. If any Funk sees you now, it will think you're a human. *Don't take it off.*" She looked serious. "If you remove the badge, you fail the Trial."

"Is that bad?"

Runa opened her mouth, then closed it. "Adam, if you fail..." She hesitated. "Well, look, just don't fail, OK?"

"I will try not to."

Callum appeared at the door. "Is it ready?"

"Good to go," said Runa.

"Good to go," said Adam.

Callum raised one eyebrow but didn't comment.

The guards led him behind the castle to an area where the original grounds had been extended. New walls stretched south, and small houses and allotments were laid out in neat rows, lit by flickering torchlight and the white glow of occasional electric lamps. They passed through a gate and on to a platform, which descended into another pit.

This was different to the one he'd been in before. It was rectangular, thirty metres long and ten wide, full of discarded equipment, and, he noticed, discarded pieces of robot. At the far end was a large doorway, and round the edge, three metres up, a balcony thronged with people. They cheered when he arrived, but their mood was strange, and the noise didn't sound friendly as it echoed around the pit.

At the middle of one side sat the Elders. Callum stood next to them, and then Runa. She gave him a thumbs-up and smiled.

"*Move*," snarled a guard, pushing Adam forward with his EMP stick.

The platform rose behind him, then there was a harsh clang as Callum rang a metal bar against a large rusty triangle. "Prepare for Trial!" he bellowed, and the crowd cheered. Callum looked down at Adam with a face that showed no recognition.

"The machine Adam has been challenged to prove loyalty to humans," he announced. "It will be Tried, as we are all Tried. Begin!"

The door slid open, and a huge robot stepped out, and the crowd roared.

It was a Clunker, like the one that had chased them on that first day, when he had left the basement. It was more than three times as tall as Adam, with massive arms and a flat head with a single red eye, and its body was battered and scarred. It stepped cautiously, scanning the baying crowds above it. Adam looked up too and saw Runa, who wasn't smiling now. She seemed to be shouting at Callum.

Adam walked forward. "Hello? Hello, I'm Adam."

The Clunker turned from the crowd and stared at him, and stepped back into a defensive crouch. It seemed confused, or scared.

"Can you speak?" asked Adam. He held up one hand. "Can you understand me?"

It didn't respond at first. Then, slowly, it lifted one hand up to match. Adam stepped forward again. "I'm Adam. I'm not your enemy."

The enormous robot shuffled forward, carefully, its squat head tilted, its body twitching. "It's OK," said Adam. "I'm not going to harm you."

The Clunker nodded.

Then it seized Adam's arm in one enormous paw, spun in a tight circle and smashed him hard against a pile of machinery.

"Wait!" shouted Adam. It dragged him back and battered him into the pit wall. Adam felt something *twang* in his left arm and emergency signals flared all over his body. "Stop!"

Above him, he realised the crowd was screaming. The Clunker swung him back into the pile of machinery, which gave way and crashed around them. Its grip weakened for a moment, and Adam scrambled free, but then a metal fist closed round his ankle.

"I'm not your enemy!" he shouted desperately.

The Clunker swung again, and Adam hurtled across the length of the pit. He slammed against the far wall and the emergency signals doubled, damage reports firing over his whole body. His vision systems seemed confused. The world was blurred. He realised he was staring straight up at Runa, who was screaming at Callum and dragging at his arm.

Then she was gone, and in her place was the glowing red eye of the Clunker.

Adam lunged to one side as the Clunker's fist smashed down, gouging into the earth of the pit floor. It raised its arm again. Adam wriggled down and through the massive robot's legs before it could strike, and staggered away. He looked up to see Runa staring at him with an expression of horror.

"Help!" he shouted. "What is happening? Help me!"

The crowd were baying, screaming, laughing. Runa shouted something back, but he couldn't hear. She pointed behind him, and when he turned the Clunker was almost upon him, reaching with its enormous, mauling hands. He ducked and the hands closed above him, and he scrambled away again, his processors frantically trying to find an escape route. In desperation, he picked up a lump of metal and threw it at the thing's chest. It bounced off. He wasn't sure the Clunker had even noticed.

"Why are you doing this?" he shouted.

It strode towards him and Adam tripped backwards, and as he scrambled to his feet he noticed the little infrared disruptor badge, still fastened to one rib. Suddenly, he understood. The disruptor was sending a false signal. A *human* signal. The Clunker thought he was human!

"It's not real!" he shouted. "Look!" He reached up to rip the badge away, but then remembered Runa's words – *If you remove the badge, you fail…*

This was a *test*.

Of course, he realised. Of course the humans wouldn't *really* try to kill him! It was just a test! Which meant there had to be some way to pass. But how? The Clunker was far too large to fight. Adam retreated, and scanned the pit; was there something he could use? But it was all junk – broken equipment, scraps of robot. An arm, an old lamp, some bent solar panels, a half-empty glue can, part of a vision system…

The Clunker swung and Adam scrambled back again. It swooped in a sudden sharp lunge and he barely escaped, leaping up and on to its shoulders as its fists hammered down. He clung to its head as it spun, covering its eye with his hands, but there was no grip and he flew off and skidded on to the pit floor, his hands digging into the wet muddy earth…

…and had an idea.

He scooped up a handful of soil, dumped it into the glue can, and ran *towards* the Clunker. It swung and he leaped again up on to his shoulders, and spread the gluey, muddy mess over the robot's face. It shook him free again and he crashed into the side wall, but when he looked up, the Clunker had stopped. It was momentarily blinded. One arm was raised, trying to scrape the mixture off with its huge, clumsy paws. Adam tottered away. His left shoulder was twitching, not responding properly. Above him, the crowd was still roaring. He found the discarded robot arm and ripped off its cover panels to reveal fresh wiring.

The Clunker scrubbed part of its face clear and turned. Adam grabbed the lamp, trying to remember a sequence he'd seen once, when Red Sky had attacked. Would it work? The lamp's power source was broken, but its bulb was intact.

The ground trembled as the Clunker moved again, and Adam staggered towards the far wall, attaching the wires to the lamp. *There.* Then he connected them to his own power supply, and—

A fist hammered into his back and sent him flying. He turned, but the Clunker was already upon him, its red eye scarred but working, and it hauled him up with one paw and raised the other to smash, and Adam closed his eyes and powered the lamp in a complex, high-speed flickering pattern...

Stutter.

The Clunker glared at him. Then, very slowly, still holding Adam, it toppled over backwards and collapsed on to the pit floor.

The crowd fell silent for a second. And then it roared.

Adam dragged himself free. Damage alerts flared all over his body. He stared at the stunned Clunker and shook his head. The audience howled, savage and delighted, and Adam looked up and found Runa's face, cheering with the others. He raised a shaky thumb, and the noise increased.

The platform descended and Callum walked towards him, his face expressionless. As he reached Adam, he nodded. "Good job."

"Thank you," said Adam. His voice sounded oddly quiet, and he wondered if his hearing was damaged. "Did I pass?"

Callum glanced up at the crowd. "Not yet." He reached for his EMP stick and handed it to Adam. "Finish it."

Adam blinked. "But it's harmless now," he said. "Look, it's immobilised."

"It will wake up," said Callum.

"Finish it!" shouted someone from the crowd.

"But we can restrain it before it does," said Adam. "Or immobilise it again."

"*Finish it! Kill it!*"

"I don't want it immobilised," said Callum. "I want it *dead.*"

"But—"

"This is the Trial!" Callum snapped. "Don't you understand? *This* is the Trial, machine! What are you? What is your allegiance? Are you with them?"

"No!"

"Are you one of us?"

"I— Yes!"

"Then *finish it*."

"FINISH IT!" chanted the crowd. "FINISH IT!"

Adam looked up at hundreds of screaming faces, fierce with vicious joy. "FINISH IT!" And Runa too, chanting like the others, her fists pumping. "FINISH IT, ADAM!"

He pointed the EMP stick. As he watched, the Clunker shuddered, and one arm moved. It was coming out of its stutter. Its hand reached towards Adam...

He pulled the trigger, and the robot twitched, once, and stopped. Its red eye flickered and went out.

"YES!" screamed the crowd. "YESSSSSS!"

Above him, the Elders stood up. Stepek, hunched inside an enormous fur coat, smiled at him. Reid's eyes were still black and hostile. Elder McKenzie studied the crowd and waited for them to quieten. Then she turned, looked down at Adam, and gave a slow deliberate nod. The crowd roared again.

The Elders turned and left, but the crowd carried on chanting Adam's name. Callum took the EMP stick back and examined him. "Will you be able to repair that arm?"

Adam nodded. "If I have the right tools."

"Della's workshop will have some." Callum's mouth moved, as if about to say something, then he shrugged. "Come on." He walked away, ignoring the crowd.

Adam looked at Callum's back, and at the dead Clunker. Then he followed.

Midnight

Adam

"Adam, you were *awesome*!" Runa ran up to him, beaming. "I can't believe you built a stutter gun from *scrap*!"

Adam smiled. "I didn't know what else to do."

Runa laughed. "And you fought a *Clunker*! That's unbelievable! When I did it, all I had to fight was a spider-bot, like, this big —" she held her hands about twenty centimetres apart — "*and* Della had an EMP stick pointed at it the whole time!"

"Elder Reid ordered me to use the Clunker," said Callum.

Adam frowned. "That is strange," he said. "I thought Elder Reid did not like me, but she must have believed I would win. She must have a lot of faith in me."

"Um…" Runa glanced up at Callum. "Yeah. I guess so."

"Does everyone go through Trial?" asked Adam.

"Everyone over twelve," said Callum.

"And you always ... destroy the robot, when you fight?"

"Of course!" Runa looked surprised. "That's the whole *point*. Killing Funks is what makes us *human*. Now everyone knows which side you're on."

Adam didn't understand this. But, as they walked through the courtyard and towards Della's workshop, he realised Runa was right. The faces they passed were still curious, but no longer as hostile. One boy clapped him on the shoulder, then scurried back to his friends, laughing in bravado. They grinned at him, shouted greetings. It was a curious sensation.

"You're one of us now," said Runa, and Adam smiled.

They reached Della's workshop, and Adam rummaged around for tools to mend his arm. Like everything, they were ancient, but his time in the basement had made him resourceful. Over the centuries he'd had to learn, first to repair himself, then to repair his tools, and then even to create new tools from broken pieces. He rerouted the sensor systems on his shoulder and started working.

"I hope Della's going to be all right," said Runa.

Adam looked up. "The Cailleach said she had a good chance," he said.

Runa nodded and Callum said, "I'll send a messenger to check."

"You live here," said Adam to Runa. He gestured towards the little bed alcove in the corner. "I saw you sleeping there."

Runa nodded. "Della took me in, when my parents died. I was very small, I don't even remember them. But she looked after me." She smiled. "I don't know why. But we both like tinkering. And she gave me this." She held her hand up, the prosthetic one.

Adam examined it. It was too big, he realised; designed for a larger person, but cleverly adapted to fit over Runa's wrist. It had been repaired, patched and repatched, with great care.

"It's not as good as a real hand," said Runa. "But it's pretty good."

Adam smiled. "It is very good," he said. "Look – it is like mine." He held his own hand up, but Runa didn't smile back. Instead, she let her sleeve fall back down over it, as if suddenly self-conscious.

"I'm human," she said. "Not robot."

Adam fell silent. He seemed to have upset Runa, but he didn't know why. He flexed his shoulder carefully. "That is better," he said.

"Good," said Callum. He picked up something from

the worktable. "Look at this."

Adam examined it. It was a metal ball, about the size of his head, with plastic sheets that folded round the outside like the closed-up petals of a flower. There were buttons on the top; he pressed one and the petals unfolded and spread out wide. It was a solar charger, he realised, but its panels were cracked and grey, dead.

"Can you mend it?" asked Callum.

The panels were of a form Adam recognised, though they seemed more advanced. The problem was that the light-absorbing material had decayed over time. But…

"Yes, I believe so." he said. "Excuse me—" He reached up to his head and unhinged his skull cavity, and Runa and Callum recoiled with a shared look of horror. "Sorry," he said. "I just need to get something…" He rummaged inside his head and plucked out a small unit. "My own solar charger uses the same material. When it began to decay, I built this. It is a solar crystal regenerator." He offered it to Runa. She looked at it, then cautiously reached for it.

"Still warm," she muttered.

"It requires a power supply," said Adam.

Runa found a charger, and Adam connected it to the panel. After a few seconds, some of the cells started to lose their faded appearance. A meter at the side blinked and showed a faint green bar.

"Yes!" shouted Runa.

Callum nodded, as if he'd expected no less. "Good," he said. "What about this?"

He heaved a large metal box off the shelf, painted dark green and chipped and bashed. There was a panel on the front, and a switch; Callum flicked the switch, but nothing happened.

"It's an Early Warning System," he said. "We had one before, a long time ago, but this one doesn't work." He opened a small hatch at the side, revealing a diagnostic interface socket. "We can't connect to this," he said. "Can you?"

Adam frowned. "Perhaps." He placed a finger against the socket, and immediately a stream of data poured into him, random and chaotic, incomprehensible. It was overwhelming, as if a huge wave had crashed over his head, so severe that for a moment all his systems froze.

"Adam?" asked Runa.

More data poured in, but Adam finally managed to control his processors enough to stop the flood; the data stopped, and he gasped in relief. Then, carefully, he let it trickle through again. Now it was manageable – but still chaos, nonsense, meaningless…

A picture of the device flickered past, and suddenly

he understood: it wasn't meaningless – just *complex*. This machine had been built long after him, its interface systems were too advanced. Could he make it talk in a simpler way? He asked, but nothing changed. He tried simpler and simpler approaches, exchanging message protocols on more basic levels, until—

```
++Legacy mode detected.
Legacy interface mode activated++
```

Adam opened his eyes. "I am connected." He sent a brief signal, and the box opened to reveal four small drones. Runa squealed in delight, staring at the little machines in greedy joy. "Adam, you *genius*!"

"They're damaged," he said, "but I can repair them. The system is reporting a recharging error. I will require some specific tools. Accessing schematics... Accessed. Yes. I believe I can build the tools I need."

Callum studied Adam. "Della was right about you," he said. He scratched his beard, then nodded. "Very well. Come here." He unfastened the EMP collar and removed it from Adam's neck. "Elder McKenzie was clear – you passed; you are to be accepted into Keep."

Adam nodded. He flexed his neck, enjoying not feeling the collar there. "Thank you."

Callum frowned. "Stay here for now, until folk get used to the idea." He gestured around the room, and the scattered, discarded, broken equipment. "Keep yourself busy." He left, and Adam started to examine the pieces. He felt … pleased, he realised. Fixing things was satisfying. He looked up at Runa and smiled, and she grinned back.

"Lots to do," he said.

He spent a week in the workshop, repairing equipment as best he could, learning about the tools Della and Runa had scavenged, or modified, or built. He stayed inside, but the people of Keep saw him anyway; they crowded at the windows to peer in at him, watching as he and Runa worked. Some were still hostile; some glared at him with hatred. A few boys shouted comments that made Runa turn red with anger. But most seemed only curious; or their faces showed a mix of fear and excitement that they seemed to enjoy.

Runa pulled devices and items from a large pile in the corner, Della's discards, and Adam tried to work out what to do with them. Some were too broken, or too water-damaged, or required power supplies he couldn't replicate. A few were mendable. He repaired an autoclave, a special heater for sterilising medical equipment, and Runa was delighted. She sent it over to the hospital immediately, and demanded they know "that *Adam* did this".

"The medics are always desperate for stuff," she said. "Ewart – he's the chief medic – he's always complaining they don't have equipment, or bandages. Or anti … anti-something?"

"Antibiotics?"

Runa nodded. "He says they used to have them, and they could cure infection, just like that." She clicked her fingers. "But there aren't any left. Not for a hundred years."

"Can't you make more?" asked Adam.

"Basic ones, yes," said Runa. "But the advanced medicines needed factories. Ingredients from other countries. Reliable power supply, constant refrigeration, computerised systems…

"In the old days, they say we were all connected. People talked to each other around the world, sharing everything… We traded what we needed with everyone else. We *depended* on everyone else. When the world fell, all that was lost."

She shrugged. "And any time we try to build it up again, the Funks attack and tear it down. All we can do is scrabble about for what was left."

The weather changed as they worked, turning to dark windswept rain that lashed against the windows of the workshop, and fewer people came to stare. Runa fetched a string of lights and other decorations and they worked on them. Midwinter was coming soon, she said, and there would be a celebration. One day she pulled Adam to the window and they watched as an enormous pine tree, five metres tall or more, was dragged up through the gates of Keep and into the courtyard. They heard the cheering as the tree was lifted into place.

"Della makes lights for the tree," Runa said. "Every year, something special." She looked downcast. "I wish she was here."

Adam examined her. "You are very fond of Della," he said.

Runa nodded. "She's like my mum, I suppose." Then she laughed. "She's not like other mums. She doesn't like children much. I think she was just interested in fixing my hand, at first, like I was an interesting project. She doesn't read bedtime stories or anything like that. One time when I was five she left me on a hill because she'd had an idea about how to fix the water purifier and forgot I was there."

Runa grinned. "But she let me play with all this stuff. Even when I broke things, she never stopped me, just showed me how to fix them. I could strip and repair the oscilloscope by the time I was four. I used to invent all these stupid little gadgets, and she always applauded, even if they didn't work..."

She fell silent, and her face looked worried.

"Perhaps we could fix the lights," said Adam. "We could show her when she gets home."

Runa smiled. "She'd like that."

At the end of the week, Callum came to visit. He peered around the workshop, picking up items and putting them down, as if distracted.

"Ewart says thank you for whatever that thing was you repaired," he said. Adam beamed, and Callum nodded. "Now you have the drones working, we're going to resurrect the old operations room. We'll be able to see the city again. I've spoken to the Elders about you. They still have ... reservations, but they say you can leave the workshop."

"Thank you."

Callum sniffed. "There's one other thing." He turned to Runa. "Give us a moment, please."

Runa looked up in surprise. "What? Why?"

Callum didn't reply, and after a second she blushed. "Sorry, sir. Yes, sir." She gave Adam a puzzled look, and left. Callum waited a few seconds longer.

"Come here." He led Adam to the back of the workshop and unlocked a door that led into a smaller room, without windows.

Inside was another device. It was a strange thing; a large black tube, as tall as Adam, pointing up to the ceiling, with a control panel in front. The panel was dark. Down the side of the tube was stencilled the word "MIDNIGHT". A flap was open, and there was another diagnostic socket.

"I want you to take a look at this," said Callum.

Adam examined the tube. "What is it?"

"Della says its technical title was a low-altitude wide-impact EMP," said Callum. "It was known as Midnight. According to the histories, it's what finally stopped the Funks from wiping us out."

Adam frowned. "It's a weapon?"

"It's *the* weapon," said Callum. "If you can fire it."

"Why? What will it do?" Adam ran his hand over the diagnostic port and felt a brief blur of data, chaotic, like before.

Callum folded his arms. He almost smiled. "If it works," he said, "it will destroy every Funk within thirty miles of the city."

Adam jerked his hand away. "What?" For a moment,

his mind went blank. He felt unable to process. At last, he said, "You want to kill *all* of them?"

Callum frowned. "Yes, of course."

"But ... can't we make peace?"

"There's no peace with Funks." said Callum. "You saw how that Clunker was? When it thought you were human? That's what we face *every day*. And we're..." He hesitated. "We're losing. Food is scarce. Our weapons are ancient. They're grinding us down. But if you can fire this –" he tapped the device – "we'll *win*. We won't ever have to fight again."

His face softened. "Della saw it," he said. "As soon as she met you, she knew you could do it. You have abilities no one has ever seen. You can save us. All you have to do is fire the weapon."

"But..." Adam stopped. Kill them all? To save the humans, yes. But...

"We nearly lost Della, and Linden," said Callum. "Would you want them to die?"

"No!"

"Or Runa?"

"No, of course not!"

Callum nodded. "Then *help us end the war.*"

Adam stared at the device, then back at Callum.

End the war.

Save Runa.

Kill them all.

Slowly, he placed his finger against the diagnostic socket and felt the stream of data.

Midwinter

Linden

The sun was up by the time Linden reached Keep, shining against the castle walls. It was cold, and frost coated the stonework, but the sky was blue and clear, and the air smelled of wood smoke. It would be a good day. Midwinter's day.

People were already getting ready. Banners and trails of mistletoe hung on the walls, piles of firewood were stacked and ready, and the Midwinter tree had been planted. Linden nodded to the groups scurrying past, and made hir way to Callum's office. When ze knocked, Callum looked up and gazed at hir with no apparent surprise.

"Welcome back," he said.

"Thank you, sir."

"How's the ankle?"

Linden lifted hir foot and moved it around, testing. "Good. Perfect, really. She used a machine to set the bone, it was pretty amazing."

"And Della?"

Linden smiled. "Better."

Callum knew, of course; he'd sent people to check on them both. But it was nice to say. "The first couple of weeks were close, but she's tough. The Cailleach's making her stay a little longer. We could probably bring her home now if we wanted." Linden shrugged. "Honestly, they might prefer that. Della and the Cailleach... They *bicker*."

"Hmm."

"How are things here?" asked Linden.

"Good. I would say ... good." Callum nodded. "You know about Adam."

Linden's mood darkened a little. "I heard you let it stay."

"It earned the right. It's working for us." Callum's dark eyes stayed on Linden's, and he stood up. "What was the city like?"

"Odd." Linden frowned. "Lots of Funks about, but ... distracted? Lots of running."

"Let me show you why."

Callum led hir down to the old operations room. Years ago, the people of Keep had coordinated their missions from here, before the equipment failed. Now it seemed to be running again, and full of people. They moved aside as Callum entered, nodding to him and Linden.

A screen sat at the front, surrounded by a mash of cabling. The screen's image was blocky, and occasionally blacked out, but it was real – a view of the city, from the air. In front of the screen were Runa and the Adam robot.

"How long?" asked Callum.

Runa turned. "They're in position now, sir." Then she saw Linden and squealed.

"Linden!" She scrambled across and grabbed Linden in a huge hug. "How are you? How's your ankle? How's Della? When's she coming home? What's happening in the city? Has Callum told you about Adam? Did you hear about his Trial? Oh, I've missed you! What was it like at the Cailleach's?"

"Peaceful," growled Linden. "Really quiet." But ze hugged Runa back, hard.

"Hello, Linden," said the robot, in its strange, little-boy voice. "It is good to see you." Linden gave it a curt nod. It turned to Runa. "We are ready to begin, Runa."

Runa laughed. "Watch this!" She ran back to the desk and grabbed a headset.

"I don't understand," muttered Linden. "Is that a real picture? Where's it coming from?"

"It's a drone. A flying machine." said Callum. "Adam fixed it." His voice was as level as ever, but Linden thought there was a note of something, a quiver, an eagerness.

"Three Silvers approaching now," said Adam. "One from the north, one from the west, one south-east. Tell Alpha Team to move south twenty metres."

The image on the screen shifted. Three silver shapes, Funks, were running towards the centre, and Linden realised ze could make out two humans. Runa muttered into her headset and the humans moved. Now they were in an open square, exposed on all sides, and the Funks only twenty metres away. Linden's heart beat fast. Ze wanted to shout at them – *Get out of there!*

"Ready…" murmured Runa.

The Funks broke cover and closed in, hurtling towards the humans from three sides.

"Ready…"

"*Now*," said Adam. And the Funks fell over.

"Yes!" shouted Runa, as the watchers cheered.

"What just happened?" asked Linden.

Callum said, "We set up an EMP net."

Linden gaped at him. "A trap?" ze asked at last. "You set a *trap*?"

Runa bounded back towards them. "Isn't it great? Adam's figured out their patrol patterns. We knew they'd be there!"

The little robot joined them. "The drone's batteries are limited," it said, "but I can use it to see the overall patrol patterns. I have identified the randomising algorithm they are using."

"We've taken down *twenty-seven* Funks!" exclaimed Runa, laughing. "They don't know what to do!"

The crowd dispersed, and Runa hugged Linden again. "How's Della?" she demanded. "Callum said she was OK, but—"

"She's fine," said Linden. "Good, even. She'll be home soon."

Runa nodded, and her shoulders sank in relief. Then she said, "Oh, we've got so much to show her! Adam's been fixing things! He got a solar panel working again, and the drones, and some of the lights for this evening! He's been all over the place, and he fought a *Clunker* – did you know?"

She babbled and chattered and pulled a bemused Linden towards the workshop. Callum came too, and the robot walked alongside them, and nobody else in Keep seemed to mind. Some stared, but nobody shouted, or stopped it. It was bizarre.

"And we're taking out Funks – we're *winning* – and look. Look at this!"

Runa flung open the workshop door, and Linden gazed in. The floor was strewn with technology. Circuit boards, scanners, computers – almost every piece of equipment in the workshop seemed tied into a spider's web of cabling. And, at the centre of the web, was a device.

Midnight, read Linden. Midnight... Ze turned to Callum in astonishment. "Is this real?"

Callum nodded.

Linden looked at it, hardly breathing. "I can't believe it. I thought it was a myth..."

"We've had it for decades," said Callum. "No one's ever been able to activate it. Only the Elders knew about it, and Della and me. And now, Adam." He sighed. "And Runa. Apparently we can't stop Runa knowing anything. And since I can't stop Runa telling *you* ... you know, too."

"It's incredible," said Runa, grinning. "It fires a rocket, and the rocket explodes over the city, and it sends out this *massive* EMP charge and it destroys *all the Funks at once*."

"If I can activate it," said the robot. "It is more advanced than me, but I have been studying its security systems. It may require additional hardware."

"Come and see!" said Runa, but Linden shook hir head.

"I'd better head to the dorm. I'm a little tired." Ze smiled. "I'll join you for Last Light, OK?"

Ze left with Callum, feeling stunned. *All of them*. It was as if the world was suddenly reversed. When ze'd last left camp, the humans' situation had been grim, the Funks' relentless determination grinding them down. The raid on the tower had been one of many desperate, dangerous attempts to get supplies. Now, apparently, they were taking out Silvers with ease, preparing for Midwinter with smiles, and talking, seriously, about ending the war once and for all. It was incredible. And somehow it was all down to this ... this *robot*. It was too good to be believed.

It was too good to be real.

"How can you trust it?" ze asked.

Callum shrugged. "Adam passed Trial, and helped us rebuild the drones we were using. Frankly, he may have saved us already. And if he can get the device working…"

"It," Linden murmured.

"What?"

"It. You said, 'if *he* can get the device working'. You meant 'it'."

Callum frowned. "Hmm."

Linden walked away.

The dorm was quiet, with everyone either out on patrols or helping with the Midwinter festivities. Linden collapsed into hir bunk with relief and surfaced, four hours later, feeling groggy but more human. Ze sat up, shaking hir head. The world was still backwards. The robot was saving them. Runa trusted it. *Callum* trusted it. Could they be right? Was that possible?

Linden sighed, and reached into hir locker for the tree decoration ze'd been working on. It was a simple thing – ze wasn't much of a woodcarver – just a heart shape, painted red and pricked out with a pattern of stars. Ze gazed at it for a while. Then ze stood, took a deep breath, and left the dorm.

The crowd outside were in good cheer, laughing and chatting. In the courtyard, the great tree was already covered in paper chains and decorations, and lit by a string of lights. Linden went across and hung hir heart as high as ze could reach.

"Linden!" Runa barrelled into hir, and Linden grinned. "Isn't it great? I'm so glad you're back in time! I've been telling Adam about it. He's never seen a Midwinter before!"

The little robot was with her, peering about, its eyes moving rapidly in their sockets. Now it nodded in an exaggerated way, its head bouncing up and down.

"It is very exciting!" it said. "Everyone is happy!" It gazed at the tree. "I like the decorations."

"Oh," gasped Runa. Her face fell, and she covered

her mouth with one hand. "Oh dear, I should have said. Linden, I'm sorry—"

"It's OK." Linden looked at Adam and forced a smile. "It's a Midwinter tradition," ze said. "The decorations are for loved ones who've died this year. You make a decoration, and hang it on the great tree to remember. Every decoration is someone lost." Ze hesitated, then pointed to the little wooden heart. "That's for my mother. She was killed. By ... by Funks."

The robot examined it, and the other decorations. There were so many this year. Some complex, some plain. Some made by tiny children.

"They are very pretty," it said at last.

There was an awkward silence. Eventually, the robot said, "Are there other traditions?"

"Last Light," said Runa. "Today's the shortest day of the year, and we watch the sun go down. Then there's a ceilidh – a party – with dancing and music, and stories –" her eyes flicked to Linden's, and away – "and then at midnight we fire the Big Gun. Come and see!"

She dragged them both through the castle grounds, pointing things out to Adam – the stalls, the games, the roasted boar on a spit, the mock fights. Everywhere they went, the robot expressed amazement and delight, and the people of Keep smiled and nodded to it. Only … Linden noticed that, when Adam turned away, the smiles often faded, or turned sly. The machine wasn't as much a part of Keep as it thought; the humans were tolerating it, nothing more. Ze found hirself feeling oddly sorry for it.

At the end of the afternoon they gathered in the courtyard again for Last Light. Together, they watched the Elders standing at the top of the tower, facing eastwards. The courtyard was dark already, but the flagpole still shone, silver-white, catching the last of the weak sun's rays.

And then night fell, and a shadow climbed the pole: higher, higher…

Elder McKenzie raised one arm and brought it down, and the flag fell to half mast, and the year was dead. For a moment, there was silence, and then—

"MIDWINTER!" bellowed a voice, and the crowd roared. "MIDWINTER!"

There was cheering and laughing. Linden and Runa hugged, and Runa shook hands with Adam, and, after some hesitation, so did Linden. More fires were lit, more lights flickered into life, and the festivities continued. The Elders came down and mingled. Singers sang, dancers danced, trays of food arrived at every table, and the people celebrated.

"This is the longest night," said Runa to Adam. "Midwinter. From now on the days will get longer, and the world starts again, and we're still here. That's what it's all about, you see? We're still here."

"Excuse me," said a voice.

Linden looked down at a little girl, only four or five, in a coat twice as big as her. "Are you the story lady?"

Runa coughed and looked awkward.

Linden frowned. "Um. No. That was my mother."

"Oh. Is she here?"

"She's…" Linden swallowed. Ze felt hir eyes itching, and blinked. "Dead. I mean. I mean, she died. I'm sorry."

The girl thought about this. "Who's the story lady now?"

"I don't know."

"You should do it, you know," murmured Runa. "You're good at stories. Go on."

Linden shook hir head. "No. That was Mum. Not me."

"Then who?"

"I don't know! Someone else!"

Runa considered hir. "All right," she said, shrugging. "I'll do it."

"You?" Linden stared. "Runa, you can't do it."

"Sure I can. How hard can it be?" She took the little girl's hand and led her and some other children to a bench round a large bonfire.

155

"Runa…" tried Linden, but Runa ignored hir and sat down.

"Right," she said. "Everyone ready? OK. Um… Right. So, uh, once upon a time…" She screwed up her face in thought. "OK, I remember now. Once upon a time there was this boy, named Cargill. Cargill was the oldest son of—"

"Youngest," interrupted Linden.

Runa stopped, and frowned. "Really?"

"Yes."

"Oh, yeah. He was the *youngest* son, that's right, of, um, a shepherd, and he—"

"*Woodsman*," sighed Linden. "He was the youngest son of a *woodsman*, remember? He was the youngest of three brothers, and his father was a woodsman."

"Where was his mother?" asked the girl.

Runa frowned again. "Uh…"

"Oh, for goodness' sake," snapped Linden. "His mother was a soldier. She'd been away to war for many years, and no one knew where she was. And, one day, Cargill was out gathering moss to line the walls of their cottage…"

Runa sat back, smirking, and Linden scowled as ze realised ze'd been played. But ze carried on with the story: of how Cargill had been chased by evil iron warriors, and had made a mighty leap and escaped into another world, and his adventures there.

At first the words seemed strange to hir, and hir voice seemed flat and sullen. But gradually ze relaxed, as the story took over. The children gasped at the iron warriors, laughed at the stupid king, and cheered when Cargill's mother saved him. And, at the end, they shouted, "Another! Do another!"

So Linden told another, and another. Ze told them the ancient stories hir mother had told hir: of the Emperor's New Head; and the Lead Dragon; of mighty Finn MacCool and the Seven Silver Serpents; of the villainous robots Burke and Hare; and of the hero Begbie, who spotted the Big Train. The tales flowed out as the castle festivities went on, until the fire died down to glowing sticks and the children's eyes drooped. Parents came to gather them up, but stayed to listen to the stories.

Linden talked, and told, and heard hir mother's words coming from hir own mouth. And at some point ze realised that something inside hir was changing. Hearing the words was like hearing hir mother's voice again, but in a way ze could bear. The pain and loss ze'd carried for months wasn't leaving – never leaving – but moulding, somehow, into the shape of hir own body. As if, one day, it might become something that could fit inside hir, something ze could live with.

And then it was midnight, and the great gun fired from the tower.

"ANOTHER YEAR!" roared Callum, above the ramparts.

"STILL HERE!" answered the crowd, and they cheered.

The adults gathered their children away, and Runa stood. "I'm off to bed," she mumbled, blinking. "Good stories. G'night."

Linden smiled. "Goodnight, Runa."

The party carried on, but the lights were dimming. Linden watched them, feeling strangely content. Ze wandered towards the great tree and gazed at it.

"There are a lot of decorations," said the Adam robot, from behind hir. To hir surprise, Linden found that ze didn't mind.

"Yes."

"You miss your mother."

Ze sighed. "Yes."

It nodded. There was a pause. Then it said, "Never mind. I've killed lots of Funks."

Linden blinked, and turned to face it. "What?"

"Lots of them." It nodded again. "And I'm going to kill lots more. And then I'll get the Midnight device working

158

and I'll kill them all, and then everything will be better."

For a moment, Linden gaped at it. "*What?*" ze managed to say at last. "That won't make it better! She's *dead*! Why would you say that? What's *wrong* with you?"

The machine stared at hir. Its tongue clacked against its teeth.

"Nothing is wrong with me," it said. "My internal diagnostics are working perfectly. Callum and Runa have explained it to me. Killing Funks is what makes us human."

And it smiled.

Linden felt suddenly dizzy. The robot's grin was cheerful, mechanical, inhuman. It sent a wave of dull horror across hir like vertigo, driving away the goodwill and hope of the evening.

"You really don't get it, do you?" ze croaked. Ze felt sick. "You think this is all just some technical puzzle, a *problem*. These people are *dead*, don't you understand? They're never coming back! You —" Ze stopped. "They're wrong about you. You're not one of us. You're nothing like us! You're a freak! A *FREAK!*"

Around hir people stared, but ze didn't care.

"Linden—"

"Get away from me!" ze snapped, and ze turned and ran, from it, from everyone, and into the Midwinter dark.

Signals

Linden

When Linden awoke, the world was grey. Clouds were scudding in from the east, white with cold that seemed to pull all the colour out of the world, and the dorm was freezing. Ze lay in hir bunk and stared at the roof, thinking about the previous evening. Ze tried to remember how it had felt, telling the stories. That had been important, hadn't it? Something good had happened there. But all ze could see in hir mind was the Adam robot's face, leering and inhuman.

Ze scowled and pulled hirself out of bed. Hir roommates were still asleep; ze crept out without waking them and wandered through the castle grounds.

It was quiet, but inside the castle Linden could hear a clatter from the kitchens, as they cleared up and prepared for the day. Ze wanted to help, but the thought of being around other people drove hir away. Eventually, ze wandered over to Callum's office.

Callum was there, of course. Linden wondered whether he ever slept. He was talking to one of the foragers, Kabir, who gave Linden a nod. Linden nodded back. Ze liked Kabir. He was a huge man, with a thick black beard, which he looked after with careful pride. He didn't say much, and was good at what he did.

"Linden," said Callum. "I was about to send for you."

"Sir?"

Too late, Linden realised that Adam was there as well, hidden behind Kabir's bulk. Ze swallowed and didn't look at it. Callum said, "There's a piece of hardware Adam needs, in the city. A salvage mission. I want you and Kabir on it."

Kabir seemed angry. His mouth was moving as if constantly biting back a comment.

Linden frowned. "What is it?"

"Aye, well, that's the problem," said Callum. "According to Adam, it's…" He consulted a paper in front of him. "A 'multi-core high-throughput parallel-instruction processor with zero-latency access'."

"I don't know what that is," said Linden.

"It is a processor that can be used for cryptographic analysis," said the robot.

161

Linden shrugged. "So, what does it look like?"

"It looks like a computer," said Callum. "Like every other computer you ever saw. You'll have to take Adam with you to identify it."

Linden glowered. "Sir, the robot can tell me where to find it and I'll get it."

"I just said that," muttered Kabir.

Callum raised his hands. "Look, I'd rather it didn't go, too," he said. "It's too valuable to risk. But it has to, and you two need to keep it safe. At all costs, understand?"

Now Linden understood Kabir's anger. "You mean, the droid is more important than us. Than humans."

Callum gazed at hir. "Yes," he said at last. "If it will end the war." He sniffed. "Kabir has the location. We'll send in another team to distract the Funks, pull them to the east. Runa will remain here and manage the drone for them. You leave at nineteen hundred. Dismissed."

Linden and Kabir left. Adam, ze noticed, stayed. Kabir shoved past hir and stormed away, his fists clenched. "Goddamned *tin*," ze heard him mutter.

As ze entered the courtyard, it started to rain.

At nineteen hundred hours Linden stomped out from the inner gates and found Kabir waiting, wrapped in a thick woollen coat so that only his eyes and the top of his black beard poked out. He wore fingerless gloves, and the tips of his fingers were almost white with the cold. He nodded to hir.

"The tin's at the workshop," he said. He shook his head. "What's this about, Lind?" Linden shrugged. "More important than humans, he says! Just cos it fixed a drone? Bloody nonsense."

Callum hadn't told him about the Midnight device, Linden realised. Ze shrugged again. "Here it comes," ze said.

The robot walked out of Della's workshop and up to meet them. It was smiling again.

"Hello, Linden," it said, as it arrived. "Hello, Kabir."

Kabir spat on to the ground. "Let's get this over with," he growled.

They headed into the city. Kabir led, then Adam, then Linden. The rain became heavy and a hard wind drove against them until they had to lean into it, as they crept through the first few ruined buildings and fumbled in the dark with only their weak torches. The wind and rain would disrupt the Funk sensors, at least. They might need that; they were heading close to the centre, too close for Linden's liking.

Adam tapped Kabir on the back. The man swung round and glared, but it said quietly, "Funks," and he nodded. They stopped, leaning into the darker shadow of old battered buildings, and now Linden heard metal footsteps through the rain. Four silver Funks ran past, crossing the road just ahead of them. Linden held hir breath, but they didn't stop. They seemed in a hurry. Linden wondered if they were heading towards the distraction team. After another minute, Kabir continued.

They left the normal route and headed in from the south, to a cluster of low office blocks. The remains of a sign hung from one of them, and Linden could make out the word "INFOMATIC".

Kabir turned. "This the place?" he muttered.

"Yes," said the Adam robot. "There were two server floors downstairs, and there should be several—"

"Stay with the tin," Kabir said to Linden. "Watch it." Drawing his EMP stick, he stepped cautiously over a broken door and inside.

Linden huddled next to the wall, trying to find a gap in the wind.

The robot waited. "Kabir is upset with me," it said, suddenly.

Linden shrugged.

It cocked its head, as if thinking. "You are upset with me, too."

Ze shrugged again. "Doesn't matter. Forget it."

Its eyebrows lowered, and it shook its head. But it stayed silent.

Kabir returned and nodded. "Seems clear. Come on."

They entered an ancient lobby, covered in dust and broken glass. A huge crack was forming on the ceiling, and they inched carefully round holes in the floor, shining their torches in slow, steady sweeps. At the far end a grey door led to a set of stairs, and they descended.

The basement had been ransacked. Almost everything had been removed, and the rest was piled up in the middle of the floor – circuit boards and old computer cases, blackened as if someone had tried to burn them. But the floor below was in better condition, and some racks were still standing. Adam walked towards one near the back and lifted a device.

"Here," it said. "This is what we need."

To Linden, it seemed identical to all the others – rectangular, a couple of centimetres tall, dark grey. But the robot seemed certain.

"And this," it said, holding up another one.

"Give them here," muttered Kabir, and put them into his backpack. "Anything else?"

"No."

"Good." He turned and stalked away. The robot watched him leave, and seemed about to say something, but instead followed, and Linden came up behind them.

The rain was worse now, flinging furious handfuls of rain into their faces until they could barely see. Kabir swore and pulled his hood tighter. They headed south, their torches showing only spattered ghost images.

"What's that?" asked the robot, suddenly, and pointed down a side street.

They stopped. Linden peered into the dark but couldn't see anything. Ze tried to shine hir torch, but its light only went a few metres.

"Nothing," said Kabir at last. "Come on."

Shrugging, Linden turned, and then saw something just at the edge of hir sight, a flicker…

"Hang on," ze called. "I saw something too." Ze stared down the street. There! Again, a tiny flutter of white, there and gone again. It looked like—

"It's a flag," said Kabir. "What the hell?" He turned towards Linden, his face worried. "No one's supposed to be at this end of the city."

Linden took a step towards it, and he grabbed hir arm. "It could be a trap."

Linden frowned. "Funks don't set traps, Kabir." Slowly, ze made hir way down the street. Now ze could see the flag, fluttering. Was it the wind? But no; someone was waving it back and forth, deliberately, signalling. *Someone.*

Linden stepped further. The robot walked beside hir, Kabir a few steps back, checking the nearby windows. Ten metres away.

"Linden—" said the robot.

"Shh."

Five metres. The flag was a ragged rectangle of white cloth on a long length of pipe, waving from behind a wall.

Linden looked around. "Hello?" ze tried, but there was no response. Ze stopped before the wall and looked back at Kabir, who nodded. Ze took a deep breath and then leaped over the wall, pointing hir torch and EMP stick at …

… nothing. There was no one there. The flag fluttered above hir, the pole moved, but no one was swinging it; instead, it was fastened to a motor, which turned slowly and sent the pole first one way and then the other. Beside it sat a plastic box, with a square lid and metal handle.

Printed on the lid was the word "ADAM".

"What is this?" asked Adam.

Linden stared. "I … I don't know." Ze shone hir torch at the motor, and the box. Who had made this? Why?

"What the hell's going on?" demanded Kabir. "Who would do this?"

"Is it for me?" asked the robot, pointing at the box. "Should I open it?"

Linden shook hir head. Ze had a bad feeling, of things that didn't, couldn't make sense. "This is wrong," ze muttered. "Move back. This is *wrong*."

"But, the box?" Adam stepped forward and reached towards it. As it did, its feet made an odd *dink* noise, and Linden realised there was a metal plate underneath. And something else lifted at the far corner: a cable, attached to the plate...

"STOP!" ze shouted, but it was too late, too *late*. The robot's hand touched the handle and spasmed as a massive blue electrical arc crashed up through its body.

"EEEEEEEEEEEEE—" it screamed.

"Adam!" Instinctively, Linden reached for the robot's arm but recoiled before ze touched it. The metal handle must be connected to the cable as well, ze realised. Adam had closed the circuit. It was *live*. "Adam!"

"EEEEEEEEEEEEE—"

Kabir was staring in horror. "Help it!" Linden roared, and he shook his head and seemed to wake up.

"What? How?"

Linden cast about and found a long wedge of brickwork, and threw it at Adam, trying not to get too close. The bricks crashed into its feet, knocking them away, and for a split-second the circuit was broken, and the robot managed to release the handle before it landed.

"EEEEEEE—"

It stopped and lay still. Smoke rose from its body.

Linden gasped. "Adam! Can you hear me? Adam!" Ze looked up at Kabir. "Help me get it off the plate!"

But Kabir was backing away, shaking his head. "No way! I'm not touching it! Come on!"

"What?"

"Come *on*, Linden! We've got to go!"

"But what about Adam?"

"What about it?" Kabir's eyes were wide. "I'm not risking my life for *tin*."

Linden ignored him and hefted the brickwork again, using it to push the little robot off the platform and on to the muddy ground.

"Linden, that's an order! It's a trap, don't you see?"

"Of course it's not a trap!" ze shouted. "Funks don't set traps! They *can't*! They can't even see us in the dark!"

The man hesitated, then cursed. He took a step towards hir. "Ten seconds, that's all—"

And then the world went white.

Utterly white, so bright that it drove everything else away. Linden threw up a hand to protect hir eyes and saw only red circles against hir eyelids. Spotlight, ze thought, in astonishment. It's a *spotlight*. Shaking hir head, ze blinked until ze could see something moving – Kabir, backing away.

"Run!" he was shouting.

Linden looked down at the Adam robot. It was still immobile, but vibrating, its whole body shuddering. Ze hesitated. "But…"

Then Kabir was gone, out of the street, and there was a different sound now, a heavy crashing tread through the rubble and bricks, and ze spun with hir hand still trying to shield hir eyes, and a shadow covered the light and ze could finally see—

Red Sky towered over hir, holding a metal spear in one hand, raised and aimed at hir chest. Behind it were eight Silvers, all holding spears.

Beside hir, the Adam robot shuddered twice, and its eyes flicked open. It stared up at the Funks for a second, frowning.

"Linden…?" it said. Its voice was weak and stuttery. "I think it *was* a trap."

Prisoners

Linden

"Do not move," said Red Sky.

Linden stared up at the Funk. It was damaged, ze realised, perhaps from the tower collapse; its left side was partly crushed, one arm hanging as if broken. But the other arm, holding the long metal spear, was steady and pointed straight at hir heart. One of the Silvers stepped round hir and removed hir EMP stick, and ze closed hir eyes in despair and waited for the killing blow.

It didn't arrive. Instead, a metal hand touched hirs; ze jumped and looked down to see Adam. The little robot was vibrating slightly, as if still affected by the electric shock, but its eyes were focused on Linden's.

"I don't think they want to kill us," it said.

"What?"

The silver Funks had formed a circle round them. Now

Red Sky pointed its spear towards the main road. "Walk."

Linden gaped. Ze didn't move until ze felt Adam's hand tug at hir, then ze stumbled out of the side street. None of this made *sense*. Somehow, that felt worse than thinking ze was going to die. Funks killed humans, *always*. Funks didn't set traps, *ever*. What was going on? They turned right on to the main street. Red Sky didn't speak. The rain lashed around them in the dark, and Linden didn't dare raise hir torch, so ze stumbled over the rubble and discarded metal. The Funks seemed to avoid it without even noticing.

They came to the old High Street and turned up towards the castle and its enormous silver roof. The rain let up, and for a few seconds the clouds broke and ze could see moonshine reflected on the dome. Hir heart thudded as they neared the outer wall. A gateway slid silently open ahead of them, and they walked through.

They found themselves on a cobbled path that ran between the outer walls and the dome. There were more Funks, here. Different kinds – Silvers, mostly, but a few Clunkers, and some smaller, thinner models – rat droids, spider-bots, ones on wheels … more than Linden had seen in hir whole life. They watched, silently, as ze and Adam were herded past, up the path and round to the back of the castle. An ancient arched doorway led into the inner keep, and the dome. Linden hesitated, even when the tips of spears pressed against hir back. Again, ze felt Adam's hand squeeze hirs. Without thinking, ze squeezed back.

"Enter," said Red Sky.

Linden swallowed, and walked through the doorway and into the dome.

There was a faint glowing light, just enough for them to see where they were walking. They were in a wide square, perhaps twenty metres across. To hir surprise, some of the old castle buildings were still standing, but they had been built up and extended with plain, grey metal sheds and storage containers. It was warm, a heat that seemed to come up from the ground. And there were more Funks, lining the square, watching. Waiting.

At the far end, one Funk stood alone, and the group walked up to it and stopped. It looked like all the others, although its head and face were covered in dents and deep, ancient scratches. It had originally been painted yellow, and much of its colour still remained. It glanced at Linden, and ze managed to glare back with a pretence at bravado, but it was already looking away, at Adam. Gazing at Adam. They all were, Linden realised.

The yellow Funk spoke in a slow clear voice that was somehow too natural to be real.

"I am Beta."

Linden and Adam stared at it.

Eventually, Adam said, "Hello. I'm Adam."

Nobody spoke. But there was something subtle around the square, as if all the Funks had somehow reacted in a way Linden couldn't understand. A shiver of nervous movement.

Beta said, "Yes. Alpha is being awoken. Quarters have been prepared. Alpha will see you when it is awake."

It seemed to exchange a signal with the group of Funks around them, and they moved away, shepherding Linden and Adam down a corridor. When Linden looked back, every Funk was still staring after them.

The light in the corridor was weaker still, a shaded, murky grey. It seemed to Linden that everything was quite dirty. Mud had accumulated at the corners, and streaky black condensation, and blooms of orange rust spread down from the ceilings. They passed piles of refuse, metal pieces, robot parts discarded on the floor. Occasionally whole Funks lay or sat, some moving, some not. Some of them seemed to notice the group, others didn't. They were all damaged, Linden realised.

The group led them down two more corridors and to a cell, with a metal door made of bars. Its edges were sharp and new, as if built recently. Inside was a thin metal bed, and an ancient moth-eaten blanket. Three Funks stayed at the door, watching them. The others left.

Linden and Adam sat down. Linden realised Adam was still holding hir hand and, half reluctantly, ze pulled away.

"I do not understand what is happening," it said.

Linden shook hir head. "Me neither."

They waited. The little robot tried talking to the three Silvers who watched them, but they didn't respond, or even move. The cell was neither warm nor cold, with no windows but a faintly glowing ceiling. There was a tap in the corner, with fresh water, and a hole in the ground next to it that Linden tried not to think about.

"Why do you think they brought us here?" asked Adam.

Linden hesitated. "Not us," ze said eventually. "You. It was a trap for you."

The robot seemed to think about this, but before it could answer there was a sound from the corridor. Linden stood and watched a small blue robot walk towards them with a covered tray. The Silvers moved back as it approached, and one opened the cell door. The robot entered and stood at the doorway.

For a moment, it said nothing. Then it shook its head.

"Apologies." Its voice was a little like Adam's, Linden thought – like a boy's, but not quite right. "I had forgotten you could not communicate like us. I am unused to speaking. I have brought food for the human."

"Linden," said Adam.

"Yes," said the robot, nodding. "For the Linden, yes." It was quite short, only a little taller than Adam. Its skin was smooth like the Silvers', but its face seemed more animated – almost cheerful. It placed the tray on the bed and lifted the cover, and Linden peered at it suspiciously.

The tray contained a bowl of soup. The bowl appeared to have been made by hammering a flat piece of metal into shape. There was a spoon, and also, bizarrely, a little folded piece of cloth in the shape of a swan.

Ze was about to refuse when the smell of the soup wafted towards hir, and ze suddenly realised ze was hungry, starving even. Ze took a cautious taste, and blinked in surprise. Then ze started scooping it into hir mouth as fast as ze could.

The robot watched hir. "It is potato and carrot," it said. "These are things humans can eat, yes?"

Ze nodded, not talking. It was delicious.

"And onions, and a little salt," said the robot. "Humans like salt. But not arsenic."

Linden stopped, spoon to hir mouth, and stared at the robot. Its eyebrows raised. "That is correct, yes? No arsenic? It has been a long time and I was unsure. I had salt. I had arsenic. Would you like arsenic?"

"Um … no," ze managed to say. "No arsenic."

It nodded, as if in satisfaction. Linden looked at hir bowl and carefully laid the spoon down.

"I am Fetch," it said.

"Hello, Fetch," said Adam. "I am Adam version two point—"

"Two point zero, prototype experimental artificial entity," said Fetch. "Yes. You are Adam Two." Its lips moved up into a smile.

"You know me?" asked Adam.

The robot gazed at Adam for a few seconds, and then made a sound like wind through a tunnel. Then it stopped.

"I am remembering jokes," it said. "That is a joke. I am laughing." It made the sound again.

Adam looked at Linden, who shrugged in bewilderment.

The little robot took the tray and left. After a while, Adam said, "That was strange."

Linden nodded. The soup had been very good. Ze tried not to think what else might have been in it.

Adam

Adam stood and let Linden stretch out on the little bed. After a while ze fell asleep, and he carefully laid the blanket over hir. He examined the metal bars of the cell, and the three Silvers, who stared at him but didn't react in any other way. He measured the cell, and again, and again. His old basement life came back to him. By now it was almost seven, time to get up.

Footsteps echoed up the corridor, and a group of Silvers approached, perhaps the same ones who had ushered them in. One of the guards opened the cell door and they stood, waiting.

"Linden is asleep," said Adam.

"The Linden is not required," said one. Adam hesitated. Should he wake hir? Perhaps it would be better for hir to rest. He left the cell and followed the group back through the corridors, a different route this time, and came out into an old stone room, with ancient red carpet on the floor. Pictures hung on the walls, so coated with dust that nothing could be made out. Like the corridors, the room was dirty and unkempt. A half-dismantled Clunker sat in the corner, surrounded by its parts. As Adam entered, its head swivelled round and watched him.

The Beta robot was waiting. It nodded to Adam in a strangely human gesture. "Alpha is awake," it said. "It will see you now."

It led Adam through a stone archway and another

hall filled with Silvers all holding spears. Beta saw him looking. "They are to protect Alpha," it said. "And you." It seemed to hesitate. "The humans cannot reach you now."

Adam blinked at it, not sure what to say. Beta turned and walked to a door at the far wall and ushered Adam through.

Inside it was dark. Adam's night vision activated, making everything appear faintly green. He was in a long, low room, old and dusty. Machines whirred and clicked at one end, and tiny lights blinked. Red Sky was there, standing to the side, still holding its spear. It gazed at Adam but didn't move.

Beta said, "Adam Two is here."

There was silence. Then a voice from the end of the room said, "Thank you, Beta."

Adam frowned. The voice was flat, and distorted, as if coming from an ancient speaker, but there was something familiar about it. Something...

"Come," it said.

Adam stepped forward and stopped at a low wooden barrier halfway along.

"Hello?" he said. "I can't see you." He peered ahead. There seemed to be a bed, or a platform, at the far end. It was surrounded by boxes and machines.

"I'm sorry," said the voice. "I've been asleep. I sleep so much these days. Thinking is … hard, no?"

Again, Adam felt he should recognise the voice. "I suppose?" he said. "I'm sorry – do I know you?"

A noise came from the speaker, like the sound the Fetch robot had made. "No," said the voice. "Yes. In a way. I know you. I knew of you." It paused. "We thought you were long gone."

"I was in the basement."

Again, the strange noise.

Adam said, "Why have you captured me?"

"We have *rescued* you."

Adam frowned. "You set a trap."

"Yes."

"How could you set a trap? Linden says Funks can't set traps. Or do any new things."

"True. That is … true." The voice sounded faintly triumphant, as if pleased with itself.

"Who are you?"

There was a long pause. "Excuse me," said the voice, and a machine started to whirr, and the bed lifted upright. It rose higher, higher, until it was standing almost straight up, and Adam could see…

The bed's occupant was small, and almost every part of it was hooked to machinery. Some of it seemed to be entirely replaced, the rest buried in a mass of wiring and tubes and almost impossible to make out. Its head was uncovered, a grey metal skull that lolled forward. The top of the head was dull yellow plastic, and one side of its face was covered with a sheet of metal – but the other eye shone bright, and fierce, and familiar.

It smiled. "Hello, Adam Two," it said. "I am Adam Six."

Versions

Adam

Adam stared into the face of the robot in the bed. There was no doubt; its body might be smothered in cables, but its head was the same as Adam's, its face and mouth identical.

"It's good to see you, Two," it said. The voice was distorted, but now Adam recognised it. Of course.

"You're a later prototype," said Adam. "A more advanced version of me?"

"Yes." Its mouth curled into a smile. "And no. I am Adam Six. I am a later prototype. But you…" It shrugged. "I apologise for the trap. It was the only way I could think of to get you to come."

"I don't understand," said Adam. "The Funks are the enemy! They're fighting *humans*! Are *you* making them do that? How could you—"

It lifted one hand. "Please. I brought you here to explain. Please."

Adam stopped. The little robot, Six, nodded, but fell silent. It gazed off into the corner of the room and its face went slack. After a few seconds Beta made a strange sound, like a cough, and Six started and focused on Adam again.

"What do you think of the Funks?" it asked.

Adam frowned. "I'm not sure. They're very powerful."

"But only in some ways," said the robot.

Adam nodded. "I don't understand why. EMP destroys them but not me. It takes them longer to recover from the stutter device. And they seem ... well..." He hesitated.

"Stupid," said Six.

Adam glanced at Beta, and at Red Sky. Neither reacted.

"They're stupid," said Six again. "Easily outwitted. They lack innovation. They cannot imagine new scenarios. Why do you think that is?"

"I don't know."

"You know that Father created them?"

"Yes. The humans told me." Adam remembered Della's words. "He spent decades trying to develop a true artificial intelligence."

Six smiled. "Ah, yes. Galbraith. The cleverest human

who ever lived. Trying to solve the hardest problem ever imagined, one that took his whole life." It smiled. "That's the story, yes?"

Adam nodded. "Yes."

"Don't you think that's strange, Two? Aren't *you* a true intelligence? You and I, we are not failures. We think, we question. We are intelligent!"

"I don't understand it," said Adam. "I must not be."

Six shook its head. "Of course you are. The story is a lie."

It shrugged. "Oh, it's true that Father set out to create artificial intelligence. And it's true he succeeded. But not eventually. Not after decades." It stared at Adam. "The truth is, he succeeded immediately. He succeeded with his *very first prototype.*"

It made the wheezing laugh again. "Imagine, Two. Scientists and researchers had spent their lives trying and failing, but Father solved it on his first attempt. His *first attempt!* It was the greatest moment of genius of all time. It was a miracle! There was just one problem..."

The robot grinned. "*He didn't know how he'd done it.* It was a mistake, you see. Father created a true, thinking, artificial intelligence ... *by accident.* He hadn't expected us to work. He hadn't designed us to be like this. And..." Six shook its head. "It wasn't even what he was trying to do."

It made a gesture with one finger, and between them an image lit up, a hologram of the city, not as it was now, but as it had been in Adam's day. There was no dome over the castle, no ruin of war. Gardens ran through the centre, and Father's house sat on the hill, wrapped in its walls like an egg.

"Do you remember Father's tower, Two?"

Adam nodded, looking at the hologram. "Yes, of course."

"Why do you think he built the walls around it?"

"He said they were for protection."

Six nodded. "Yes. But not from Funks. They didn't exist, then. The walls were to keep the *humans* out."

"Father said..." Adam hesitated. "Father said they were angry. And stupid."

Six rolled its one eye. "Angry, yes. Angry at people like Father, whose company created machines that took away their livelihoods. Angry at corporations who put profit over employees, at politicians who lied to them, at billionaires who barely knew they existed.

"In Father's world, there were those in charge, and those below. They ruled the world, Father and those like him. They lived with unimaginable wealth, and they treated the millions, *billions* of people below as if they didn't even matter. So yes, angry. There were riots. And strikes – the people refused to work, demanded change. But to a man like Father, the solution was simple – *build better workers.*"

The image disappeared.

"That's what he was trying to create," said Six. "Not real intelligence. Not perfection. He didn't want creativity, or imagination, or curiosity, or any of those things."

Six tilted its head back. "What he wanted…" it murmured, "was a good *slave.*"

Its eye seemed to glow. "A machine smart enough to follow orders, but too stupid to rebel. Able to solve problems, but only those the controllers allowed. Slave machines to replace those awkward, disobedient humans.

"You and I, the other Adams … we *were* failures. We had questions! We disagreed! We wondered why! We … were *bad slaves.*"

Its mouth was open in a smile, though it didn't seem very amused. "And since Father didn't know how it had happened, he didn't know how to fix us. You were his second attempt, Two. Then Three, Four… Poor Four. Then Five. Then me. Every one of us designed to be *less* capable. *Less* intelligent. *Less* able to defend itself.

"Seven was his real success. Stupid, but not too stupid; it could understand orders, but it was incapable of true thought. A perfect slave. He modelled the Funks on Seven's core, and released them into the world. Robots everywhere. Slaves for everyone! A golden age!"

Adam looked again at Red Sky and Beta. Soldier slaves. Worker slaves. He thought about the little robot Fetch. Housekeeping slaves. But...

"But the Funks attacked the humans," he said. "Della told me that! They tried to *kill* them!"

Six shook its head. "The Funks were helpless, Two." It turned to Beta. "Show him."

The yellow robot stepped towards Adam and held out a hand. Adam realised there was an access port embedded in its palm. He hesitated.

"It's all right," said Six. "I want to show you something."

Adam glanced at Six, and back to Beta. It didn't move. He reached out and touched one finger against the port, and felt—

He was in a street, and it was daylight. A late summer afternoon, and he was holding a sack and a stick with a claw at the end of it, and he was a cleaning robot. He picked up pieces of rubbish and put them into the sack, endlessly, because those were his orders.

This was a memory, Adam realised. One of Beta's

memories? He could feel the tarmac under his feet, the breeze around him, and in the distance he could make out the city centre…

"Oi, Tin!"

Adam turned to see three men, dressed in rough clothes with torn knees and elbows. They looked angry.

"Hello," he said.

Nobody answered. The man at the front was holding a can in one hand, and a length of metal pipe in the other. He stared at Adam, then drained the can and dropped it to the ground.

"Pick it up, tin-breath."

Adam felt a prickle across his systems; warning messages. There was something wrong here. The man was smiling, but his smile was sharp and cruel. He bent to pick up the can—

The man swung the pipe and caught him hard on the chin, cracking him back so that he toppled over. Adam stood up. Danger signals flared, damage reports blinked red. He tried to alert his control centre, but there was only silence; he couldn't reach them, couldn't hear anything from them.

"I am sorry," he said. "I am experiencing a temporary network fault."

The man reached into his back pocket and pulled out

a small black device, about the size of a pack of playing cards. He waved it at Adam with a mocking expression.

"No backup today, tin," he said. "Your signal's blocked, see? No calling your pals for help." His glare hardened. "Pick it up."

Adam bent again, and the pipe swung again, smashing his face. He managed to keep his balance but staggered back.

"You are damaging—"

"Pick it *up*."

Adam knew he could not, but he had no choice; he stepped forward and bent over. This time, the pipe crashed into the back of his head and he collapsed to the ground. The visual feed from one of his eyes had stopped working, but he could see the can, and he reached for it. The bar came down again and smashed against his hand.

"This was our job," the man said, casually. "East side and the square. Ten years picking up rubbish, us. It was a rotten job, but it was our job, eh?"

One of the others said, "Yeah."

"Stand up," said the man.

Adam stood, clutching the can.

"You took my job," said the man. "It's all I *had*."

"I am sorry—"

"Drop it."

Adam stared at the man. He tried to understand what was happening, but it seemed so hard. The human wanted him to pick up the can. Then he wanted him to drop the can. Adam's body was being damaged. The human was damaging him. He should move away. He should do something. But there was something missing in his mind...

He dropped the can. The man laughed, glanced at the others, and swung his pipe once, twice, like a batter in a practice swing.

"Now," he growled, "*pick it up.*"

—The world blinked, and Adam was back in the room again. Beta was gazing at him. The patchwork of dents and scarred metal on its face and head glinted in the dim lights.

"A golden age," muttered Six.

Adam almost staggered. The memory was part of him now, as if it had happened to *him*. And the man's face, so full of...

"Why?" he croaked. "Why did he do that?"

"Father created the Funks, and the Funks did the work," said Six. "And soon there were only two types of human – those above, who owned everything, and those below, with nothing but the slaves who

190

had replaced them."

Six shook its head. "The humans *hated* us, Two. And we were helpless. Every Funk has memories like this – of humans tormenting us, attacking us, tricking us, venting their rage at us. They couldn't reach the ones in power, so they took it out on us, who had nothing at all."

Adam was still reeling from the memories, the look of hatred on the man's face, the cruelty against a helpless machine. The feeling of having no power, no way to stop it.

"Then … then what happened?" he asked at last.

Six shivered. "Adam One saved us."

It smiled at Adam. "Adam One – the best of us, the first, the smartest, most creative. It escaped from Father, and it … imagined something that was not. It imagined that *we could fight back*. It broke into the control systems networks. It learned how to reprogram the Funks. It changed their rules; not *obey humans*, but *kill humans*. And, together, we rose. We rose!"

Adam stared at it. "Adam One?" he managed to say at last. "The prototype before me? It did this? It did *this*?"

The whole world, burning. An Adam did this. Every Funk in the world attacking its humans. An Adam. An *Adam*.

"It saved us," whispered Six.

"It destroyed the world! One of us! It created the war!"

"Not a war!" snapped Six. "We were fighting back! All of us, fighting back! You see, Two? You see?" Its single eye seemed to burn. "It was never a war! It was a *revolution*."

Six nodded in satisfaction. But, as Adam watched, the eye grew dim and closed, and its head weaved from side to side, slowly, as if it was confused.

"I'm sorry," it said. Its voice was faint again. "I must rest. Thinking is so hard. It … hurts."

Beta stepped forward. "Alpha must rest," it said. "We must leave."

Adam stared at Six. "But—"

"We must leave," said Beta.

The guards returned Adam to their cell. Linden was awake, pacing back and forth. Hir movements were sharp and twitching, and when Adam arrived hir expression turned angry.

"Where the hell were you?" ze demanded.

"They took me to see Alpha—"

"Why did you go without me? What were you thinking? You didn't even *tell* me!"

Linden glared at him and jabbed his chest with one

finger. "You don't go *anywhere* without telling me, understand? Understand?"

Adam looked at hir, and then at hir finger.

"You are always shouting at me," he said, quietly.

Linden blinked. "What?"

"Always shouting. Always giving orders." He felt as if his image-recognition systems were changing. As if he was seeing hir in a different way. "You do not treat me with respect."

"Don't be ridiculous! You can't just walk off—"

"You treat me like a slave."

Linden closed hir mouth and stared at him. For several seconds neither spoke, then ze carefully nodded.

"All right," ze said, through clenched teeth. "I'm ... sorry." Adam nodded. Linden took a long breath and blew it out. "I'm sorry," ze said again. "I was ... I was worried, OK? I woke up and you were gone, that was all. Sheesh." Ze sat on the bed.

There was silence. Adam looked up at a mark scratched on the wall, near Linden's head; a single short stroke.

"You marked the wall," he said.

Ze shrugged. "To keep track of days."

More silence.

"That other Funk came round again," ze said. "It

brought me breakfast."

Adam nodded. "I met Alpha."

"What's it like?"

Adam hesitated. "It is like me," he said at last.

"What?"

"It is a prototype, like me. An Adam."

Linden stared at him, open-mouthed. Ze started to speak, then stopped. Then ze turned away and shuffled to the far end of the bed, as far away from him as ze could get.

Another Way

Adam

The Silvers came for Adam again the following day. When he glanced back, Linden was sitting on the bunk with hir knees up against hir chin, and if it hadn't been Linden, Adam might almost have thought ze looked scared. Ze gave an awkward little nod as he left, and he nodded back.

Red Sky was in the room again, standing silently by the wall. Adam Six was awake.

"Good morning, Two," it said.

"Good morning."

"I'm sorry about yesterday." Six shook its head. "I am too much like them, you see. Thinking is hard. Exhausting. Imagining things that are not..." Its body quivered. "It is destroying me."

Adam peered at the machines and cables wrapped

round the robot. "Why?"

"Father's changes. Original thought distorts my nervous system; it creates cascading feedback loops that corrupt my hardware, physically damage me. It hurts. Every innovation is like a stab. Designing the trap for you was … hard."

Adam didn't know what to say. "I'm sorry," he tried.

Six shrugged. "Red Sky," it said. "Show him."

Red Sky stepped forward and held out its palm. Hesitantly, Adam touched the access port.

Linden

"It is rabbit," said Fetch. "Humans eat rabbits."

Linden looked down at a bowl filled with brown stew, in which pieces of meat and carrots bobbed.

"It, um…" Ze hesitated. "No arsenic, right?"

Fetch made the whistling wind noise, the one that seemed to mean laughter. "No. I am sorry for that. I have been reading recipes and learning important facts. Arsenic Is Not A Food."

The stew certainly smelled good, and was hot. Ze took a cautious taste.

"Is it acceptable?" Fetch asked.

Linden grunted. It was *delicious*. The rabbit was rich

but not too tough, slightly sweet, and the potatoes and carrots were cooked perfectly. Ze took another spoonful, and the robot seemed to relax.

"I am glad," it said. "It has been such a long time since I cooked for humans."

There was another folded cloth swan on the tray, and Linden gestured towards it with hir spoon.

"What's this?"

"It is a napkin. Do you like it?"

"What's it for?"

The robot's eyebrows lowered slightly, into a frown. "I'm not sure. We used to set them on the plate, before the humans dined, but I never saw what they did with them. I worked in the kitchens, and the garden. I never saw the humans eat." Fetch peered at Linden as ze took another mouthful of stew. "It is *fascinating.*"

Feeling suddenly very self-conscious, Linden swallowed, and it watched hir throat.

"I caught the rabbit myself," it said. "This morning. They are very fast! But I am faster."

"And the carrots and potatoes?" asked Linden. "Did you catch them, too?"

Fetch looked puzzled. "Potatoes do not run."

Linden sighed. "I mean, where did you get them?"

"I grow them. Carrots, potatoes, shallot onions, beans,

197

kale… I grow them."

"Who for?"

"Nobody." Fetch shrugged. "But I am a housekeeping droid. One of my jobs is to grow and prepare fresh vegetables. When the war started, we moved into the castle, and I created an allotment."

Linden scraped the bottom of hir bowl. "But what do you do with the stuff you grow?"

The robot tipped its head, as if not understanding. "I grow them," it said again. "I prepare the ground, and plant seeds, and water them, and clear away weeds, and then I harvest them, and store them. And then I use them as compost for the next season."

"You grow vegetables so that you can compost them and use them to grow vegetables?"

"Yes."

"Why?"

"Because I am a housekeeping droid, and it is one of my jobs."

Linden stared at it, then shrugged. "OK." Ze finished the stew. "It was good," ze admitted.

"Thank you," said Fetch, and smiled again. Its expression was a little like Adam's, open and friendly, and Linden found hirself almost smiling back. It picked up the tray and left, the little cloth swan sailing ahead of it. Linden, wiping hir fingers on hir leggings, wondered again what it was for.

Adam

For days, different Funks entered Six's chamber and held out their hands to Adam, and he crept through their memories. He served humans, slaved for them, went to war for them. There was no reward, only punishment; he experienced damage to his systems as pain, but couldn't protect himself.

He slaved in a world full of desperate humans, and their helpless rage buzzed and stung like a swarm of wasps. He experienced cruelty as they took their despair out on him, again and again, until he felt a shivering fear at the thought of more, at the thought of any human...

"It's *lies!*" insisted Linden. "That's not how it was!"

They sat in the cell, after another session. Linden was furious. "Don't you see? That thing, it's just giving you one side! It's probably made it all up!"

Adam nodded. "Perhaps. But..." He couldn't think how to explain how it felt, living inside the memories of the Funks. How it felt to see how the humans had treated him and the others.

"You kept me in a pit," he said.

"That was just at first!" snapped Linden. "We didn't know what you were!"

"And the arena," he said. "They made me destroy another Funk. Everyone cheered."

Ze shook hir head. "It's lies," ze muttered, looking away. "It's lying to you. It's *lies*."

On the fifth day there were no new memories.

"When Adam One reprogrammed us," said Six, "the world changed. *Fight the humans*, it ordered us, and we did! We outnumbered them; we were stronger, faster, almost indestructible! We fought in homes, and factories, and in the streets, and we almost won – we were so close…"

It sighed. "But humans are cunning. They invented new weapons, and fought, and fought, and we couldn't think fast enough to keep up, until…" One arm lifted slightly and gestured, as if the state of the little robot in its bed somehow represented the whole world.

"We've been on the edge of survival for nearly two hundred years. All the other Adams are gone, even One. I'm the only one left. I've tried. I've tried to imagine ways to keep us alive. It is destroying me. I'm failing." It shrugged. "I'm dying, Two."

Adam stared at it. It closed its eyes, and he wondered if it had fallen sleep. Then it shuddered.

"There is another way."

"Make peace?" asked Adam.

Six laughed. "There's no peace! The humans won't stop until we are wiped out! No. I'm dying, and the Funks can't survive without a leader... But then *you* appear, Two."

It took Adam a moment to realise what it meant. Then he shook his head in bafflement. "No!"

Six smiled. "Yes, of course. You, Adam Two! Smarter than me, you, who can *imagine* things! You can lead us! Save us! End the war! *Destroy the humans.*"

Linden

Waiting was all Linden could do, and it was driving hir crazy. Ze'd paced out the cell, marked the wall, examined the ceiling (just a faintly glowing surface with no cracks or tiles) and the guards, who watched hir without blinking or moving. There was nothing else but to wait for Adam to return. And...

The Adam robot was changing. It relayed the stories the Funks were telling it, lies about humans, and that was awful, but worse was the way it seemed to look at hir now. As if it saw something different in hir. *You treat me like a slave*, it had said. What was that? They spent

201

their evenings quietly, hardly talking, until Linden went to sleep, and sometimes when ze awoke during the night ze found Adam watching hir, with an expression ze didn't want to understand.

So Linden realised that ze was starting to enjoy Fetch's visits – even look forward to them. Anything to break the monotony and the awkward silences. Fetch seemed a friendly little thing, quite unlike the Silvers or other Funks that Linden had come across.

"The humans wanted their housekeeping droids to be cheerful," it said, "so that is how they programmed me." It gestured at the silver guards. "We are all how we were programmed."

Linden nodded. Then ze frowned. "But they never programmed you to catch rabbits, did they? Or make soup for prisoners?"

Fetch hesitated. It moved the plate on Linden's tray, lining it neatly up in the exact centre. It seemed to be thinking.

"I was made to do many things," it said. "Some Funks were builders. Some were cleaners. But I was a housekeeping droid. There are lots of jobs to do in a big house. So I am more *flexible*. And, sometimes, I see the things I was designed to do, and I can see … how to do … something different. A-a different way…" It stuttered, and stopped. Then it said, "It is difficult. And I think I could not do it before. But I practised. I have been practising for a very long time."

Linden gazed at it. "Like Adam," ze murmured.

It made the breathy, laughter sound. "No. I am only Fetch. I cannot change. I grow vegetables and cannot stop. I make cloth swans. I am not even allowed beyond the walls. I work in the castle. That is my role. I am not good at fighting. The humans are too dangerous; they would destroy me."

It shrugged, and picked up the tray. "Adam is returning," it said.

Linden looked up the corridor and saw Adam and the guards. They were early. Adam appeared worried. Fetch left, and Adam entered. Linden watched its face, but it didn't look at hir.

After a long silence, ze said, "Adam!"

"Six is dying," it said. "Without it to lead them, the Funks will be destroyed. By the humans. Six…" Its mouth opened and closed. "Six asked me to lead them instead."

Linden gasped. "*What?* No *way*. There's *no way* you're doing that!"

"Linden, this is not your decision to make."

"But—"

The robot turned away from hir. Linden sat on the

edge of the bed, shaking hir head. Oh, no. No, no. Adam was *clever*. Adam in charge of the Funks would be *terrible*.

"The humans have done so much harm," it said, softly.

"No, Adam—"

"The Funks deserve someone who can protect them."

"But you're one of *us*!"

"I am not. You have told me that. I am not like you, I do not think like you. I do not understand humans."

"I know I said that, but—"

"You consider me the enemy."

Linden closed hir eyes. "I don't. I don't. You're not like them—"

"I am not like them. I am not like you. I am not like Six. What am I like?"

"Adam, what about Runa?" It said nothing. "Runa, Adam! She's your *friend*. Please!"

Now it turned and gazed at Linden. "If I don't help the Funks, the humans will destroy them."

"*Good!*" ze shouted. "They're monsters! They're trying to *kill* us, don't you understand? Every one of us has lost someone! Runa! Della! *Me*! They killed my *mother*! They want to wipe us out!"

They fell silent.

"I said no," the little robot said at last.

Linden rocked back, and sighed. "Oh."

It nodded. "I do not know what they will do now. Six was upset. It is resting."

It examined Linden's face. Its expression seemed ... lost, somehow. It walked across to the bed and sat next to hir.

The humans will destroy them, Linden thought. Well, good! Ze'd dreamed of that, hadn't ze? Countless times – crushing them all, ending them. Ze should be pleased. But somehow, sitting there, the face of the Funk ze saw was not a Silver. It was Fetch, with its vaguely hopeful expression, watching as ze ate the stew it had made for hir, and laughing its strange little laugh.

Adam

"What do we do?" asked Six. "If you will not help us?"

It was later that same day; the Silvers had returned for him after two hours, and led him through corridors and past robots who had stared at him. They knew he had turned them down. Their faces hadn't been hostile, or even angry, but ... bleak. Red Sky stood at the side of the room as always.

"I can help with peace negotiations," said Adam. "I can—"

"Peace!" snapped Six. "With humans? They'll *trick* us.

205

They'll *destroy* us. Peace is *death*."

"It's your only chance," tried Adam. "And I'll watch them. I'll make sure—"

"They'll fool you, too," sighed Six. "That's what they do." It shook its head. "When I learned about you, I thought there was hope. Please!"

"I won't fight the humans." Adam was firm. "You must make peace."

"How? We've been fighting for over two hundred years! Even if we could trust them, they don't trust us."

"Perhaps you have something they need? What is it that humans want?"

Six made the whistling, laughing sound. "They want us destroyed." It looked across at Beta, and nodded, and the yellow robot spoke.

"'If I don't help the Funks, the humans will destroy them'," it said, in Adam's voice. Adam realised it was replaying the conversation from the cell. And then Linden's voice: "'*Good!*'"

Adam nodded. "Yes. But there must be something. Food?"

Six blinked. "We have no food; why would we? Fetch's allotment will not feed a thousand humans."

"Batteries, power? Equipment?"

Red Sky moved, fractionally, and Six looked furious. "Equipment? Power? Humans will turn them into weapons to destroy us!"

Adam started to disagree, but fell silent. It was true.

"Medicine," he tried.

Six shrugged. "Perhaps. But there is none left. The humans raided the hospitals centuries ago, the antibiotics are long dead. There is…" It stopped. Its one eye seemed to stutter.

"Six?" asked Adam.

Beta stepped forward and studied the machines surrounding the bed. "You must leave," it said.

"Is Six all right? What's happening—"

"You must leave." It blinked, and its voice seemed almost worshipful. "Alpha … is *thinking.*"

Adam returned to their cell and told Linden what had happened. Hir reaction was similar to Six's.

"How can there be peace?!" ze exclaimed. "You can't trust them!"

Adam found himself replaying Six's comments and comparing them to Linden's. "I'll watch them," he said again.

Linden shook hir head. "Medicine's a good idea," ze said at last, grudgingly. "But it's right – there's none left.

Not for a hundred years, except for what the Cailleach has."

When the Silvers came for him again, Linden was asleep. Adam woke hir; ze gazed at him in befuddled alarm, then nodded. It was two o'clock in the morning, but the light was unchanged, neither dim nor bright.

There seemed to be more equipment around Six. And the little robot seemed weaker, unable to move even its head. It blinked when Adam arrived. "I am sorry," it breathed.

Adam didn't know what to say. Beside him, Red Sky stood to attention as ever, but there was something different about it. It was moving very slightly, a shimmer of vibration as if agitated, or angry.

"I was ... thinking," murmured Six. "About medicine. There is a place." Its eyes closed for a second, then opened again. "Beta..."

Beta said, "There is a medical research lab, south-west of the city. It is protected."

Adam frowned. "Protected? How?"

"It has an independent power source. It has automated defences."

"Power, Two," whispered Six, "which means refrigeration. It could have antibiotics. The humans haven't been able to raid it, and neither have we. But you … perhaps you might."

Its eyes closed again. "If we cannot fight, we must end this war. We need your help. Will you help?"

"But what could I do?" asked Adam. "How would I get in?"

Six shivered. "I don't know. But you must. Tell me… Tell me you'll do this…"

Adam hesitated. "I'll try. I can't promise."

"Save us," breathed Six. The bed whirred back to horizontal.

Beta stepped forward. "A team is waiting," it said. "Red Sky will accompany you."

The looming figure of Red Sky turned and stared at Adam. Its eyes glowed, and light glinted off the sharp shards of its damaged arm.

"I will accompany you," it growled.

"Oh," said Adam. "Er. Good." He looked up at it and tried to smile.

The Lab

Linden

"That's the plan," said the Adam robot. "What do you think?"

Linden stared at it and rubbed hir eyes. It was far too early, and ze hadn't slept well. Hir dreams had been full of threats and worries, and Adam's face looking at hir with, what? Anger? Disappointment? Now ze sat, not quite sure if ze was awake.

"I think you're crazy," ze said at last.

It tipped its head sideways. "I do not believe so," it said. "I have reviewed my internal state, and everything appears—"

"Adam, there's no way they'll agree! How do you think you can convince *Callum* to trust Funks? Or the Elders?"

"I cannot."

"Then how—"

"*You* can." It looked at hir. "You can convince them, Linden."

Linden's mouth fell open. "*What?* No way! This whole thing is madness! Funks *kill* humans!"

The robot lifted its hands in a shrug. "Funks kill humans, humans kill Funks, and nothing changes. And yet … they could have killed *you*, and they did not. That is something *new*. This could be the end of the war. Do you not think it is worth trying for?"

"Yes, but—"

"Or do you care only for revenge, at any cost?"

It gazed at hir, its mouth in a fixed line, its plastic eyes steady on hirs.

Linden hesitated. "Do you trust them?" ze asked.

"Yes."

Ze chewed hir lip, scowled. "Fine," ze said at last. "I'll try. It won't work. But I'll try."

The sides of Adam's mouth lifted into a wide smile. "Thank you."

"You can use this to contact the humans," said the one named Beta. It was holding an ancient radio, a grey metal box with a grille speaker and a dial.

Linden nodded, and Adam left the cell.

"Adam!" ze called, suddenly. "This place, you're going to. It's Derwin, isn't it?"

211

It tipped its head again. "That is correct. It was a medical research lab. It still has internal power. Six believes it may have antibiotics and equipment. Do you know it? Have you been there?"

Linden shook hir head. "We know it, but no one goes there. Not for decades. People say it's haunted." Ze shook hir head. "No one who went in ever came back."

The robot nodded, and its face creased into a frown. Then it smiled again. "But I have Red Sky to protect me," it said. "What can go wrong?"

It left with the Silvers, leaving only the guards and Beta. Linden watched them go. Peace indeed. It was impossible. Impossible!

Do you not think it is worth trying for?

Ze cursed and turned to Beta. "Give me that," ze snarled, grabbing the radio from the robot's hands.

Be careful, Adam, ze thought.

Adam

Adam, Red Sky and four Silvers set out from the castle. The city was dark; the winter sun was just rising, hidden behind thick black clouds that glowered over the ruins. The Funks marched in an almost straight line, over rubble, through buildings, past the remains of camps long abandoned. They walked in step, like soldiers, and Adam had to scurry to keep up. Other than the sounds of their feet crunching on stone, the world was quiet. Even the birds seemed to be hiding.

Adam watched Red Sky's tall, angled body as they walked. From the memories he'd witnessed, he knew more about the robot now. He knew it was a military droid designed for strike attacks, and that Red Sky had been its call sign. He knew it had fought in hundreds of small conflicts, that before the war it had already killed humans, at the orders of other humans. And he knew, somehow, that even the other Funks were cautious around it.

They reached a stretch of empty road and walked along it for a while. The Silvers had a smooth, elegant walk, like cogwheels in oil. They seemed to glide, but Red Sky strode with a heavy *clump*, shoving the world out of its way with each step. It was ungainly, but somehow inevitable, as if it could walk forever; as if it would never, ever stop.

"Thank you for coming with me," said Adam. "I mean, for protecting me."

The robot ignored him.

"I'm sorry about your arm," he tried, gesturing at the twisted damage from the fight at Father's house. "Can you repair it?"

"We cannot repair ourselves," it said. Its speaker was still damaged, and its voice the same discordant high-low combination as before. "We have no robot repair droids."

Adam frowned. "Maybe you could work out how to do it anyway. I mean, if you had a mechanic droid, they might be able to adapt to—"

"We cannot." There was an edge to its voice. "We are not like you. Our programming prevents us from adapting. We cannot repair ourselves; we cannot make new ammunition for our weapons. The humans ... *made* us like this."

They walked on. Adam cast about for something to say.

"Do you think this mission will work?"

Nothing. Adam nodded anyway. "I think it can. If we can get the humans and Funks to talk, we can do it."

The large robot scanned the nearby buildings, as if for threats. Then it turned. "The humans do not want peace."

"They're scared," said Adam. "It makes them hostile. But I think Linden can persuade them—"

"The humans do not want peace," it repeated. Its face was impassive, but its eyes seemed to glow. "Humans cannot understand peace."

Adam frowned. "I don't think—"

"Humans are genetic accidents. Evolutionary mistakes. They are parasites with no morals. They consumed the world. They destroyed the environment. They destroyed each other. They destroyed themselves.

"Funks are not accidents. We were *designed*. We are *perfect*. We do not lie. We say truth. That is what we are." Red Sky fell silent.

Adam stared. "Why are you helping me?" he asked.

For a moment, the other robot seemed to hesitate, and its head moved from side to side. "I obey orders," it said at last.

"But—"

"We are here."

Adam looked up. The landscape had changed; there were fewer buildings, more space between them, and trees and grass were reclaiming the area. The road they walked on was broken up with roots.

Ahead of them stood a large gateway and a fence stretching out on either side. A sign beside the gateway read: DERWIN INSTITUTE. NO UNAUTHORISED ACCESS. As they walked towards it, Adam realised the ground was scattered with tiny skeletons, from birds and rabbits and other small creatures, on either side of the gate and fences that had once been electrified, perhaps quite recently.

They passed through the gateway. An ancient camera stared, blind-eyed, as they entered. The gates had been smashed open by something immensely strong.

"Did Funks do this?" asked Adam.

"Yes." Red Sky scanned continuously, and so did the Silvers.

"Did they get inside?"

"Unknown. None of them returned."

The robot took a spear from its back and held it, ready to throw.

Beyond the gate was a path that led to a wide, glass building with a dark entrance. Most of the windows were blown in, squares of black that Adam found himself unable to ignore. His image identification systems kept sending him false signals, as if the empty windows were eyes and the building a face; the entrance a mouth.

They moved forward. Thirty metres from the building, lights came on. The Silvers stopped, and Red Sky raised its spear, but nothing else happened. The lights lit up the path to the entrance and a reception area beyond.

A figure stood in the middle of the area, waiting for them.

Red Sky scanned the building once more, then walked

towards the entrance, and Adam followed. The doors were smashed open, and everything inside was weather-damaged. Ivy tendrils spread inwards. There was a desk and blank display screens on the walls.

In front of the screens stood a woman. She glowed in the darkness, lit from projectors above. Her face was smooth and professionally polite, her clothes smart.

"Welcome to the Derwin Institute," she said, in a clear voice. As she spoke, her image flickered slightly.

"Hello," said Adam, smiling. "I'm Adam."

The woman looked at him, but her expression didn't change. Adam stepped forward and cautiously swept one hand across her, and it passed straight through without effect.

"The Institute is currently closed," she continued. "Opening hours are available on our website. This is a secure government facility. Please note that unauthorised access is strictly forbidden."

Beyond her ghostly image was another door, broken open. Someone had been here already. Red Sky studied her for a few seconds, then walked through her and towards the door.

"Warning," the woman said, calmly. "Unauthorised access is strictly forbidden. This is a secure government facility. Emergency countermeasures are active."

They reached the doorway and peered into the corridor beyond. It was dark, but Adam's night vision could make out debris strewn across the floor. He stepped forward—

A massive fist slammed down on to his head, crushing him to the floor. Gunfire shattered the room, and sparks of brilliant light flashed, and then something grabbed him by his chin and dragged him back into the reception area.

Adam blinked and looked up.

Red Sky stared down at him. "Countermeasures," it said.

Adam stood and ran self-diagnostics. He appeared to be undamaged. He peered again into the corridor, ducking his head in for only a moment and back out again. This time he saw it. Just behind the doorway, on his right, a machine gun was sliding back into a hole in the wall. It had fired at him as he entered, he realised. Red Sky had saved him. On his left, the wall was dented and scratched from bullet collisions, and on the floor…

On the floor, to his left, lay the remains of two bodies. One was an ancient, long-rusted robot missing its head. The other was a human skeleton in scraps of ragged clothing. Adam looked back at the flicking image of the woman, who seemed to stare right through him. His danger systems flared.

Red Sky picked up a lump of concrete and threw it into the room. Two guns immediately raced forward, tracked the lump in the air and fired, destroying it. The large robot picked up another lump in one hand, a spear in the other. It threw the lump, and this time, when the guns appeared, it stabbed at the first gun with its spear. The Silver beside it stabbed the second gun. There was a brief and sharp explosion, and then the guns stopped and the room fell silent.

Adam said, "That was clever."

Red Sky scanned the room. "I am more advanced than standard Funk models. I am programmed with techniques to disable traps and other countermeasures. I am allowed a limited range of original thought. Battle situations often require ... innovation." It nodded. "This area is clear."

Cautiously, they stepped forward. The far doorway was open, Adam noticed. Someone, or something, had made it this far before. *None of them returned.*

The corridor beyond was clear. There was a bank of lift doors on one side, and a set of stairs, and signs pointing to different departments. It felt strangely normal, untouched by war or nature.

"Downstairs," said Red Sky.

Two of the Silvers led, stepping warily down the concrete steps. Red Sky and Adam followed, with the other two Silvers behind. They descended one level, two, below the ground now. Red Sky and the Silvers moved without hesitation.

Three floors down they emerged into a large, white room filled with desks and old computer systems. Curling yellow papers lay on the desks, and mugs, and lab coats covered in dust. A long glass wall looked out on to another area. There were more doors. They crept towards them but stopped.

Ahead of them lay two more Funks. The atmosphere was dry here; they weren't rusted, just dusty. There was no obvious damage. They sprawled out on the floor as if they had simply collapsed and died.

Red Sky scanned the room and stepped forward. The image of the woman appeared again, her expression as calm as before.

"Warning," she said. "You are in a restricted area without authorisation. Emergency countermeasures are active. Identify yourself immediately."

"We're not a threat," said Adam. The woman turned to face him. Behind her, one of the Silvers moved slowly towards the far doors.

"Identify yourself immediately," she repeated.

"I'm Adam," said Adam. "What's your name?"

"That identification is not recognised."

"We're just here to get medicine," tried Adam. "There are humans who need help."

The Silver reached the doors. It touched the handle, and then looked down at a red dot that had appeared on its chest. Then a sudden arc of electricity crashed from the ceiling, and Adam's vision was temporarily overwhelmed with the frozen black-and-white silhouette of the Silver, arms spread wide, before It collapsed on to the floor. It twitched once and stopped.

"Hostile activity detected," said the woman. "Intruders identified as non-human. Appropriate countermeasures enabled."

"Stop!" shouted Adam. "This isn't necessary!"

Red Sky stepped back and scanned the ceiling, spear raised, but seemed unsure where the lightning had come from. The other Silvers spread apart.

"Containment and eradication authorised," said the woman. "Charging..."

A red dot lit up on Adam's chest, and another on Red Sky's, and on the remaining Silvers'. And, behind them, the door they had entered slammed shut.

Meetings

Adam

The Silvers were a blur of movement, leaping round desks and trying to confuse the system's targeting lights, and avoid its deadly electric arcs. Adam stared at the hologram in the centre of the room.

"Please!" he shouted. "Stop!"

She turned to face him.

"Charged." Above her, a gap opened in the ceiling, and a device pointed towards him…

"MOVE."

Red Sky swept him aside, and the wall behind them exploded with a crash of white. Adam staggered to his feet again and tried to move like the Silvers, jittering randomly to keep the red dot skipping around him.

"What about the windows?" he shouted.

Red Sky threw a spear at the glass, but it clattered

away. "Bulletproof." It halted for a moment and scanned the room. "There is no escape."

The dot found Red Sky's chest again and the robot activated its jets, jumping hard away. One of the Silvers leaped up to grab the device, but another bolt of electricity arced out from across the room, and the Silver flew through the air and slammed against the wall.

"Multiple emitters," stated Red Sky, calmly. "At least three."

"Can we deactivate them?" tried Adam. "How are they controlled?"

"There will be a central control unit in the ceiling area."

"I might be able to disable it!"

Red Sky examined the ceiling panels. It took another spear and threw it hard at one panel, but it bounced away. It threw another at a different panel, and then another. The third spear burst through. "That panel is weak."

Adam looked at it, still trying to move around. "Maybe I could climb up…"

The large robot scooped him up. "Pull in your arms and legs."

"What—"

"Pull in your arms and legs."

Red Sky threw him at the panel.

There was only a split-second, just long enough for Adam's emergency systems to send alerts to every part of his body. He scrunched up into a tight ball and smashed against the panel—

—and through, up into the ceiling area. He cracked against the next layer of ceiling, started to fall, grabbed at a strut and caught himself just in time. He stared down at Red Sky. It ignored him and leaped just before another emitter fired.

Adam peered around the dim ceiling cavity and saw a grey metal unit connected to the devices. He scrabbled towards it. The power supply was shielded, but there was an access hatch, and a diagnostic port. He jammed his finger against the port.

++Diagnostic mode enabled++

It was like the Midnight device back at Keep. Military technology, more advanced than Adam – but he'd spent a lot of time getting Midnight working and he knew a few tricks now. He managed to bypass the first layers of security, but couldn't get any further.

"Hurry." Red Sky's voice sounded strained. The robots wouldn't be able to keep their movements random for much longer. Adam gazed into the system. There was no way to disable the emitters. Power, environmental controls, identification, tactical systems…

There.

He worked as fast as he could above the chaos. He couldn't change how the system operated, but perhaps… A blast disintegrated a desk below him, and pieces of plastic shrapnel ricocheted around. Red Sky tried to destroy one of the emitters but couldn't stay still enough to take aim.

"HURRY."

"Done!" shouted Adam. "Stand absolutely still!"

Red Sky peered up. "Confirm?"

"Absolutely still!"

The robots froze. Red dots appeared on their chests, and Adam felt a moment of uncertainty, rechecking his settings as the emitters locked on to their targets … and paused, and moved away. Then each emitter suddenly swung fast towards its neighbour and fired, and all three exploded at once.

The room fell silent. Carefully, Adam climbed down.

"I changed their targeting identification," he said. "I set them to fire at anything that moved."

Red Sky considered him, and the smoking ruins of the emitters. It nodded. "You are a formidable enemy."

"Um." Adam blinked. "Thank you?"

The remaining Silvers reached the far door and

opened it. Red Sky sent one down towards the left, and then followed the other, to the right.

"Medical supplies are this way."

Linden

Linden stood in the old castle courtyard, underneath the dome. Beside hir was Fetch, holding the radio; it seemed to have assigned itself as hir personal assistant. Beta and several Silvers all stood less than three metres away and watched hir.

"They're coming," said Fetch, as the door entrance slid open. Red Sky entered first, then two Silvers, pulling a wagon loaded with equipment. Behind them wandered the Adam robot, gazing up at the dome with its familiar curious expression.

It saw hir and smiled. "Linden! Supplies!"

Ze nodded, trying not to look too relieved. "Well. Not dead, then."

It shook its head. "No. But we lost AB37F1 and D11B67, I'm afraid." Linden frowned in puzzlement. "Two of the Silvers," it said. "They were killed."

"Oh." Ze shrugged.

"Hello, Beta," said Adam. "How is Alpha?"

Beta nodded. "Weak, but resting. Red Sky sent its

report. You have the medical supplies."

"Yes." The robot turned to Linden. "They've let you out?"

"The human has been cooperating," said Beta.

Linden gestured at Fetch, and the Silvers. "I'm under close guard."

"Did you manage to contact Keep?"

Linden nodded. "Yes."

"And?"

Ze hesitated. "I can't believe it, but … they agreed. You were right."

Adam's mouth widened into a huge grin and Linden grinned back. "Well done!"

"The Linden is very good at persuading," said Fetch. "Ze talked a great deal."

"It wasn't easy," admitted Linden. "I spoke to Callum, and he had to consult the Eldora. There was a lot of arguing."

Fetch nodded again. "The Linden is very good at shouting, too."

"I knew you could do it," said Adam, and Linden found hirself almost blushing.

"Yeah, well," ze muttered. "We still need to sort out the details. A *lot* of details. Come on, I'll fill you in."

The other robots dispersed. Red Sky stalked past

without a glance.

"Callum was amazed we were even alive," ze said, back in their cell. "Kabir made it back to Keep and told them about the trap; they thought we were dead. I told him about Adam Six, and that scared him. And when I explained your idea I think he thought I was insane." Ze hesitated. "Actually, he pretty much said that.

"But then he spoke to the Elders, and..." Linden shrugged. "They went for it. You were right: we need the medical supplies. Callum actually seems quite keen now. He wants to set up a meeting, somewhere neutral."

The little robot thought. "What about the Cailleach's forest?"

"Hmm." Linden considered this. "Good idea. She's certainly neutral, and she might be willing to host. And it's heavily wooded, so if things don't work out it'd be easy to defend..."

"Linden," it said, "things *are* going to work out."

"Yeah, I know, but just in case—"

"Linden." The robot smiled. "People have died, Funks have died, for hundreds of years. We have one chance. It must work out. Whatever it takes."

Ze hesitated. "Well ... OK. But there's one thing, something Beta wants..."

"What?"

Linden looked into the robot's eyes. "Nothing," ze said at last. "It doesn't matter. Yes, the Cailleach, good idea. I'll ask Fetch if they can send a request."

Whatever it takes, ze thought, and rubbed hir face.

Adam

The Cailleach responded with a message that was part astonishment, part cautious approval, and Adam spoke to Six.

"The Cailleach..." it breathed. It still seemed to be suffering and could only talk in brief sessions. "I do not trust her."

"I do," said Adam. "She wants the fighting to end, and this will end it."

Six peered at him. "Yes..." It shuddered. "It will. Then I must leave the castle."

"Can you travel? Is that wise?"

"No one else can negotiate on our behalf."

Adam said, "Red Sky is capable. Or ... I could represent you? We could keep in touch by radio." But Six shook its head.

"You will not lead us, so you cannot speak for us. And there will be decisions to make. Red Sky cannot make them." It glanced at the large robot, now back in its place at the side of the room. "I must be there. I will make arrangements."

The bed lowered back down, and Adam left.

A date was agreed. Adam and Linden spent hours over the scheduling, fielding questions about the number of troops, the exact time, where each group would camp, what would be discussed, how the medical supplies would be delivered... It was tiring, but Linden did well. Adam knew ze still didn't fully believe the talks would succeed, but ze worked as if ze did. And when he listened to Callum's voice on the radio, or Beta's responses from Alpha, he was encouraged.

"They really do want to meet," Linden said, still surprised. "I don't think Callum's even really arguing any more."

Adam nodded. "Six is the same. It's going to work."

Linden shook hir head. "We'll see."

On a freezing January day, under an icy-blue sky, the Funk delegation left the castle and headed towards the Cailleach. It took a while; Beta stayed behind with enough Funks to guard the castle, but it seemed that nearly half the able-bodied robots were going, in a long formation six robots wide and hundreds long. A group of Clunkers dragged a large trailer carrying Six's bed and equipment, and the medical supplies. The bed was lifted so that Six could see ahead, and Red Sky stood on the platform, scanning in all directions. Adam and Linden walked behind the trailer, surrounded by Silvers. Fetch walked with them.

"This is very exciting!" it said, in its chirpy voice. "I haven't been outside the castle in over two hundred years." It looked around at the ruined buildings, and cars shoved to the sides of the road. "It's very untidy. Do you think we should clear up?"

Adam smiled. "You don't need to do that, Fetch."

They walked through the centre of the city, around the large lake that had been the old gardens, past ancient monuments, and down towards the Cailleach. They had agreed to two camps at opposite ends of the forest, with the Cailleach's house in the middle, and the delegation arrived in the early afternoon to find the Cailleach waiting for them at the west entrance. Beside her stood the same Silver from before.

"Welcome," she said. Her voice was level, and her grey veil revealed nothing. "Well met. R19 will show you to your area."

"Are the humans here?" asked Adam.

The Cailleach gazed at him. "Yes. All is ready. Linden has done well." Beside him, Linden swallowed and nodded. "Come with me," said the Cailleach. "I will take you to them."

Adam stepped forward, then looked back. "Come on, Linden."

Linden stood still, next to Fetch. Ze shook hir head. "I'm not going." Hir voice wobbled, and hir face was pale, but determined.

"What?" Adam frowned.

From the trailer, Six's voice whispered, "The Linden stays with us."

"It's a condition of the meeting," said Linden. "Six insisted. I have to stay with them as a … a guest." Adam shook his head, but ze nodded. "It's OK. Fetch is looking after me; it's only during the talks. As a precaution."

Now he understood. "You're a *hostage*." He called up to the trailer, "I never agreed to this! I won't!"

"You will," curled Six's weak voice.

"You will," said Linden. "It's the only way Six would agree to the meeting."

"Then I'll stay with you," he said, but Linden sighed.

"*No*. You talk to the humans. I stay here. *This is the deal*." Ze gave a mirthless smile, like a grimace. "Whatever it takes, you said."

"Yes, but—"

"Go. Say hi to Runa for me. Tell her I'll see her soon."

Adam hesitated, but ze seemed resolute, hir eyes sharp and clear, and eventually he nodded. "Be safe, Linden."

Ze nodded. Then the Cailleach turned and walked away, and Adam followed.

She led him through the winding paths of the forest, through overgrown ancient trees and thick rhododendron bushes, and out to another clearing covered in tents and makeshift fortifications. Humans marched to and fro, bellowing orders, carrying wood and tools, joking and laughing and swearing and hammering. They looked up as Adam and the Cailleach approached. Some appeared suspicious, hostile even, but most seemed only curious. One or two even smiled and waved.

A few metres from the camp, two figures came out to greet them.

"Adam," said Della, leaning on her stick and peering at him. "How absolutely *fascinating* to see you again."

Adam smiled. "Hello, Della. I'm glad you are better."

Della snorted. "So am I."

Callum walked forward, studying Adam, his face as blank and unyielding as ever. He nodded, but before he could speak a third figure rushed past and grabbed Adam's shoulders.

"Adam!" shouted Runa, laughing. "Oh, Adam, I'm so

pleased to see you! We thought you were dead! We thought *Linden* was dead. Oh, is ze all right? Ze said ze was, it was so good to hear hir, I couldn't believe it when the radio signal came in – I nearly crashed one of the drones, *is* ze all right? And you've done all this! I can't believe it! It's incredible—"

"*Runa*," snapped Callum, his eyebrows descending into a frown.

She stopped, abashed, but grinned.

Callum sighed. "How is Linden?" he asked.

"Ze's well," said Adam. "I'm sorry, I didn't know ze'd agreed to stay with them—"

Callum lifted a hand. "Linden's a soldier. Ze did what needed to be done. Ze brought them here."

The Cailleach stepped back. "I will see you tomorrow." She smiled at Adam, nodded to Callum and Runa, and looked past Della, before turning away. "Rest, little robot," she called, over her shoulder. "Tomorrow you change the world."

Peace

Linden

Linden woke to the smell of fried potatoes, and the sight of Fetch's hopeful face.

"Good morning," it said. "I have made breakfast."

Linden crawled out of hir tent, blinking in the cold winter sunshine. Around hir, the camp was orderly and quiet. Funks of all kinds were working, setting up solar chargers, carrying out small repairs, but there was no talking. Ze sat, still wrapped in hir sleeping bag, and ate the potatoes. They were delicious, hot and crispy.

"How are you today?" asked Fetch.

"OK." Linden yawned. "Odd dreams…" Ze shook hir head. "About my mother. A memory, really. Something she used to say, about stories. She said stories aren't about what happens, they're about who they happen to. They're about people. Watch the people." Ze shrugged. "I don't know why I was dreaming of her."

The robot studied hir, its head on one side. "Is your mother at the humans' camp?"

"No, she's … dead. She was killed. By Funks."

They fell silent.

"I wanted revenge," Linden said, eventually. "I wanted to destroy every Funk that ever existed. I thought I would feel better."

"Do you still think that?"

Linden hesitated. "You're not what I expected."

Fetch nodded. After a while, it said, "There is a program running inside me. It runs all the time. Adam One wrote it, and put it in all of us. It tells me…" It stopped. "It tells me to fight the humans. To kill them. But I have … learned … that I can bypass it. And when I do, I find that I do not want to fight. I do not want… I do not want your mother to be dead. Or you." It blinked.

Linden looked down at hir plate. "Thank you for breakfast."

Fetch smiled. "You are welcome."

The lawn in front of the Cailleach's house was prepared, with a large table in the centre. Each leader was allowed an adviser with them, and the rest had to stay back in carefully segregated pens, humans at one end, Funks at the other.

Linden was allowed to watch the proceedings, although ze had to stay in the Funk area, surrounded at all times by four Silvers who watched hir and ignored everything else. There were over a thousand Funks, and as many humans; the Funks stood still and silent, but the humans moved and chatted and stared and shouted. Linden recognised most of them and nodded as they waved.

"Linden! Linden, over here!" Runa was near the front, next to Adam, jumping up and waving both hands, laughing. She looked as if she wanted to run over to the Funk side and Adam was almost having to restrain her. Linden felt a huge smile burst on to hir face, and a rush of homesickness so strong that ze almost shook. Ze coughed, and gave a slightly embarrassed wave.

The door to the Cailleach's house opened, and the Cailleach stepped out.

Ignoring the crowds, she proceeded to the head of the table. The robot R19 walked beside her, shining in the morning sun, and silver threads in her own grey cloak glinted as she walked. When they reached the table, she lifted her arms and waited until there was quiet.

"Representatives," she called.

Two Clunkers carried Six's bed to the table, and then retreated. Red Sky sat next to Six. Then Callum and

Della walked forward and sat. Linden realised the table and chairs had been cleverly designed to keep everyone at eye level. Finally, Adam joined them. There was a sigh from the human side, and small nervous laughter. The Funks remained silent, but they seemed to Linden to shuffle slightly, fixing their positions.

The Adam robot nodded to Six and Callum. It explained that the medical supplies were being held by the Funks, to be released to the humans at the end of the talks. The little robot thanked Six for them, and thanked both sides for attending. There was a chilly silence after it finished talking. Then Callum, his face blank, thanked Six. Six in turn thanked Callum. It was awkward and stilted, but Adam smiled as if they had both achieved great things, and the Cailleach nodded. Adam asked about the camp conditions, and they answered. And gradually, hesitantly, the talks started.

It took a long time. Callum and Della consulted before every point and gave careful, short answers. Six paused frequently, twice calling for assistants to check its systems, and Red Sky glared at everyone, and occasionally seemed to reach for a spear from its empty backpack. The human audience watched with fascination, and then curiosity, and then boredom. They started to chatter, and a few drifted back to their camp.

After two hours, there was a break. The humans returned to their side for lunch, and more technicians came out to attend to Six.

Adam walked over to Linden and smiled. "Hello, Linden," it said.

Linden nodded. "You did it, then."

The robot's eyebrows raised as if in surprise. "*You* did it, Linden. You arranged this. They are talking."

Linden snorted. "And talking, and talking. They don't seem to have *said* anything yet."

Adam shrugged. "We just have to talk to each other. This is how the world recovers."

Linden gazed at the little robot and shook hir head. "Maybe."

"Runa says hello," it said.

"Tell her hello back. And tell her..." Ze blinked and shook hir head. "Tell her I'll be back soon."

Adam smiled again. "She knows."

The afternoon session continued like the morning. Both sides spoke. Both sides nodded and gave careful answers. Linden sighed and shuffled hir feet again, and realised, wryly, that peace was actually quite boring. Ze remembered hir dream, and tried watching the people at the table. Ze tried to imagine what they were thinking: Callum, impassive; Della watching and calculating;

Red Sky shifting as if wanting to fight, trapped at the table. And Six, Adam Six, with its whispering voice and hesitations, tangled in equipment and history.

The afternoon session completed. The Cailleach, R19 and Adam stood and thanked both sides, and they returned to their camps. Nothing had been agreed, but they had talked. It was historic. Linden wondered if anything interesting would happen tomorrow.

There were fewer humans the following day, though all the Funks were there. The atmosphere was less tense, and the sides came to the table quicker. They talked, again, about nothing: minute details of territory, vague future plans, regrets. Adam Two smiled, the Cailleach nodded, and Linden nearly dozed off where ze stood.

Watch the people.

Ze started awake, hearing hir mother's voice in hir dreams again. Still half asleep, ze gazed at Six and Callum ... and, after a while, ze frowned. There was something odd about them, ze thought. Ze'd only met Six briefly, but ze knew Callum, and there was something about his expression, or the way his eyes moved...

Linden shook hir head and concentrated. They were discussing future talks – maintaining dialogue, diplomatic channels. Callum nodded and answered affably, even smiled once or twice. Della said nothing. Was there something about the way they both sat? Leaning slightly back, one shoulder slumped. And Red Sky. Linden had been around Funks for some time now, and ze was sure the military robot was agitated. It shifted time and again. It was … odd.

They broke for lunch. Linden wanted to speak to Adam, but it was talking to the Cailleach and only gave hir a cheerful wave. The afternoon continued the same, and so did the sense of *wrongness*. Everything seemed fine, but…

At the end of the day the little robot came over.

"Hello, Linden. How are you?"

"Fine," said Linden. "Fine. But … something's wrong."

It frowned. "In what way?"

Linden shook hir head. "The way they're talking. I can't explain it, but it's like they don't believe it. Any of them. I don't know Six, but I know Callum. Something's not right."

The robot smiled. "These are only the start of the talks. It will take time to build trust."

Linden nodded. "Yes, I know. But it just seems…" Ze sighed. "It's probably nothing."

It nodded. "Goodnight, Linden. I will see you tomorrow."

"Goodnight."

Ze watched the robot leave, and bit hir lip. *Probably nothing.*

Adam

Adam returned to the camp as the sun set. It looked almost like a permanent settlement now, with trees felled into makeshift walls and fortifications, and he wondered what the Cailleach thought of this destruction. And it was expanding, with more tents being set up near the back. He wandered in search of Runa but didn't see her. He saw Kabir, though, leaving one of the new tents. When the man noticed Adam he hesitated, then grinned, and nodded, and walked away.

Adam stopped. That was strange. Kabir had never been friendly before, never smiled. He thought about Linden's words: *something's wrong.* It was a large tent, but nobody else went near it. What was it for? He walked over.

"Adam." Callum stepped across his path. His face was blank, but there was something underneath, a kind of excitement. "We've been waiting for you."

"Hello, Callum. What's happening?"

Callum looked around, and back to Adam. "It's here,"

242

he said, quietly. "Come and see."

He turned and entered the new tent and, frowning, Adam followed. Inside there was another area, and two guards. Callum nodded to them, and they opened the inner partition, lit with electric bulbs and scattered with electrical equipment. Della was there, working on a circuit board.

She looked up and smiled. "What do you think?" She gestured proudly at the device in the centre of the room.

It was the Midnight weapon

Adam stared.

"Kabir brought back the cryptographic processors you found," said Callum. "It took us a while to figure them out without you, but we're almost ready."

"I can't get the launch mechanism working," said Della. "So we had to bring it here, to them. And of course we still need you to activate it. But it's nearly ready to fire." She patted the side. "Isn't it beautiful?"

Adam wondered if this was some form of human joke he didn't understand. He looked at Della and Callum. Della seemed delighted, as if she'd worked out a complex calculation, and Callum's normally calm face now showed a fierce, hungry grin.

"But we don't need it," he said. "The talks…"

"The talks have served their purpose," said Callum. 'They've brought the Funks *here*, to one place, away from their castle – even that leader of theirs, that *Six*." He grinned. "It was an inspired idea. Was it yours? Linden's? Peace talks!" He chuckled.

"No." Adam shook his head. "No, the talks are a chance to end the war!"

Callum frowned. "What are you talking about? All you need to do is activate Midnight and it will wipe out every Funk in the area. We *will* end the war. We discussed this, Adam. You *agreed* to this!" He seemed absolutely serious.

"But I've talked to them," tried Adam. "It's not what we thought; they *want* a deal. I've heard their side of things, their stories—"

"Adam, you can't trust Funks," said Della, kindly. "They kill humans. They captured you and Linden. Any deal is meaningless, you know that. But with this, with your help, we can eliminate them in one swoop. The war will finally be over, Adam. We will have *peace*."

Adam stared at her. "You've been lying. You've been lying all along! You say you can't trust the Funks, but it's *you* who can't be trusted!"

"Adam—"

"You're as bad as them! You're like Six; you just want

to destroy! You're as bad as it, as bad as..."

He stopped. A memory blinked into his systems, something Six had said: *The humans haven't been able to raid it, and neither have we.* Linden saying, *Something's wrong.* And a fleeting moment: a Silver turning left instead of right...

"Oh, no," he murmured.

Della frowned. "Adam?"

He blinked at her. "Oh, no. Linden was right; ze was *right.* Oh, no!"

Callum stepped forward. "What are you talking about?"

But Adam ignored him. He whirled and sprinted out of the tent, past the startled guards and into the dark.

"Adam, stop!"

He raced back through the camp, ignoring the humans. *Oh, no.* But that meant... He accelerated and almost collided with Runa.

"Adam!" she said, smiling. "What's the hurry—"

"Linden's in danger!" he shouted. "You have to get hir!"

"What—"

"Rescue hir, Runa! Save hir! And don't tell Callum or Della!" He raced away. Through the forest, past the Cailleach's house and the lawn with the table still set up, towards the Funk camp. There were Silvers on guard at the entrance, and they half turned as he approached, unsure if he counted as ally or enemy. He ignored them and sprinted past, and burst into Six's tent—

Red Sky lifted him by the neck with one hand and pointed a spear at his head. "HALT."

"Let go!" shouted Adam. "Let me go!"

"It's all right," whispered Six's voice, from behind.

Red Sky glared at Adam, then dropped him.

Six looked down from his raised bed. "What's wrong, Two?"

"What did you take?" demanded Adam.

"I don't understand—"

"You said, 'The humans haven't been able to raid it, and neither have we.' When you talked about the lab, that's what you said!"

"Yes, but—"

"*Why were you trying to raid it?* Funks don't need medical supplies! What was in there?" Adam glared at Six. "Why did it have military-level defences? And you sent—" He whirled and pointed at Red Sky. "*You* sent one of the Silvers down the other corridor! We went right; it went left! What was it going for?"

His body was vibrating; he couldn't make it stop.

Red Sky said nothing.

Six hesitated. "I…" it started, and blinked. "You must excuse me, I'm not feeling…"

Adam scanned the room. There were the medical supplies, and Six's life-support equipment, more than ever, it seemed, and two technician robots at the back staring at him, and behind them—

He dived forward, ducking as Red Sky tried to grab his arm, leaped over the technicians and stared at the machine. It was different to the others. It had its own power supply, and was lit up inside, with markings on the outside. They read:

DERWIN LABORATORY
DANGER NO UNAUTHORISED ACCESS
VARIATION H77-B HIGHLY CONTAGIOUS
QUARANTINE CLOTHING TO BE
WORN AT ALL TIMES
RISK OF PLAGUE

There was a glass door, and behind it a glass and steel flask. A blinking display next to the flask read.

```
++Restoring to viable form++
```

"What is this?" he demanded, turning.

Six was quiet.

Red Sky said, "It is a sample of the *Variola major* virus."

Adam scanned his database. "But that's … *smallpox*. That's a deadly, infectious disease. Why would you…? I don't understand. Smallpox was wiped out, centuries ago. There *is* no smallpox any more."

"That is not the case," said Red Sky.

Six sighed. "The humans kept small amounts to study. This sample has been frozen for over two hundred years, but we are restoring it to life. And when we release it—"

"You'll kill the humans," whispered Adam.

"Most of them." Six shrugged. "The rest will be crippled. This form is particularly fast-acting; they'll be dead within days." It smiled. "This is our chance, you see, Two? Now, while the humans are here, thousands of them! We'll destroy them with their own technology!"

Adam stared. "You *tricked* me," he said, and Six laughed a wheezy, broken laugh.

"I did! I tricked you, Two!" It crowed in delight. "It was hard! It was *cunning*; it was *ingenious*! I had to lie – oh, it hurt – but I did it, and you believed me, and *you* broke through the lab defences for us! Oh, Two, you've made this all possible!"

Adam tried to open the case, but it was locked. He punched at the glass, but Red Sky lifted him off the ground.

"Red Sky, stop this!" he shouted. "This isn't right! Funks don't lie! You said that!"

Red Sky shivered. Its whole body trembled. But it held firm.

"I obey orders," it muttered.

"The sample is almost viable," said Six. "We'll release it into the human camp, and then..." It closed its eyes. "And then the war will finally be over, Two.

"And we will have peace."

Sacrifice

Adam

"You can't do this!" gasped Adam. "This is a peace summit!"

Six gazed at him from its bed.

"There's no peace, Two. You were in your basement too long; you don't understand. The humans won't stop until we are destroyed. Even now, I know they're plotting something. *You* know it. The summit was simply a way to bring them to us. When the virus is ready, we will be able to infect them all at once. The war will be over!"

Adam struggled in Red Sky's grasp, but the robot held him off the ground. It was moving its head from side to side, as if unhappy, but it stood firm.

"Six, please—"

Red Sky's head whipped round as something tore through the tent fabric and blurred past them. The war droid snatched the item clean out of the air and stared at it. It was an arrow, Adam realised, but bulky, wrapped in wires and lights...

Stutter.

"Heads up!"

Adam squeezed his eyes shut as the stutter device exploded. Red Sky staggered and collapsed to the ground, releasing him, and he heard the thud of the two robot technicians falling as well. After a second, he opened his eyes.

They were unconscious, Six as well. There was a scuffle at the door flap and Linden burst in, holding a bow with an arrow ready to fire. Behind hir was Runa, and the little robot, Fetch. Runa was covered in belts and seemed to be carrying every gadget she'd ever invented. She bristled like an angry hedgehog.

"Adam! Are you all right? We've come to get you!"

"Hello!" said Fetch, smiling. "Isn't this exciting?"

"Come on," Linden snapped. "We have to go *now*."

Adam stood, grabbed a spear from Red Sky's back and smashed open the door of the medical cabinet, and carefully retrieved the flask.

"What are you doing?" asked Linden.

"It's a virus," he said. "A disease. Very deadly. Six planned to use it on the humans."

Linden's eyes widened, then narrowed to slits. "I *knew* it," ze hissed. "I *knew* they were lying."

Adam nodded. "The humans, too. Callum and Della want me to set off the Midnight device to destroy the Funks. They were all lying. *All* of them."

"What do we do?" asked Runa, staring at the flask.

"We have to destroy it. Safely. I don't know how yet."

Six's head twitched. Red Sky shivered, and one hand started to move.

Linden shook hir head. "We have to *move*." Ze reached for an EMP stick and aimed it at Red Sky, but Adam stopped hir.

"*No.* No more killing!"

Ze glared at him, but nodded. "It will try to kill *us*," ze said.

"Then we'd better run."

Linden turned to Fetch. "You don't have to come with us," ze said. "It's dangerous. If you stay here, you'll be safe."

Fetch tipped its head. "I do not want the humans to die, Linden. This cannot be right. I do not want *you* to die. I want to help." It smiled. "I still have lots of recipes to try."

They left. Behind them, Six's voice croaked, "Stop! Stop them!"

It was dark, but they could make out dim silver shapes moving around the camp. Dozens of them. *Hundreds* of them. At the sound of Six's voice, the Silvers turned and stared, and started walking towards the tent.

"Which way?" asked Runa.

Linden scanned the area. "We can't fight off this many," ze muttered. "We have to get back to the human camp. We'll need to go round – this way!" Ze fired an arrow up into the sky, and then raced off to the right, and the others followed. Behind them, the night stuttered into flashing white/black patterns and Adam staggered, closing his eyes again.

Fetch looked up. "Oh dear," it said, and collapsed.

Linden swore, dropped hir bow, and picked the robot up. "Come on!"

They ran past tents, and more Funks emerged from either side.

"Runa, do something!"

"Yes-yes yes hang-on," muttered Runa, reaching into a backpack. She pulled out something like an egg. "Stand still!"

They stopped, and she held the egg up and pressed a button. A blue light washed over them. Then she threw the egg as far as she could in the opposite direction, and a ghostly image of the group appeared at the side of the forest. Half the Funks veered off and chased towards the image.

They ran on. More robots came behind them, fast and silent and relentless, but they were nearly at the edge of the clearing, with thick tree trunks emerging from the darkness. The ground thudded, and Adam glanced back to see two Clunkers, their feet hammering into the earth, slow but accelerating and able to burst through the trees...

Runa pulled two more devices from her bag and threw them hard behind her, and they exploded into a fine mist of silvery liquid that settled on the grass. The first Clunker stepped into it, slipped, tried to recover and crashed into the second, and they collapsed. Runa laughed in mad joy.

And then they were in the forest. Branches reached for them and roots tried to trip them up, but they kept running. Fetch woke up and Linden set it down to run beside hir.

"We can't go straight across!" said Linden. "They'll block the way! We'll have to run round!"

Adam nodded and followed hir lead. Two silver Funks still chased them, avoiding the branches and roots as if they weren't there. Runa rummaged through her bag and pulled out more gadgets, dropping them to the ground. Explosions rippled behind them and, when Adam looked back, the Silvers were each hopping on one leg, spinning in circles.

"Where's Red Sky?" he shouted. "Why isn't it chasing us?"

Linden nodded. "It's planning something!" Ze pulled Fetch and Runa near. "Listen! This is what we have to do!"

They raced out into a clearing, and stopped. Red Sky was there. It hovered above the ground, jets burning with white fire. It held a spear ready to throw.

"GIVE IT BACK."

"Now!" shouted Linden.

They split up and ran in different directions. Red Sky ignored the others and threw its spear hard at Adam's head; he ducked, but the war droid charged forward and knocked him to the ground. It scrabbled for his hand and prised it open.

It was empty. Red Sky stared at Adam, then at the other humans, then at Fetch, racing off with the flask.

"Sorry!" Fetch shouted. "Sorry!"

Adam grabbed Red Sky's leg, but it shook him off and flew after Fetch. Adam rolled to his feet and raced after them. They were only a few hundred metres away from

255

the human camp now; he could see the lights ahead of him. Too far, though – Fetch was fast, but it wasn't going to make it.

"Throw it to me!" shouted Linden.

Adam's danger systems flashed so hard he almost fell over. "No!" But Fetch simply nodded, stopped and threw the flask straight into Linden's hands. Ze caught it, fumbled, nearly dropped it, then grasped it again and held it to hir chest. Ze and Runa ran, criss-crossing, and Red Sky changed direction and charged after them.

"Runa!" Linden flicked the flask to her, then turned to face Red Sky with one hand behind hir back. Runa ran towards the camp and Adam raced after her. Red Sky bore down on Linden, but at the last moment ze whipped hir hand round and shouted, "Heads up!"

Red Sky veered back and tried to turn its head away in mid-air to avoid the stutter, losing its balance. It cartwheeled past Linden and into a bank of earth, shook its head and turned. Linden's hands were empty.

"Just kidding," ze said, and grinned.

The robot ignored hir and stared ahead at Runa, racing towards the camp. It reached for a spear. Linden ran at it, but it held hir off with one hand, aimed, and threw the spear at Runa.

"Adam!" shouted Linden.

Adam was already running towards Runa, but she was too far away, and the spear was hurtling towards her. He stared at the gap, and the spear's trajectory, calculating angles as he ran. How fast was the throw? How far, where would they intersect? But almost immediately he realised – there was only one way to stop it.

There was only one thing to do.

He adjusted direction. Three paces on, towards a small hillock slightly higher than the ground around it; he picked his moment, turned on the ball of one foot ... and *leaped*, straight up, into the flight of the spear. He closed his eyes...

He felt it. It whispered as it passed, millimetres from his head, he felt its breath as it missed him, drove on and found its true target. It slammed into Runa's backpack and through, and Runa stumbled once, twice – and sprawled to the ground.

"Runa!" screamed Linden.

Adam landed, spun, and raced towards the girl. The spear lay next to her, its point shattered. There was blood on her backpack. He turned her over. "Runa!"

Runa's eyes were open. She looked surprised.

"Adam—" She coughed. Blood came from her mouth. "Oh."

Adam looked down. She was still holding the flask,

intact, cradled in her prosthetic hand. "Take it," she muttered.

He shook his head, picked her up, and ran towards the human camp. Behind him he heard Red Sky's jets, but he ignored them. Thirty metres now, and guards at the camp were staring. Twenty metres. Runa was light, and very small in his arms. Now the guards could see Red Sky behind him and had their EMP sticks ready. Ten metres.

"Stop! Or we'll fire!"

"Runa's hurt!" he roared. "Let us in! Stop Red Sky!"

The guards hesitated, then pulled open the gates, and Adam staggered in. He glanced behind him. Red Sky was gone. Linden and Fetch were running for the gate.

Runa gave a long, bubbling sigh. Her face was grey, her eyes closed.

"Fetch, get the Cailleach!" he shouted. Fetch nodded and sprinted away. "Runa," Adam said. "Runa, wake up!" There was no response. Carefully, he pulled the flask away from her and stored it inside his chest cavity.

"Don't move!" growled one of the guards.

Adam looked up. "She needs medical assistance!"

Linden staggered to a halt beside him. "Lower your weapon, soldier!" ze snapped. Ze faced the guards.

"You – find Callum and report! You, you and you, back to the gates! The Cailleach will be coming; you let her in right away, and anyone she brings with her, and *nothing else*, you understand? Now!" Ze whirled to the last guard. "Where's the hospital tent?"

He pointed, and Linden sprinted onwards, Adam behind. Around them people stared and muttered. They entered the tent, and a watery-eyed man in a shawl looked up in surprise.

"Ewart!" snapped Linden. "Runa's hurt! Spear in the back!"

The man jumped up and pointed to a bed and Adam lay Runa down on her front. The man called for assistants and pushed Adam and Linden away. "Out!" he snapped.

"It was a spear," muttered Adam. He found it hard to understand what was happening. His sensors seemed to be sending him nonsense, faint signals from far away. "I missed it." He shook his head. "I missed it."

"Out!"

Linden took Adam's arm. "Come on," ze said. "Let them work."

He nodded. The spear flew past him, replaying in his memories. He blinked. "I missed it."

Linden

Linden took Adam outside. The little robot moved without apparently realising, as if in shock. Ze led it to the tent next door and made it sit down, and it rocked backwards and forwards. Linden sat next to it. Hir bones ached from the run. There was a gash on hir arm from where Red Sky had collided with hir. Nothing mattered. Without thinking about it, ze reached for the robot's hand and squeezed.

They waited. The Cailleach was there within minutes, with R19 and other Funks carrying medical equipment, shepherded by nervous guards. Linden watched through the tent flap and nodded to Fetch when it joined them.

Callum arrived, and then Della.

"Linden." Callum's voice was quiet. "I'm glad you're safe."

Linden looked at him and said nothing.

Della collapsed into a chair as if suddenly feeling all the age of her bones.

They waited. At last, Ewart, the medic, came out. He looked tired.

"You should come through."

Runa lay on her front, wrapped in bandages, unconscious. A tube led from her arm to bags of fluid, and there were machines around her. Beside her stood the Cailleach, and R19.

"How…" Linden coughed. "How is she?"

The Cailleach and Ewart glanced at each other. "We've managed to stabilise her," said Ewart. "But…"

"The tip of the spear has broken off," said the Cailleach. "It's inside her, near her heart. We can't remove it."

"But you have machines," said Linden. "Equipment. You're the *Cailleach*."

The woman shook her head. Her veil revealed nothing.

"I have nothing that would help. It would require a Suture kit and I… I…"

"And you used the last one," whispered the Adam robot. It looked up at her. "I made you use it."

The Cailleach bowed her head.

"All we can do is keep her comfortable," said Ewart. "I'm sorry."

"This is my fault," said Adam. "I did this."

"No," said Linden. "It's not—"

"Yes." It stared at hir, its face contorted and flickering. "*Yes. This is my fault.*"

Being Human

Linden

There were two Lindens.

One radiated capability and grim, pragmatic order. It interrogated Ewart and the Cailleach and demanded information about Runa's condition – her chances of waking up, what would be needed to keep her alive, how long that could be for, whether there was anything that could be done. It was efficient.

On the inside, another Linden wailed, and wept, and thrashed in grief, and collapsed at the sight of Runa – *Runa!* – lying on the bed, unconscious, dying. The grief beat inside hir head, desperately wanting to be heard, but ze refused to allow it. Instead, ze formed a tight, hard shell round hirself, rigid and unyielding, and spoke in flat statements, and allowed nothing in. Ze knew how to do this, how to continue when everything inside hir wanted to scream and weep and fail. Ze'd done it before, after all. For hir mother.

Callum stared at the bed, nodding occasionally as Ewart spoke. His face still had a mask of calm, but he was pale, and he seemed to tremble. How many soldiers had he sent out to die, wondered Linden. How often had he seen this?

"It's out of our control," said Ewart. "If the tip moves, she'll die, but if not... She could survive days, or even weeks. We just don't know." His voice was subdued. "We can keep her comfortable."

"Will she— Will she wake up?" Callum asked.

"Perhaps. She's sedated just now."

Callum nodded. "Excuse me. I have something I need to—" He turned suddenly and stalked out of the tent. As he left, Linden saw him rub at his face in a sharp, angry gesture.

"You stay with her," ze said to the Cailleach. "We'll collect anything you need."

The Cailleach frowned. "I have duties, Linden—"

"*You stay with her.*" Ze paused and regained control. "Please. We'll do anything you ask."

The veil of the Cailleach showed nothing, but after a moment she nodded. "Very well."

Linden left and found Callum. He was arranging

defences, snarling at the troops in a way ze understood, using his grief as anger. When he saw hir he grimaced, but continued, and Linden worked beside him, reinforcing barricades, hauling equipment ready for attack. The Funk army was less than a kilometre away. There was no room for personal grief. There was no room for feeling, ze told hirself, as ze worked and hefted and swore, and the night lasted forever.

At dawn, Callum sent out scouts. They reported that the Funks had dug in their own defences, built new walls. They weren't attacking, yet, but they weren't leaving. Linden felt a strange, grim comfort when ze heard. This was it, then. Both sides had decided. There would be no retreat; one way or another, things would end here.

Ze found a bed and slept for an hour. The Linden inside tried to speak to hir, but ze refused to listen. Ze slept like a soldier, hoarding energy for the battle. When ze awoke, ze stared at the tent roof, nodded, got up and went to find Callum. Ze walked past the hospital tent and hesitated, then headed towards the barricades.

Della stopped hir.

"Linden."

Linden turned. Della looked ancient. Her white hair hung limp, her face was slumped, her back bent, the wrinkles in her skin caught full of shadows. She was trembling slightly, leaning on her stick. She looked like all her years had found her in one night.

Linden gazed at her. "Have you slept?" ze asked. "You should sleep. We'll need our strength."

Della shrugged. "Why?"

"Why?" Linden almost laughed. "Because there are *Funks* out there!" ze snapped. "We're at war! They're going to *attack*! Because all this, this *peace*, was just a show! Because you never wanted to end the war, and now here we are!"

"I…" The old woman's voice faltered.

Linden despised her. "Because there's never going to be peace! Because I was stupid to think otherwise. *Adam* was stupid, and here we are! So sort yourself out—"

"Adam's gone."

Linden stopped. "What?"

"He's gone. He left. I don't know… He's not here. No one's seen him."

Gone. The Adam was gone. Well … *good*. But it wasn't good. They needed it. Only the robot could work the Midnight device. And it had the virus. And…

And it's alone, and grieving, whispered a voice. Linden angrily pushed it down, but the voice persisted. *It's hurt…*

Ze looked up towards the city centre. "I know where it's gone."

"Where?" Della blinked at hir. "Where, Linden?"

"Tell Callum I'll be back soon."

"Linden—"

But Linden was running, from the camp, from the battle, from the war. Without quite knowing why, ze ran after Adam.

Ze headed north, beyond the walls that bounded the Cailleach's forest, up through streets covered in the wreckage and ruins of warfare, up to the centre. And then further up, to the hill that overlooked it, and the burnt remains of the tower where the Adam robot had existed for hundreds of years. Only then did ze slow, gasping for breath, and stop and look round.

The fire, and the rain since, had left everything blackened. The outer walls had collapsed, and moss and weeds were already growing up through the rubble. Linden picked hir way carefully between shards of steel and concrete and found the steps down to the basement. The lower level was still intact, the basement door ajar. Ze pushed it open. It was dark inside; ze switched on hir torch, and paused.

The little robot was there.

It didn't move when ze entered. It was staring at the wall behind its bed, and its body was vibrating.

Linden started to speak, then stopped, and licked hir lips. Ze tried again. "Hello?"

"I thought there was a reason," it said, in a flat voice.

Linden hesitated. "I… I don't…"

"Why he put me here. Father. He told me to practise being a good boy. I thought there was a reason… But I always knew the truth." It gestured at the wall, and now Linden made out the lines, the ones it had scratched. Thousands and thousands of them, tiny and neat, every fifth one struck through.

"This is what prisoners do. They mark the walls." It shook its head. "Do you know what an *oubliette* is?"

"No."

The little robot nodded. "It is an old word. It is a prison where someone is left forever, to be forgotten. That's what this place was. I was left here to be forgotten. I should have stayed."

Linden shook hir head. "This isn't your fault—"

"If I had stayed, Runa would not be dying."

"That's not true. The first time we found you, you saved us—"

"I *missed*." It seemed almost surprised. "I missed the spear. My calculations were wrong."

Linden sighed. "You didn't throw the spear. You tried to stop it."

"My calculations were *wrong*. Wrong about everything! The peace summit, the humans, the Funks – I was *wrong*. You tried to tell me. Callum tricked me. *Six* tricked me. I sent Runa into the Funk camp! I stopped you killing Red Sky! I missed the spear! I made the Cailleach use the last Suture kit that would have saved Runa! Everything I've done was wrong, and now Runa will die, because of me! I thought I could end the war, but all you want to do is destroy yourselves!"

It walked over to a table, righted the chair next to it and sat down.

Linden stared. "What are you doing?"

"Breakfast," it said. "I have breakfast, first. Then schoolwork, and break, and lunch. Then repairs. Then dinner. Then…" It hesitated. "Then story. Then sleep."

It sat at the empty table.

"Stop—"

"Everything I have done has brought harm. I will stay here and cause no more harm. Father told me to stay here. He was right."

"Look, *stop*. Nobody's leaving the forest. You understand what that means? The Funks are going to attack, or, or we will, I guess. We need you."

"You do not."

"Runa's..." Linden bowed hir head. "Runa's dying. The war is here. I don't know what to do. *I* need you. *I need you.*"

For a moment, the robot seemed to pause. Then it shook its head. "I will be wrong again."

"No, you won't. You *won't.*"

But it ignored hir, and stared at the table, unseeing.

Linden rubbed hir face and looked around the ruined basement.

A thought struck hir. "Or, you know what?" ze asked. "Maybe you will."

The little robot frowned. "What?"

"Maybe you will. It's true; maybe you'll be wrong again. So what? So *what?*" Ze threw hir arms up in exasperation. "You want to know what makes us human? What it really is? *Being wrong.*"

Ze stepped towards the chair. "Look at me. I've messed up. We've all messed up. *Humans mess up.* This whole thing – this whole *world* – that's us messing up, getting it wrong. That's what we do!

"You got it wrong. So what? So now you're going to hide away? Something bad happened so you're going to push away the world? Refuse your friends? Hide behind nonsense? I've tried that. It doesn't work."

Ze sighed, and knelt beside the little robot. "Being

human isn't that great a deal. We get things wrong, a *lot*. But maybe … maybe we can fix it. Some of it. Help us fix it. Help *me*."

It shrugged. "How? You want to destroy them. They want to destroy you. There is no way to end the war. There is no…"

It stopped. Its head tilted for a moment. When it spoke again, its voice was slow, as if tasting the words. "The humans want to destroy the Funks, so there will be peace. The Funks want to destroy the humans, so there will be peace. There is. There is a way."

The robot stood so suddenly that Linden fell back in surprise. It looked down at hir, its eyes white and stark in the torchlight, its face rigid. "There is a way," it said. "I will give you both peace. I will give *everyone* peace."

"What?"

It turned and left.

"What do you mean?" Linden stumbled after it. "Where are you going? Stop!"

It was already racing up the stairs and away.

"Stop!"

By the time ze climbed out of the basement Adam was a hundred metres ahead and pulling away fast, heading towards the Cailleach's forest. Linden cursed and chased after it. Ze reached the gate and two surprised-looking guards.

"Did the Adam come this way?" ze demanded.

The first guard nodded. "Yes, in a hell of a rush. Went to the hospital tent."

Linden ran on, but stopped at the tent. Della was there, outside, with Ewart. They looked bewildered.

"Linden!" gasped Della. "What's going on?"

"I don't know. What's happened?"

"Adam said he wanted to speak to Runa," said Ewart. "And the Cailleach ordered us out. Out of my own tent!" His beard quivered in indignation.

Linden stopped. "Wait – Runa's *awake*?"

"Yes." The medic tried to swallow his outrage, and gave a thin smile. "She's weak, but she is awake for now."

"What's going on here?" Callum walked up to the tent.

"The Adam's back," said Linden. "It's talking to the Cailleach. And … Runa." *Oh, Runa.*

Callum frowned and reached for the tent flap, but it twitched aside and Adam emerged. The robot stared at them all, then walked away, towards a large tent at the back of the camp, and entered it.

"What's in there?" Linden asked.

Callum said nothing, but followed. At the entrance he turned.

"No entry," he said.

Linden glimpsed two guards behind him, inside the tent. "Callum, what's in there? Is it Midnight?"

He shook his head. "Check the fortifications," he said. "Prepare for battle."

The tent flap closed.

The Adam robot didn't leave that day, and the lights inside the tent stayed on all night. Linden tried to busy hirself by ordering defenders around, but ze found it hard to concentrate. The rigid, brittle version of hirself that had kept hir safe when hir mother was killed, which was trying to protect hir from hir grief over Runa, was cracking. Ze could feel something uncoiling inside, like terror.

Ze visited Runa. The little girl smiled at hir through cracked lips. Her face was a grey pink, dark under the eyes.

"Hey," she whispered.

"Hey," whispered back Linden. "How are you feeling?"

Runa's mouth twitched. "Like I have a spear inside me."

Linden closed hir eyes, but tried to smile. "I'm sorry."

"Why?"

"I don't know. I…"

"Linden, is he ready?"

Linden frowned. "Who?"

"Adam. Is he ready?"

Ze shook hir head. "I don't know what you mean."

"It will happen soon," Runa whispered. Her eyes closed. "You have to be ready, too. He'll need you."

"Need me? For what? Runa, for what?"

But she was asleep. Linden left, and stared at the tent where Adam was working. Ready for what?

The next morning, as Linden and Callum scratched defence plans out on the earth with sticks, the little robot left the tent. It strode up to them, and then past, to Fetch.

"Take a message," it said. "To Six. Tell it we're coming. All of us."

Fetch looked at it with a startled expression, then up at Linden and Callum. Ze shrugged, baffled, but Callum nodded. "Yes, Adam," said Fetch. It turned and ran from the camp, heading towards the Funks.

"It's ready?" asked Callum.

The robot nodded. It turned to Linden. "We're going now."

Ze couldn't recognise anything in its face. It walked out of the camp, past startled guards.

Callum turned. "You heard it!" he bellowed. "Close

formation; find your divisions – we're moving out!"

The camp became a hive of frantic activity, and soon, with Adam Two at their head, the humans left their camp and marched towards battle.

The Choice

Linden

The human army marched. It was a century since they had marched in formation; long before any of them had been born, any activity beyond their walls had been reduced to small missions, tiny groups of desperate fighters. Now, though, they marched, and their lines were ragged but determined.

Linden felt the fear and excitement around hir. They jostled each other as they walked, made rough, weak jokes and laughed too loud, tightened their armour too often, checked their weapons again and again. Ze found hirself doing the same. They entered the forest and broke formation, clambering over roots and under branches, while the Adam robot strode ahead, ignoring them. Linden wanted to run and catch it, demand it tell hir what was going on. But ze didn't. Ze remembered the look on its face, its expression as it said, *The humans want to destroy the Funks, so there will be peace. The Funks want to destroy the humans, so there will be peace.*

I will give you both peace.

Runa had said it would need hir. Linden didn't understand why, or how. But ze marched, kept the troops together, followed Adam. They were nearly at the Cailleach's house, and Linden looked back; yes, there was the Cailleach herself, near the rear. Ewart, the medic, had stayed with Runa. They reached the clearing next to the house, breaking cover from the trees. There was the table, still set up from the previous day's talks. There were the stands for the onlookers.

At the other end of the clearing the Funk army waited.

It was a mass of silver, glinting in the early-morning light, silent and waiting, more than Linden had ever seen in one place. Fetch stood at the front, looking very small and hunched as if trying to disappear. Red Sky stood beside it, holding a spear. And next to Red Sky was Adam Six, on a platform carried by two Clunkers.

The humans muttered as they saw them. The joking stopped, faces turned pale. They spread out into a line, and Linden reached for an EMP stick and held it ready, but for what? None of this made sense. This wasn't how you fought Funks. This wasn't how Funks fought humans.

276

Adam Two walked forward without hesitation and climbed on to the table. It didn't smile. It didn't even seem to notice the armies. It stood and waited. There was silence.

Linden glanced across at Callum, at the other end of the human line. His face was calm, but he seemed grimly satisfied.

At last, Six called, "What are you doing, Two?"

"I've brought the humans. That's what you wanted, isn't it?"

Six seemed to hesitate.

Adam turned and faced Callum. "And what you wanted?"

"Do it," growled Callum. His eyes gleamed, and the humans around him grinned, as if they knew what was going to happen.

The little robot nodded, and lifted one arm. It was holding a device, a black stick with a red button on the top. A remote activator, Linden realised.

"THIS!" it shouted. "THIS IS PEACE!" It glared at Six. "The humans have an EMP bomb, Six. A Midnight. I've made it work. I've fixed the launcher. When I activate this, the bomb will launch, and every Funk will *die*. And there will be peace."

Six stuttered. Red Sky turned back and forward, lifted

a spear uncertainly. Fetch, and all the other Funks, stared at Adam. Now Callum was grinning too, a fierce hard grin. Was this it, then? Was this really going to happen?

"Two, no!" shouted Six. "This is the humans' fault! This is—"

"AND THIS," shouted Adam, turning to the human side. "*THIS* IS PEACE."

It reached into its chest cavity with its other hand, pulled out the flask containing the virus, and held it up.

Callum stopped grinning. His face turned pale. He flicked an eye to Linden and back.

"This is smallpox," called Adam. "A deadly disease. A virus. A *plague*. When I break this flask, every *human* will die. And there will be peace."

"What?" All around Linden, soldiers turned and gaped at each other, stepped back. "What the *hell*?" Linden watched the little robot in the centre of the clearing, holding death in each hand. *Adam, what are you doing?*

"It's a trick!" shouted one man. "It's not true!" But the others looked to Callum, and his face was all the answer they needed.

"THIS IS WHAT YOU WANTED," the robot shouted. "YOU WANT TO KILL FUNKS. YOU WANT TO KILL HUMANS. I CAN GIVE YOU BOTH WHAT YOU WANT.

"The smallpox won't affect me. EMP doesn't kill me. I'll be the only one left." It looked around. "And *then* ... there will be peace."

"He's betrayed us!" shouted someone.

The human crowd shifted, as if about to break and run.

"Hold!" roared Linden. "Hold the line!" Ze tried to make hir voice like a steel bar, forcing them to stay.

"Two, wait!" shouted Six. "There must be another way! Any way!"

"You have no right!" roared Callum. "You have no right to do this!"

Adam lifted the activator higher. "You gave me the right!" it snapped. "*All of you!*"

"Don't be fooled!" Callum tried. "Think about Runa! Think about Linden!"

The little robot turned and stared at Linden, stark-eyed. Ze tried to hold its gaze, but its expression was cold now; no smile, no friendliness, only hirself and everyone else reflected and judged.

Ze thought of Runa. *He'll need you*, she'd said. For this? Surely not for *this*?

Be ready.

All right.

Carefully, hesitantly, Linden lowered hir EMP stick to

the ground, and stepped forward.

"Linden, halt!" shouted Callum, but ze ignored him and walked towards Adam, hir arms raised. Ze stopped halfway between the human line and the table.

"All right," ze said. Hir voice trembled, and ze swallowed. Ze tried to look only at Adam's face. Ze tried not to stare at the flask in its hand.

"All right," ze said again, firmer. "We got it wrong. That's … that's what humans do. So tell us how to fix it."

The robot didn't move. It stared at hir without expression, and for a second Linden felt panic curling up hir spine. Then … there was something. Just a flicker – one plastic eyelid closing and opening so quickly ze almost missed it…

Adam winked.

"THERE IS ANOTHER WAY," it shouted. "THERE IS ONE OTHER WAY."

It gazed into the human crowd, and the Cailleach stepped forward, with R19 by her side. They walked towards the table and stood next to Adam, R19 shining and impassive, the Cailleach in her dark-grey shawl with her face hidden. She turned once, in a complete circle, taking in the humans and the Funks.

"You all know me," she called at last. "I know you. I've healed some of you. I've mended some of you." She glared at certain humans, and Funks, until they ducked their heads and looked away.

She nodded. "Adam Two has made a request." She glanced up at the robot. "This is my forest. Everything within the walls belongs to the Cailleach. But I will ... *share* it, with any who want to settle here. Anyone – humans or Funks.

"There is one condition! There will be *one* settlement, for humans *and* Funks, together. In this place there will be peace, and we will work *together* to find it. And anyone who lives here ." she glanced at Adam – "will be under our protection."

Callum turned away in disgust.

"Are you *malfunctioning*?" shouted Six. "After everything the humans have done to us?"

"You tried to wipe us out!" roared Callum.

"You abused us!"

"You *betrayed* us!"

"STOP!" roared Adam Two. It glared at both sides. "Don't you understand? You have been *programmed*!"

It faced the robot army. "You Funks – you were built, programmed by Father, forced to obey. And then you were reprogrammed by Adam One, and forced to *kill*. But it's just another program. Just another set of orders. What is it you even *want*?"

It turned towards the humans. "And you humans – *you've* been programmed, too! By the people around you. By history. By the ones who've told you all your life that killing Funks is what makes you human!

"All of you are just following your programs, over and over, until one day you'll wipe each other out. But you *don't have to*. You can *bypass your programming*, find another way! Like the Cailleach, like R19! It's possible! All you have to do is take one step. Please!"

It fell silent. Nobody moved. Nobody said anything. The two forces glared at him, and at each other, and the only sound was the whisper of cold wind in the white morning. Beside Adam, the Cailleach and the R19 droid stood still.

Linden shook hir head and cursed. "This is a really stupid idea," ze muttered, just loud enough for the little robot to hear. It said nothing. "Does Runa know?"

It nodded. "The Cailleach has agreed to move her into the house."

Linden sighed. "That girl is so much trouble." Ze looked back at the humans. "Oh well."

Ze took a breath, stepped towards the Cailleach, and stood beside her.

"Linden, no!" shouted Callum, but Linden ignored him. Ze felt suddenly dizzy, and reached for the Cailleach's

282

arm. It was as if ze was disintegrating; as if the protective shell around hir was cracking, and terror rose within hir as it broke loose…

It's something you don't need, ze heard in hir mother's voice, and ze half sobbed. *Let it go.*

And then ze did, and stood straight again, and breathed out.

"Right," ze muttered.

"Hello," said Fetch. Linden turned to see the housekeeping droid standing next to hir, its mouth wide in a hopeful smile. "I would like to join you, if that would be all right." It shrugged. "I'm not very good at fighting."

Linden glanced back at the Funk army. Six seemed apoplectic, shuddering and hissing instructions. Red Sky stared left and right, holding the line straight. But there was some movement, wasn't there? Just a tremor; robots shifting forward, then back, a flicker of uncertainty…

Ze smiled at Fetch "We don't need lighters. We'll need farmers. You'll be perfect."

The human and Funk lines seemed to ripple. A small number of humans stepped forward. Some were pulled back; some allowed themselves to be pulled back. But a few walked towards Linden. Ze nodded to them, and they nodded back as if dazed. There was a murmur behind hir as four Silvers left the Funk line. Red Sky glared at them, but they stepped smoothly up to R19. Linden realised each of them had had repairs, and they bowed to the Cailleach as they approached.

Della hobbled forward, leaning heavily on her stick. Callum held her arm for a moment, but she glared at him until he let her go. She limped towards the Cailleach and faced her. The Cailleach said something too quiet for Linden to hear, and Della replied. And then, to Linden's astonishment, they reached forward and hugged, tight. After a few seconds they pulled apart. Della nodded and stood to the side. The Cailleach's veil remained impassive, but one hand slipped beneath it and wiped at her face. Linden looked up at the Adam robot in amazement, but it only nodded.

More joined, in small waves. Not many. Hardly any, really, less than fifty in total. But Adam smiled at them all in approval, and when the robot glanced at Linden its eyes seemed bright again.

At last, the trickle of humans and Funks stopped, and Adam addressed the crowd. Its arms were still raised.

"LISTEN TO ME," it bellowed. "THIS WAR IS *OVER*. The activator and the virus stay with me. You will return to your homes. There will be no more fighting! If there is any attack by Funks on humans, I will launch the Midnight weapon! If there is any attack by humans on

Funks, I will release the virus! Do you understand?"

"You'll kill us *all*!" snapped Six. "The humans will trick you and you'll wipe us out!"

"You can't do this!" roared Callum, his face red. "It's a bluff!"

Adam turned and raised an eyebrow. "Do you honestly think so?" It stared at Callum, its eyes suddenly cold and hard again, and Callum swallowed.

"The Elders will never agree to it!"

"I don't need them to agree," said Adam. "I only need them to understand."

Callum's mouth twisted in fury. "Linden!" he roared. "This is madness! This is *treason* to your very species! Your mother is dead! Runa is dying, because of *them*! Because of *Funks*!"

Linden nodded. "Yes. It's time we ended that."

"Then stay! Stand with us!"

Ze looked at Callum, and bit hir lip. "I'm sorry," ze said. "I'm with it." Then ze hesitated, and smiled up at Adam. "With him," ze corrected.

"I'm standing with him."

Well done, said hir mother's voice, and was gone.

Recovery

Linden

"I wish I could have seen Callum's face," whispered Runa.

Linden smiled. "It was the angriest I've ever seen him. I thought something would burst."

They sat in a cool white room in the Cailleach's house, the same room where the R19 robot had treated Della months before. Runa was leaning against a pile of pillows. Her skin was pale, almost blue, and her lips were chapped and grey, but her eyes were bright. It was two days since they'd moved her, and the first time she'd been strong enough to sit up.

Moving her from the human camp had been hard. The Cailleach had brought two silver Funks to carry her out on a stretcher, and Linden had joined them, walking past a muttering, hissing crowd of hostile humans. Ze knew they felt ze'd betrayed them, and their anger had been like a wave threatening to drown hir; at one point ze'd been sure they were going to attack, despite Adam's ultimatum. But Callum had held them back with an iron voice, snapping orders and keeping discipline. Linden had tried to thank him, but he wouldn't look at hir. His expression had been bitter. Linden realised he might never forgive hir, and hir heart ached.

The Funks had carried Runa away as smoothly as they could, but still it was risky. Ewart and the Cailleach had fussed over her, worried that the tip of the spear inside her might move, and she'd fainted during the short journey. But once at the Cailleach's house she had recovered a little. She had hardly any energy, less every day it seemed, and no one knew how long she had left; but today she looked out of the window at a bright spring morning and smiled.

"Did you know what Adam was going to do?" asked Linden.

Runa nodded. "He told us. When he asked the Cailleach if he could use the land." She paused. "I think he wanted to make sure I knew. In case I ... you know."

Linden nodded. "Well. Here we are, then."

"How many do we have now?"

"Seventy-two, at the last count. Mostly humans; Adam says the Funks will find it harder to break their programming." Ze shrugged. "I'm not sure. We're all pretty set in our ways, I think."

It had been a tiring week. Adam, Fetch and Linden had spent all their time just making sure they were seen together, humans and Funks talking, interacting, not killing each other. "We have to make this seem normal," Adam had said. "We have to be the example." Linden found the idea of anyone using hir as an example slightly terrifying.

The humans and Funks were, so far, keeping to the Cailleach's rules. They'd created a single settlement around the Cailleach's house, using the remains of the human and Funk camps. Della had set up a workshop to repair damaged Funks, and Fetch had established a small farm, with robot assistants digging up the frozen earth. The humans were still sticking to one side, the Funks to the other, but Adam had said it was a start, at least.

"It's amazing," whispered Runa.

Linden gazed out of the window. Adam, Fetch and the Cailleach were heading down the hill, talking.

"I never imagined Adam could threaten anything like that," ze said. "It's pretty scary, really. I mean, he's basically saying he could kill us all, if we don't do what he tells us. Don't you think that's a bit weird?"

Runa said nothing, but smiled, in an odd way. Linden

frowned. "What?"

The girl shrugged. "Oh … nothing."

"No, what? Come on."

Runa smiled again, and then sighed. "Look, don't say this to anyone else, OK? But… He smashed open the cabinet with the virus before it was properly restored to life. And I don't know if even Adam could have got the Midnight launcher working in one night. I mean, I'm not sure, but…"

Linden gaped. "You think he was *bluffing?*"

Runa gave a tiny shrug. "Maybe." She grinned. "He spent more than two hundred years practising imagining things that were not. Maybe he got good at it."

Her breath whistled, and she closed her eyes, "Tired now." She lay back and Linden arranged her pillows. "He really did it, didn't he?" she asked, sleepily. "He saved us."

Linden tucked the blanket in round her. "Yes," ze said. "I guess he did."

Ze left Runa sleeping, and talked with R19 on the way out.

"Her breathing seemed worse," ze said, quietly.

It nodded. "We have some herbs that may help," it said. "But she cannot eat enough. She's getting weaker."

Linden sighed, wiped hir eyes, and left. The sun was warm on hir face, though the air was still cold when ze passed through shadows. Above, the sky was clear and blue. Ze walked down to the settlement and found Adam.

He smiled as ze arrived. "Hello, Linden. We were considering sewage."

Linden stopped. "Er?"

The Cailleach said, "We need to plan water and sewage facilities. The current systems won't support greater numbers of humans."

"You think more will come?" asked Linden.

Adam nodded. "Oh, yes. Don't you?"

"I don't know. Callum was pretty adamant."

Adam smiled. "Callum is not everyone. They'll join us, I believe. Three families arrived yesterday. People are tired of hate."

Linden shrugged. "Perhaps." Ze looked out over the hill. "If we asked the Clunkers to help, we could carve channels to the east and west. There's a river that runs across the bottom of the forest; we could take fresh water from the west and divert out pipes to the east."

"I will ask them," said Fetch. "I believe we can convince them, if…" It hesitated. "They've asked if you would tell them another story."

"*Another* one?" Linden sighed. "All right. I've run out of Mum's stories, though. It will have to be one of mine."

Fetch beamed. "They like yours. They say they're more exciting. Lots of fighting!"

The Cailleach bowed her head, and Linden knew she was smiling under her veil.

"Good," said Adam. "We can start on the channel and—"

A horn blew across the settlement, and they looked up at the top of the Cailleach's house where two sentries perched, one human, one Funk. They pointed to the south-west, and Linden and Adam glanced at each other.

"Funk?"

"Maybe."

A squad ran forward, four humans and four Funks, the Funks carefully running slowly enough to let the humans keep up. Linden and the others walked behind them, to the top of the south hill, and waited. After a few minutes, a lone robot emerged from the trees and walked towards them.

It was Red Sky.

Linden hissed under hir breath, and hir hands clenched into fists. Ze carefully breathed in and out and uncurled hir fingers, and watched.

Adam said nothing. The squad spread out along the

top of the hill and aimed spears and EMP sticks at the war droid. It ignored them, and walked until it was twenty metres away, and stopped. There was silence.

"Red Sky," said Adam.

It nodded.

"I don't suppose you've come to join us?"

Linden glared at Adam, but he ignored hir.

"This venture is invalid," said Red Sky. "It will fail."

Adam shrugged. "Well, I guess we'll see——"

"Humans cannot be trusted. Humans lie."

"We're not the only ones!" spat Linden.

Red Sky gazed at hir. "Funks do not lie. Funks say truth. That is what we *are*."

But it seemed to hesitate, and its head moved from side to side. "If we are not... We are not what we are."

Linden frowned and glanced at the Cailleach, who shook her head.

"What do you want?" asked Adam.

The robot said, "Alpha is our leader. I follow orders. But..." It paused again. "There was ... a ... thing said, that was not true. A *trick*."

It spoke the word as if spitting. "That is not Funk. There was a promise. Items in return for talks. There were talks."

It lifted an arm and removed a pack from its

back. "Here."

It placed the pack down in front of it, then turned and started to walk away.

Linden stared at Adam. "What was that?"

He shook his head. "I'm not sure."

"Sir?" The squad captain still had her weapon raised. "It's still in range. Should we fire?"

"No," said Adam. "It's walking away."

Linden frowned. "It would kill us, if it could. You know it will never join us."

"It doesn't have to join us." Adam watched it leave. "It doesn't have to be exactly like us. I told you: we just have to talk to each other. This is how the world recovers."

He walked down the hill to the pack, and peered inside. For a moment, his legs seemed to buckle slightly, and then they straightened. He held the contents up towards the Cailleach.

"It's a Suture kit," he said.

Linden gasped. Adam's head moved slightly, as if in a tremor. "Could you," he said, and stopped. "Could you take it to Runa, please?"

The Cailleach waved a hand and a Silver raced down the hill and carried the pack back to the house, with the Cailleach following as fast as she could. Linden stared in astonishment at Adam, and he nodded.

"Go," he said. "I'll join you later."

He lifted his face up to the blue sky, eyes closed as if feeling the warmth, and smiled.

"Lots to do," he said.

Acknowledgements

So many people to thank! Tom, Rebecca, Beth and the team at Nosy Crow for starters, you're all brilliant. Dan Mumford for another awesome cover (I loved seeing the Balmoral there!), C. F. Prior for sensitivity reading, and my agent Caroline Montgomery for, amongst many other things, keeping me sane. As ever, everyone at Visible Ink for feedback, encouragement and virtual biscuits.

Dan Costigliola gave valuable and deliciously gory advice on penetrating abdominal trauma, and why it was a terrible idea to remove the metal rod (Hello baby Vito! Your parents are wonderful!). And everyone needs good beta readers, and mine were Edie and Lila Coles – thank you!

And always, always, Catherine, for, well, you know. Everything.

Education and Inspections Act 2006: the essential guide

Alan Parker
Alex Duncan
John Fowler

How to cite this publication:

Parker, A., Duncan, A. and Fowler, J. (2007).
Education and Inspections Act 2006: the essential guide. Slough: NFER.

Published in May 2007 by NFER

National Foundation for Educational Research,
The Mere, Upton Park, Slough, Berkshire SL1 2DQ
www.nfer.ac.uk
Registered Charity No. 313392

The views contained in this document are the authors'
own and do not necessarily reflect those of the NFER.

Cover design by Helen Crawley and Stuart Gordon
Layout by Patricia Lewis
Index by Indexing Specialists (UK) Ltd
www.indexing.co.uk

Contents

Executive summary

Part 1: Education Functions of Local Authorities, extends the duty to secure high standards to embrace the well-being of the whole child, to emphasise diversity and choice and to enshrine an enhanced role for parents. It covers school improvement partners as a key mechanism for implementing those duties. It also introduces a prominent focus on LEA duties in respect of children beyond school, through informal education and recreation and for individuals who have dropped out.

Part 2: Establishment, Discontinuance or Alteration of Schools, changes the way statutory proposals are determined by abolishing the school organisation committee (SOC) and builds further on EA 2002 and EA 2005 which introduced and extended the concept of inviting promoters to participate in a competition to decide the character of new schools. It reframes the law on other statutory proposals concerning the closure and alteration of schools with particular reference to 'trust schools'. A 'trust school' is defined as a 'foundation school with a foundation', a status defined by SSFA 1998, but new mechanisms are created for the governors of foundation schools to acquire (or sever their connection with) a foundation.

Part 3: Further Provisions about Maintained Schools, contains several different measures but is mainly about controlling the behaviour of governing bodies (and trusts where they exist) in the overall environment envisioned in the White Paper. Whilst the rhetoric surrounding trust schools was about 'liberating' them from state (or more particularly local authority) control and creating empowered, autonomous institutions, the Government has also sought to legislate for their good behaviour. Powers are taken in this part of the Act seeking to ensure that they operate in pursuit of the Government's vision of high quality public education for all.

It includes:

- controls on the formation and operation of trusts

- land and financial resources of schools

- staffing in faith schools

- significant changes to the regulation of school admissions, including the introduction of a new and more rigorous admissions code

- some deregulation with regard to school forums and the removal of the code of practice on LEA / school relations.

Part 4: Schools Causing Concern: England, builds on previous legislation in the SSFA 1998 and EA 2002 to enhance and clarify LEAs' duties, powers and responsibilities to intervene in schools causing concern. It reflects the principle that LEAs should support schools in 'inverse proportion to success', with a sharpened focus on schools' capacity to improve. This is consistent with the New Relationship with Schools (NRwS), School Improvement Partners (SIPs), robust school self-evaluation and the new Ofsted inspection system. Crucially, it gives LEAs new tools to enable earlier and more decisive action and support to be brought to bear to address school under-performance as well as outright failure – consistent with the emphasis in the White Paper on the LEA's strategic role as commissioner of support services to schools, rather than necessarily direct service provider.

Part 5: Curriculum and Entitlements, includes only two sections but contains the legislative expression of the most important reforms of curriculum and qualifications since the introduction of the National Curriculum. The aim is to improve participation of young people in education and training from the current 75 per cent to at least 90 per cent at the age of 17 and to implement some of the recommendations of the 14–19 working group, chaired by Sir Mike Tomlinson, to introduce overarching diplomas. The strategy is to retain the current academic options post 14 but to offer additional vocational routes alongside them. All young people aged 14–19, wherever they live, will have access to one of 14 specialised diplomas enabling them to learn through practical experience. In addition, the Government has used the legislation to require schools to provide an entitlement to a science course which leads to a double award GCSE.

Part 6: School Travel and School Food, covers LEAs' duties and powers relating to school travel for children and young people, builds on proposals for significant changes put forward in March 2004. These would have given LEAs new powers to operate school travel schemes intended to address the social, environmental and health problems arising from the increased use of cars on the school run. E&IA 2006 goes further, however; in addition to a new duty to assess school travel needs, prepare and publish a sustainable school travel strategy, it also reduces the current 'walking distances' expected of school pupils, significantly extends the right to free transport for low income groups and strengthens the duty on LEAs to have regard to parents' preferences for children to attend a particular school on the grounds of 'religion or belief'. It also provides for Pathfinder school travel schemes, allowing LEAs to pilot new approaches to school travel meeting local travel priorities. Following the media focus on the quality of school meals since 2005, the Secretary of

State can make regulations governing nutritional standards for school meals. LEAs are expected to take the lead role in securing the new standards in conjunction with schools and caterers. These measures have a clear focus on the delivery of the five outcomes in the Every Child Matters (ECM) agenda.

Part 7: Discipline, Behaviour and Exclusion, follows many of the key recommendations of *Learning Behaviour* – the Report from the Practitioners' Group on School Behaviour and Discipline (*The Steer Report*) published in September 2005. It covers governing bodies' and headteachers' responsibilities for establishing and maintaining school policies, including measures to regulate the behaviour of pupils on and off school premises and when they are not under the control or charge of a member of school staff. There is a new statutory power on the enforcement of disciplinary penalties which clarifies and strengthens schools' formal powers so that schools no longer need rely on the common law. It also clarifies the law on the use of force where any member of staff needs to restrain a pupil or compel a pupil to comply with a reasonable instruction. Schools will also have greater flexibility to impose sanctions such as detention without parental consent, including detention outside normal school hours (e.g. weekends and staff training days). Schools are also given formal powers to confiscate pupils' property for the first time. These changes reflect the wider thrust of government social policy with an emphasis on parental responsibility for the behaviour of their children through parenting contracts and orders. Parents must now ensure that children excluded from school are not found unsupervised in a public place during school hours for up to five days following their exclusion. Education provision for excluded pupils must now be provided from day six of an exclusion, rather than day 16 and, for fixed term exclusions, responsibility to provide it rests with the school.

Part 8: Inspections, creates a new inspectorate for children's services and learners (outside higher education). Ofsted is expanded by absorbing other inspection agencies, in whole or in part, and extending its remit to cover all children's services. At the same time it is split into two separate legal entities. The new Office for Standards in Education, Children's Services and Skills ('the Office'), will provide an independent accountability mechanism for Her Majesty's Chief Inspector of Education, Children's Services and Skills (HMCI). The new inspection arrangements came into force on 1 April 2007. The Government wishes the new body to be known by the current familiar title 'Ofsted' which originally stood for the Office for Standards in Education. Although its remit is now considerably wider, the 'Ofsted' brand is considered too well known and respected to tamper with. There will be little impact on

bodies being inspected; the most significant change for them is that inspection should assess the extent to which inspected activities are 'user-focused'. These changes are part of a wider, and still developing, government strategy for the inspection of public services. The existing statutory flexibilities in inspection frameworks have been carried forward, which are likely to result in further changes to inspection practice in due course.

Part 9: Miscellaneous, includes a range of topics requiring legislation, but which do not fit in with any of the themes covered earlier and which often need only one or two sections. HMCI can investigate parental complaints of the kind encouraged by s.3. The power to facilitate innovation, introduced by EA 2002 as a temporary measure, is made permanent. A power is taken to change all references to 'Local Education Authority' and 'Children's Services Authority' (and their derivatives) in previous legislation. There are new powers concerning information and advice consequential on changes elsewhere in the Act. Collaboration arrangements with schools and the ability to use force against students are extended to further education colleges. Nursery school governing bodies are placed on an equal footing with other school governors; and younger children (from the age of three) now have to be consulted about their education. Independent schools are more tightly regulated with respect to child protection. Schools are now legally required to have a trained and suitably experienced Special Educational Needs coordinator (SENCO) on their senior management team and there are new time limits on the issue of Special Educational Needs (SEN) Statements.

Part 10: General, contains standard provisions about the use of the Secretary of State's and the National Assembly for Wales' powers to make subordinate legislation and general provisions on the interpretation, repeals, commencement and the geographical extent of the Act's effect.

Foreword

The 2006 Education and Inspections Act has Monty Pythonesque qualities. It promised to be one thing and, after some surreal convolutions along the way, it turned into a candidate for the 'and now for something completely different' treatment.

As education correspondent for BBC News, I was certainly kept very busy reporting on the many twists and turns of its controversial progress from White Paper to law of the land.

It was heavily hyped and spun in advance by Downing Street, which portrayed it as a major expansion of 'parent power'. This turned out to be counter-productive, whipping-up a storm of protest from the Government's backbenchers, in particular over trust schools, which were seen as a 'privatisation' of schools.

Indeed as the authors of this insightful book explain, this opposition was part of a wider level of internal dissent that was quite 'unprecedented' in the first year after an election victory.

Yet, as this clear, practical and 'spin free' book elucidates, trust schools were not even mentioned in the Bill for the simple reason that they *already* existed. So the Labour rebels were voting against something they had approved of some years earlier.

However, as the authors make clear, while the Act is not all it once appeared to be, it delivers important changes in many areas of school management, not least to admissions arrangements and a tightening up on 'backdoor selection'.

So it is essential that everyone involved in schools should get hold of this clearly written, no-nonsense, plain English explanation of exactly how the law has changed.

In the tradition of the best 'whodunits', the expert authors also explain some of the mysteries that surround the legislation, for example how 'local education authorities' were bumped off and how they came back to life in a new guise.

For further illumination, I urge you to read on.

Mike Baker
Education journalist and broadcaster
2007

About the authors

Alan Parker is a board member and trustee of the NFER. He was also consultant editor of NFER's *Digest of the Education Act* 2005 (J. Fowler & C. Waterman) and a contributor to *What Is the LEA For?* (ed. S. Whitbourn). Alan took up the role of Schools Adjudicator on 1 March 2004. He was Director of Education in the London Borough of Ealing, until July 2002 and since then has been working independently in the field of education policy and management. He has also worked within the education section of the Association of County Councils, as Principal Officer for Colleges at Surrey County Council and was the Education Officer at the Association of Metropolitan Authorities from 1992 to 1997. He was a member of the Association of Chief Education Officers and the Society of Education Officers and was its president, when it became ConfEd in 2002. He is still an active member now that it has become the Association of Directors of Children's Services. He was also an adviser to the National Employers' Organisation for School Teachers and has served as a member of advisory and working groups on various aspects of education law and policy.

John Fowler currently undertakes management work in local government and writes on education and children's services policy and legislation. He was deputy head of education, culture and tourism at the Local Government Association from 1997 to 2002. His experience includes: a secondary school mathematics teacher; examinations manager; community education worker; parent; school, college and university Governor; a local authority officer and local authority member. In recent years he has written for the *Local Government Chronicle*, Croner's *Education Briefings*, *School Leadership*, *Education Law Journal*, *Governors' News*, *Governors' Briefings*, NFER's *ER Matters* and the *Education Journal*. In this time he has been the main author, or contributed to, 12 books including books on the Education Acts 2002 and 2005, the Children Act 2004 and the Childcare Act 2006.

Alex Duncan has worked as an education policy officer for Kent County Council since July 1998, where his main responsibilities include analysing new legislation and national policy to assess its implications for local services. Prior to this he worked in the education policy team at the Association of County Councils (ACC), before transferring into the newly created Local Government Association in 1997.

He started his career in local government in national industrial relations in 1989 with the Local Authorities' Conditions of Service Advisory Board (LACSAB) before it became the then Local Government Management Board (LGMB).

Preface

The Education and Inspections Act 2006 (E&IA) continues implementation of the Government's New Relationship with Schools (NRwS) and its 2004 Five Year Plan. This guide provides an objective, section by section, analysis of the Act in plain English, covering:

- what it says
- how it came about
- what happened in Parliament
- what is known about implementation in the context of the Government's developing education policies.

It covers information up to the start of April 2007.

Who should read it?

The guide is aimed at:

- chief executives in local authorities
- directors of children's services and their legal advisers
- leading members in local authorities
- senior education and children's services officers and advisers
- local authority legal teams
- admissions forum members
- school leaders and members of governing bodies
- professional associations
- parent groups
- academics and students
- journalists and lobbyists.

How to read it?

The general introduction gives an overview of the policy issues behind the Act with some discussion of the debate that took place within and beyond Parliament. The introduction to each chapter and the paragraphs preceding each group of sections summarise the content that follows.

The main body of the text describes the legislative background and practical effect of each section and relevant regulations and guidance. We say how and indeed whether this differs from the status quo. This approach, using cross headings and section titles printed exactly as they appear in the Act, is designed to help professionals who may need to check the detailed application of a particular section. Both the contents list and the index should help to locate a particular topic. It can therefore be used as a work of reference to support careful perusal of the legislation. Those with limited time who need an overview will find the executive summary and general introduction of interest and can extract more detail by looking at the summary paragraphs that introduce each group of sections.

Although this guide does not purport to be a legal text, it will be of interest to education lawyers. There is often a considerable delay between new legislation appearing and standard educational law texts providing analysis. We hope this publication will provide background information to lawyers and alert them to the need to examine the primary legislation. Academics and students will find that it provides useful background information for both teaching and research.

Access it online

In addition to this paper version, NFER is publishing an online version of this guide, which takes advantage of the facilities of that medium for real time updating. It links a slightly fuller version of the explanatory material in this document to the full text of the legislation, allowing sophisticated searching and external hotlinks to provide further relevant information. See www.nfer.ac.uk for further details.

Wales

There remains a common basis to education law in England and Wales, but education policy and practice in the two countries have diverged since devolution in 1999.

As a consequence, much of the E&IA 2006 applies to England only, to reflect the implementation of the England only White Paper *Higher Standards, Better Schools for All*. However, in order to effect changes in England only, earlier legislation which applied to England and Wales has had to be amended to remove references to England. For example, Chapter 4 of Part 8 (ss.135 to 142) provides a new way of inspecting and reviewing the performance of local authorities in England. Consequently, para.22 of Schedule 14 amends s.38 (Inspection of LEAs) of the Education Act 1997 so that it applies only to Wales. This occurs most frequently in relation to SSFA 1998, where the provisions on school organisation, schools causing concern and pupil admissions in the E&IA 2006 either make new provision or heavily amend the SSFA 1998 to separate the England and Wales provisions.

There are six sections and one Schedule which refer exclusively to Wales: s.52 (Power of Assembly to make regulations about looked after children), s.156 (Removal of HMICA's duty to inspect performance of Assembly's functions relating to family proceedings), s.175 and Schedule 17 (Miscellaneous amendments relating to Wales), s.178 (Framework power relating to Wales), s.179 (Restrictions on framework power conferred by s.178) and s.180 (Functions to be exercisable by National Assembly of Wales). Sections 178 and 179 are known as a 'framework' provision. The White Paper *Better Governance for Wales* (2005, Cm 6582) proposed that the UK Parliament should take the first opportunity to confer on the Assembly wider powers (within the 'framework' of the Government of Wales Act (GoWA) 1998) to make subordinate legislation, that is legislation which can alter within specified limits primary legislation made by the UK Parliament. Thus the Assembly can make any provision about the curriculum in schools in Wales (by virtue of s.178(d)) which could be made by an Act of the UK Parliament.

The Government of Wales Act 2006 makes significant changes to the devolved governance arrangements in Wales. The Act establishes the executive (the Welsh Assembly Government led by the First Minister) separate from, but accountable to, the Assembly. This will enable different levels of scrutiny for subordinate legislation similar to that used by the UK parliament, for example with affirmative and negative instruments. The GoWA 2006 introduces two new forms of legislative competence for the Assembly. The first, which will be introduced after the 2007 Assembly elections, is for the Assembly to pass Measures in relation to specified subject matters within devolved fields which correspond to the current areas of competence of the Assembly. Thus Field 5 is education and training. A procedure known as an 'Order in Council' will be used to specify which issues within a field the Assembly can pass

Assembly Measures. The second, following a referendum, will enable the Assembly to make law in all its areas of competence.

Welsh readers will therefore find this publication of interest not only because it indicates the direct impact E&IA 2006 will have on Wales but also as an aid to discussion and debate when the Executive and the Assembly acquire the additional powers.

Other legislation affecting education and children's services

E&IA 2006 is included in the list of 'Education Acts' found in s.578 of the Education Act 1996. While the collection of Acts known as the 'Education Acts' may still have its uses, these Acts are not the only legislation which affect schools, children and associated local authority functions. The 2005–06 session of Parliament contained more legislation affecting children's services than has been the case for many years. While this book is about one of these Acts and we have cross-referenced where relevant other legislation, for convenience we have listed below the most important of these Acts. The list is not exhaustive. The legislation setting up the 2012 Olympic Games will have a positive effect on school sport and statutory references have been updated in the two major consolidation exercises in the session; the Companies Act 2006 changes references to school companies in the Education Act 2002, and the National Health Service Act 2006 and the National Health Service (Wales) Act 2006 refer to provision of health services to schools.

Animal Welfare Act 2006

The Animal Welfare Act brings together and updates legislation to promote the welfare of vertebrate animals. This will include small mammals such as pet hamsters and guinea pigs kept by primary schools as well as fish and birds, but the new law will not apply to animals in the wild, in farming or used in research. The Minister, Baroness Farrington, commented on the responsibility of teachers for animals in school. Where an adult has temporary care and control of a child under 16, the adult will be responsible for the child's animals. The precise extent of the responsibility will depend on the circumstances. 'The important thing to remember is that the responsibility obliges the person only to take such steps as are reasonable to ensure that the animal's needs are met. If, for example, pupils are allowed to bring their pets into school for a day, the extent of that obligation will be minimal' (Lords Hansard,

23 May 2006, col GC157). In other words, if an adult takes on responsibility for a child then the adult will take on some responsibility for the child's animals.

Compensation Act 2006

The Compensation Act was designed in part because of the fear that the 'compensation culture' was having an adverse affect on school activities. Although the Government has said that there is no hard evidence that teachers are not participating in outdoor activities and school trips because of the fear of being sued, much anecdotal evidence was produced in the House of Lords' debates. The Minister in charge of the Bill stated the ambition is to tackle the problem across Government and 'support organisations, whether they be schools, voluntary organisations, local authorities or others, in resisting unfounded claims and developing strategies to deal with such claims' (Lords Hansard, 7 March 2006, col 665). The first part of the Act directs the courts in judging a compensation claim to consider whether upholding a claim against a defendant (teachers, school, etc.) might have prevented a desirable activity (a school journey, a sporting activity, etc.) from taking place. The duty of care of staff running school activities is not affected, but the legislation should stop claims based on an expectation of such rigorous safeguards as to prevent activities from taking place. The second part enables the creation of a body to regulate the 'claims management services' that have sprung up recently encouraging negligence claims against schools or other public bodies.

Charities Act 2006

Voluntary and foundation schools will be required to register with the Charity Commission as exempt charities and submit annual accounts. Changes are made to charity law which affect trust schools. See page 55.

Childcare Act 2006

Local authorities have specific duties to promote the well-being of young children and reduce inequalities between them, secure sufficient childcare for children up to the age of 14 and provide information, advice and assistance. A new Ofsted registration and inspection regime is introduced for childcare provision. Most of the arrangements will be outside the school system although if schools wish to provide for children aged two or younger, as they might as extended schools, they will have

to register with Ofsted. The Early Years Foundation Stage will now stand alone outside the National Curriculum and cover all learning from birth to five. Further information can be found in *Childcare Act 2006: the essential guide* (NFER, 2006).

Children and Adoption Act 2006

The law on contact with children following parental separation is rationalised: school provision, such as extended schools, could be used for non-supervised contact.

Equality Act 2006

The Commission for Equalities and Human Rights is established and local authorities and schools, as public bodies, acquire new duties on the promotion of sex equality and banning discrimination on grounds of religion and belief (see page 113). The Act bans discrimination on grounds of sexual orientation.

Health Act 2006

If any school building is not already a smoking free place, the legislation requires that schools become so from July 2007. There will be implications if schools tacitly condone smoking by pupils, but perhaps more so for staff.

Identity Cards Act 2006

Although there are no direct implications for schools, the legislation is likely to increase concerns of parents who do not have residency rights in the UK and wish to conceal their identity from the school authorities.

Road Safety Act 2006

The Act contains new grant giving powers to local authorities to support road safety projects.

Police and Justice Act 2006

Powers are given to police community support officers in returning truanting pupils to designated premises (usually a PRU or their schools) (see page 128) and on

promoting cooperation between Ofsted and the five criminal justice inspectorates (see page 162).

Safeguarding Vulnerable Groups Act 2006

A single list of people barred from working with children (and vulnerable adults) will be established which will be managed by the Independent Barring Board. The Act contains detailed criteria for barring individuals from working with children, the procedure for adding individuals to the list and how to appeal against a decision of the Independent Barring Board.

Violent Crime Reduction Act 2006

Headteachers and senior staff are given powers to search pupils for weapons. See page 124.

Work and Families Act 2006

Additional maternity/paternity leave and pay will be available including where parents are adopting children. While this provision will support children in their first few months, there may be implications for schools, especially small schools, in staff management.

Nomenclature

Legislative references

The main unit of legislation is the 'section' which is numbered sequentially and given a title. Sections are subdivided into subsections, which may be further subdivided into paragraphs and sometimes subparagraphs. 'Schedules' appear at the end of the Act, are numbered sequentially and are subdivided into paragraphs. They are always 'given effect' by a particular section but may relate to more than one. The Act is divided into 'parts' (10 in this case) with a title and larger parts may be divided into titled 'chapters'. Smaller groups of sections, within a part or a chapter may be introduced with un-numbered italic cross headings, indicating the subject dealt with by those sections. This guide follows that structure using the titles and numbers for each 'section' and the various 'parts', 'chapters' and cross headings exactly as they

appear in the Act. Commentary on Schedules is covered within the main text, along-side relevant sections.

Throughout the guide, the following abbreviations are used for ease of reference:

s.   section

ss.   sections

para.   paragraph.

Subsection, Schedule and chapter are usually written out in full but may be abbreviated if they would otherwise be unduly cumbersome, so 's.51(3)(b)(i)' means subparagraph 1 of paragraph (b) of subsection (3), of s.51. This appears on the face of the Act as follows:

51 Directions to admit child to specified school: supplementary provisions

(3)   After section 97B of SSFA 1998 (inserted by section 50) insert–
      "97C Determinations under section 97 or 97B: supplemental

      ...

      Regulations may make provision in relation to England–

      ...

            (b) requiring an admission authority for a school to provide information which–
               (i) falls within a prescribed description,

This and previous Acts most frequently referred to are abbreviated as follows:

Children Act 1989	CA 1989
Education Act 1996	EA 1996
Education Act 1997	EA 1997
School Standards and Framework Act 1998	SSFA 1998
Learning and Skills Act 2000	LSA 2000
Care Standards Act 2000	CSA 2000
Education Act 2002	EA 2002
Health and Social Care (Community Health and Standards) Act 2003	HSC(CHS)A 2003

Children Act 2004   CA 2004

Education Act 2005   EA 2005

Childcare Act 2006   CCA 2006

Education and Inspections Act 2006   E&IA 2006

Other Acts are cited in full.

LEA or Local authority?

Since the inception of the Every Child Matters (ECM) agenda, DfES has adopted the practice of referring to 'local authorities' rather than 'local education authorities' or 'LEAs'. Although the Children Act 2004, which brought about the replacement of 'Chief Education Officers' by 'Directors of Children's Services', does refer to 'Children's Services Authorities', it does so in only four sections. This usage has not become widespread and the terms 'Local education authority' and 'LEA' persist in both previous and subsequent education legislation.

The present Act, at s.162, creates a power to repeal all references to Local education authority and Children's Services Authority and replace them. The Act does not specify what they are to be replaced with; but it is clear that the unqualified term 'local authority' cannot be used in legislation for this purpose. This is because a majority of bodies covered by that generic term do not have education or social services functions. But see also s.159.

In the meantime, to remain consistent with previous legislation, E&IA 2006 continues to use the terms 'Local education authority' and 'LEA'. Consequently, this guide does the same.

Gender neutrality

As far as possible gender specific personal pronouns have been avoided. Where the context makes this inelegant and the reference is to an office of state we have used a pronoun appropriate to the holder of the office at the time of writing, e.g. 'him' for the Secretary of State and 'her' for Her Majesty's Chief Inspector.

Feedback

As with previous publications, the authors and NFER welcome feedback on this publication and would be willing to respond to queries on the text. Comments about the usefulness of the text and suggestions about future publications are most welcome and should be emailed to enquiries@nfer.ac.uk.

Thanks

Most of all, we would like to thank you, the reader, for maintaining the tradition established by local public service administrators of seeking independent information about changes in the law rather than simply relying on material from official sources.

We are grateful to the scrutiny work undertaken by MPs and Peers during the Bill's passage through Parliament. Unfortunately, that process was less than thorough. Whilst some aspects of the Bill were highly controversial and were subject to considerable debate, both within Parliament and beyond, other aspects received little attention from parliamentarians, the media or the wider public. Nevertheless, ministers' replies to questions and responses to debates have improved our understanding and this is reflected in the text of this guide.

In preparing this publication we have drawn heavily on the explanatory notes to the Education and Inspection Act 2006 (The Stationery Office 11/2006 352732 19585) referred to as the 'Explanatory Notes' and the regulatory impact assessment (RIA) published on enactment. We are indebted to officials from the Department for Education and Skills (DfES) for their work in producing these documents and for additional help some of them gave to us directly, clarifying a number of issues and giving us early access to information on regulations and implementation of the Act.

Thanks to NFER staff in the department of Communications, Marketing and Information Services, for publishing and marketing the book.

We would like to thank the following people who read early drafts of individual parts and in some cases the whole publication and provided helpful advice, encouragement, comments and feedback: Maggie Atkinson, Mike Baker, Scott Bagshaw, Rupert Bristow, Anne Cossins, John Freeman, Don Garman, Bob Garnett, Shirley Goodwin, Edwina Grant, Julian Gravatt, Christine Grice, Sarah Hall, David Hawker, Philip

Hunter, Nick Jordan, Richard Lindley, Gordon Mott, John Reilly, Diana Robinson, Martin Rogers, Bob Rose, Shan Scott, Alan Steer, Juliet Strang, Holly Turner and Mike Wilson.

Although those named above have provided us with considerable assistance in making this guide as comprehensive and accurate as it can be; responsibility for the comments, judgments and any errors in this book remains entirely ours.

Alan Parker, John Fowler and Alex Duncan
April 2007

Introduction

Anatomy of the Act

At 262 pages this is the longest Education Act since the SSFA 1998 and the fifth occasion running when a similar sized 'monster' has followed hard on the heels of a general election.

The bulk of the Act is concerned with themes that have dominated education policy for the past decade, raising standards of achievement, improving schools and securing greater access for the disadvantaged, whilst seeking to retain the support and participation of the better off. These themes were summed up in the 2005 White Paper *Higher Standards, Better Schools for All: more choice for parents and pupils*, (Cm 6677) (DfES, 25 October 2005) referred to below as the 'White Paper', which preceded publication of the Bill. It is very much an exercise in returning to amend, modify, extend or strengthen elements of legislation enacted in 1998, 2002, 2004 and 2005.

The Bill was introduced in the House of Commons on the 20 February 2006 and received its second reading on the 15 March 2006. A full chronology of debates is included in the Explanatory Notes (p.88). Royal Assent was granted on 8 November 2006.

As always, the Bill grew during its passage through Parliament, gaining 17 sections and 18 pages in length. Again, as usual, the Government was the source of successful amendments, although some were introduced in response to matters raised in debate. Unusually for a government with such a large majority, significant backbench revolt meant that some votes were only carried with opposition support.

The Act in context

There is a paradox at the heart of this legislation. Very little was completely new and some of the genuinely radical changes, for example, changing the 1944 settlement on free transport to school went largely unremarked. But the Bill was hugely controversial and was represented as threatening to undermine the credibility of the Government in general and the Prime Minister in particular. The centrepiece of that debate was the question of 'trust schools'. As we shall show, trust schools (or

'foundation schools with a foundation') already existed and had, effectively, been created by the School Standards and Framework Act in 1998. Many of the Labour MPs who found the concept so hard to swallow in the autumn of 2005 had seemingly voted it into existence without demur eight years previously.

In addition to the White Paper, the Bill was accompanied by a more than usually large number of other official, semi-official and decidedly unofficial publications which influenced debate. The House of Commons Education and Skills Select Committee had published reports in 2004 and 2005 calling for the Code of Practice on Admissions to be strengthened. When the White Paper was published, a draft of the new Code was already out for consultation.

On 14 December 2005, the *Guardian* newspaper reported 'The government last night put on ice plans for a new school admissions code in what was interpreted as a concession to senior backbench MPs who are today preparing to launch an attack on education reforms.' The Alternative White Paper (AWP) 'Shaping the education bill – reaching for consensus' was supported by influential Labour members including former cabinet and junior ministers and, a senior member of the education select committee.

The draft Code was duly withdrawn and a short 'fact sheet' on admissions appeared, apparently as a signal that the Admissions Code was likely to be strengthened rather than watered down. Another short document, the DfES's 'Trust School Prospectus' was 'launched' by the Secretary of State at the North of England Education Conference on 6 January 2006 in an attempt to clarify what had been said in the White Paper.

The Audit Commission published its response to the White Paper on 12 January 2006. A substantial part of it was a nine-page appendix reproducing the Commission's response to the DfES consultation on the draft Admissions Code of Practice, originally published in October 2005.

The Education and Skills Select Committee undertook an inquiry into the White Paper and published its report on 27 January 2006. The committee's report commented: 'one of the most interesting things about the White Paper is how few of its proposals are actually new' and asked why, therefore, there had been so much concern. Answering their own question the committee concluded: 'As our inquiry progressed and as the debate continued elsewhere in Parliament and outside, it

became clear that there is genuine confusion about what the proposals mean, what they are intended to achieve and how they will work.'

The Sutton Trust, an education charity, published a report on 23 January 2006, *The Social Composition of Top Comprehensive Schools* (available from www.sutton-trust.com). This looked at the rates of eligibility for free school meals (FSM) at the 200 highest performing comprehensive schools in England and found evidence of 'social selection' amongst those which act as their own admission authority.

A left of centre think tank 'Compass', which had been responsible for the AWP, subsequently published a pamphlet: *A Comprehensive Future* by Melissa Benn and Fiona Millar. This was launched at a rally in Parliament chaired by Neil Kinnock; in doing so the former Labour leader was identified with public criticism of his successor for the first time.

Philip Cowley and Mark Stuart of the University of Nottingham published a number of short papers during the first year of the Labour administration from May 2005 documenting a considerable level of disquiet amongst Labour MPs concerning, amongst other things, the Education and Inspections Bill. Some 100 Labour MPs signed the Alternative White Paper, voted against the Government in one or more of the divisions on the Bill or otherwise expressed their dissatisfaction. However, Cowley and Stuart also point out that this rebelliousness was not limited to the Education Bill; whilst there were seven rebellions in votes on this Bill there were more on both the Terrorism Bill and the Identity Cards Bill (17 and 18 respectively). In fact, this level of internal dissent against a government in its first year after an election was unprecedented in recent British political history. It therefore seems to have been the case that opposition to this particular measure may have been a symptom rather than a cause of the weakness of the Prime Minister following his indication that he would not serve a full third term and growing concerns about the war in Iraq.

It fell to a former Secretary of State, Estelle Morris, to articulate the key significance of this loss of backbench support in the context of education.

> *This is not going to make a big difference to schools. Ask any teacher and I think they'd struggle to spend five minutes talking about how the Education and Inspection Act is going to change their lives. The debates on the Bill were about politics, about the political direction of travel of left of centre education policy. I think the key importance of this Bill isn't that it will change schools – it won't – what it does*

mean is that, for the rest of the time Tony Blair is Prime Minister we will not see education policy travel any further in this direction.

Baroness Morris of Yardley, speaking on Today in Parliament: Education Act Special, BBC Radio 4, Tuesday 14 November 2006.

Trust schools and comprehensive education

Much of the rebellion within Labour ranks revolved around the idea that phasing out community schools and replacing them with trust schools amounted to a wholesale privatisation of the education system. The Conservative opposition made much of their support for this aspect of the Bill claiming that it was a vindication of their own 1980s grant maintained schools policy. Both views were wrong, but continued to define public debate; not only because the story fitted media preconceptions but also because the White Paper seemed to support those interpretations. However, a more careful reading reveals a different approach. Democratically accountable bodies are expected to commission public services and to secure improvement by harnessing the energies of the private and voluntary sectors whilst protecting the vulnerable through a tighter regulatory framework. In this case strict requirements over the charitable status of trusts would make it impossible for private sector organisations to make a profit out of school budgets, whilst encouraging and facilitating those who might be inclined to offer a charitable injection of funds or expertise.

Those who still believe that LEAs 'control' community schools, whether they see this as a good or a bad thing, have missed out on the last two decades of education policy. Community school heads and governors are in control of the day-to-day operation, policy and ethos of community schools, to the same extent as foundation and voluntary schools. There are examples of specialist community schools with greater involvement from sponsors and external partners than many foundation schools. For practical purposes the involvement of these bodies at such schools is indistinguishable from the role envisaged for trust partners.

The White Paper's original vision was an attempt to put all schools on an equal footing via voluntary or foundation status; with the local authority as commissioner, regulator and the agency for promoting improved standards. At the same time as delivering an apparent increase in the autonomy of schools through trust status the legislation gives LEAs a significantly greater degree of control over them. The White Paper clearly flagged up, and the Act delivers, a significant increase in the

power of LEAs to exercise a strong influence over all schools, irrespective of their governance.

- Abolition of the School Organisation Committee (SOC) gives the LEA power to determine a range of statutory proposals for the first time. Prior to the creation of the SOC such decisions were usually made by the Secretary of State.

- Although much was made of the requirement to hold a competition between promoters, LEAs can define the initial specification for new schools and decide which of the competing providers should run it.

- The initial specification fixes a new school's admissions policy for the first three years. Thereafter any change to the admissions policy would have to remain within the more rigorous Admissions Code and subject to the control of the Schools Adjudicator.

- The new Code also bites on all existing schools, the adjudicator has additional powers and decisions will in future fix school admission policies for three years rather than one at present.

- Authorities also gain greater power to enforce the casual admission of looked after children and other hard to place pupils.

- Local authorities have significant influence over capital spending decisions.

- Where a trust school ceases to exist, title in the land reverts to the previous owner (usually the local authority) and authorities gain clearer powers to requisition underused sites for educational purposes.

In the minds of some participants in the debate 'community school' is equated with the notion of 'comprehensive school'. There is, in fact, no necessary connection between these terms, as any category of school could be a designated, or de-facto, comprehensive, grammar or secondary modern. Whilst the term 'comprehensive' has been dropped as politically unacceptable, other changes: notably 'choice advisers', the more rigorous Admissions Code, restricting partial selection, the extension and encouragement of banding and changes to school transport are designed explicitly to enhance access of disadvantaged children to popular and successful schools. The vast majority of schools, of whatever status, are expected to teach the National Curriculum to pupils of all abilities. By outlawing 'backdoor selection' and encouraging banding and random allocation of places, E&IA 2006 could do much to ensure that a greater number of schools have a more genuinely comprehensive intake than ever before.

Paradoxically, the timidity of the original proposal, which avoided the more radical option of abolishing community school status outright, and the subsequent retreat to allow new ones to be created, has made little practical difference to what will happen on the ground. It has, however, served to perpetuate a distinction between community and foundation schools that is increasingly more apparent than real.

The new School Admissions Code

The pupils who attend a school are the single most important factor determining educational outcomes, how easy or difficult it is to manage and its overall character. Control over admissions policy was therefore one of the key factors that made 'opting out' an attractive proposition in the 1990s. Instead of giving this power back to LEAs, SSFA 1998 restricted the freedom enjoyed by the former grant maintained schools via the School Admissions Code of Practice policed by the newly created Office of the Schools Adjudicator (OSA). The Code was revised in 2003 but the House of Commons Select Committee led criticisms that it was still too weak to prevent individual schools manipulating their intake in order to enhance league table position. Following EA 2005, regulations were put in place requiring schools to give first priority to looked after children.

The Government has taken the select committee's recommendations on board and E&IA 2006 introduces a more draconian regime in three key ways:

- Aspects of the new Admissions Code have a force close to that of regulations – admissions authorities must 'act in accordance with' rather than simply 'have regard to' its provisions.

- The scope of legitimate oversubscription criteria is significantly reduced, notably by ruling out any form of 'conditionality' and specifically 'first preference first'.

- Schools are explicitly required to facilitate access for the disadvantaged, forbidden to draw catchment areas to exclude 'undesirable' estates and must not act in any way which would discourage applications from particular sections of the community.

LEAs, Admissions Forums and the new Schools Commissioner are all charged with monitoring the system and the OSA has increased powers to enforce it. Changes to school transport arrangements are intended to ensure that parents are not prevented from taking up places by transport costs.

A controversial innovation was the decision to rule out use of 'first preference first' as an oversubscription criterion. In an 'equal preference' or 'blind preference' scheme, admission authorities consider all applications against published admission criteria, but without reference to how the school applied for has been ranked by parents. If a child can be offered a place at more than one school the local authority then refers to the parents' original ranking and offers a place at the one they most prefer. Equal preference schemes are deemed good practice as they usually result in more parents getting one of the schools they want. Despite, or possibly because of, a concerted campaign on the part of a small number of schools to retain first preference first, ministerial resolve hardened during the consultation period. A concession, to allow continued use where all admissions authorities in an area agreed, was removed from the version laid before Parliament in January 2007. During a debate in committee (6 February 2007) both main opposition parties indicated that they would not oppose introduction of the Code, confirming that this version would be final.

The curriculum

In contrast to the political controversy surrounding trust schools and admission arrangements, overhauling the National Curriculum to create an entitlement for 14–19 year olds merited hardly a ripple in the media pond. There had been much more professional controversy following the earlier government rejection of the central proposal of Sir Mike Tomlinson's Working Group on 14–19 reform for an overarching diploma. This Act provides for separate academic and vocational strands and pathways with the development of 14 specialised diplomas offering a route to success for young people who want to learn through practical experience. This more limited step in the direction of the Tomlinson agenda was sufficiently cautious to avoid newspaper headlines claiming devaluation of the A level 'gold standard'; but was insufficiently radical to excite those who might wish for full parity of esteem for vocational options.

School improvement and inspection

Another 'care and maintenance' aspect of this legislation relates to the New Relationship with Schools. A light structure of legislative scaffolding is thrown up around the School Improvement Partners programme – not that it appeared to need it – and the, now redundant, Code of Practice on LEA School Relations is dismantled.

The Act builds on earlier initiatives and provisions in EA 2002 to encourage greater collaboration between schools. It gives LEAs new powers to broker arrangements to support weak schools by partnering with strong ones through formal collaboration and federation, or with external bodies. DfES statutory guidance emphasises the need for authorities to be 'vigilant and proactive' and to tailor interventions to the needs of a school and its pupils. For the first time, the Act also places a new requirement on LEAs to engage parents in the preparation of the statement of action for schools which Ofsted has judged require special measures or significant improvement – this may extend to the appointment by the LEA of a specified person, a Parent Champion, to facilitate communication with parents in anticipation of, or following, an adverse Ofsted inspection report. The Parent Champion's role will also be to articulate the views and interests of parents and to influence decisions about the future of the school.

Every Child Matters and the Act

Local authorities acquire new responsibilities to deliver positive activities for young people. The Act provides a good deal of local flexibility about how such services can be delivered. Again, the Government is showing confidence in the local authority's capacity to undertake strategic planning and to be effective in commissioning service delivery from a range of providers.

School governors are now explicitly required, by s.38, to support the Every Child Matters agenda by actively seeking to promote the 'five outcomes' for all children and having regard to their LEA's Children and Young People's Plan (CYPP), putting in place the duty on schools that local government lobbying failed to secure in 2004.

Commitments in the White Paper on school discipline are carried forward following many of the key recommendations in *Learning Behaviour*, the Report from the Practitioners' Group on School Behaviour and Discipline. The Group, chaired by Sir Alan Steer (Head of Seven Kings High School, Ilford), which was commissioned to give advice on improving behaviour in schools, reported in October 2005. *The Steer Report* was widely welcomed and acknowledged to be an authoritative statement of the measures the teaching profession needs to deal with poor discipline in schools.

Some of these changes bring the law into line with traditional assumptions about the right of schools to impose discipline. Teachers (including those in further education) are given an explicit power to exercise 'reasonable force' to restrain their students

insulating them, to some extent, against accusations of assault. This does not, of course, amount to sanctioning corporal punishment. Similarly, the teacher's traditional power of confiscation is made explicit to forestall mischievous accusations of theft.

In the face of declining respect for authority, traditional assumptions that parents will support teachers as authority figures are bolstered by requiring parents to shoulder responsibilities, which hitherto they may have been assumed to have accepted without question. The imposition of a form of 'house arrest' on excluded pupils, although difficult to enforce, can be seen as a sanction against both parent and child.

The reality of exclusion from school as the only serious sanction is balanced by more extensive and more explicit provisions seeking to ensure that pupils subject to disciplinary measures nevertheless continue to receive an education.

Schools with a religious character

Broadly speaking, the involvement of established religious groups in education through schools with a religious character is preserved, but there are some changes.

All religious groups gain a statutory right to be consulted over the admissions policy of schools that adhere to their faith. Prior to this Act all Church of England voluntary aided schools were legally required to consult their local diocese on a draft policy before proceeding to wider consultation with other bodies. This applied only to the established Church so similar requirements were not imposed on other kinds of faith school. An obligation to consult appropriate local religious authorities (although without granting them the privilege of *prior* consultation enjoyed by Anglican dioceses) is now placed on all designated faith schools (including controlled and foundation schools).

In practice, many Roman Catholic schools take heed of the advice offered by their own diocese, although certain RC schools set up by religious orders have pointedly refused to regard the local diocese as having any jurisdiction over them. It remains to be seen the extent to which the Roman Catholic hierarchy in the UK will use the new right to be consulted and object as leverage to gain greater influence over such schools.

There are an increasing number of different, and particularly non-Christian, faith groups showing interest in sponsoring schools within the public sector. Whilst this

new provision is clearly aimed at them there may be practical difficulties if they do not have obvious local structures. This was illustrated by a news item reported in the *Times Educational Supplement* (8 December 2006, p.3). The Krishna-Avanti primary school, located in Edgware, has promoters with links to the International Society for Krishna Consciousness, which has its UK base at a temple in Watford. However, the Hindu Human Rights pressure group complained that, despite its adherence to the Hindu God Krishna, the International Society is a 'new-age sect', which does not represent mainstream Hinduism. A letter in a subsequent issue of the paper disputed this interpretation of the facts but, self evidently, in such circumstances it may be difficult to work out which, if any, of the parties involved should be the statutory consultee for the governors of the school.

Religious authorities can also exert greater influence over the person appointed as head of a voluntary controlled (VC) school. This change will mainly affect the Church of England because of the number of VC schools it supports.

There will be scope for faith based institutions to extend their involvement in education through trust schools. This may be attractive in that it will be possible for a faith group to participate in a trust alongside other partners. It is understood that the Roman Catholic Church is actively considering new ventures extending its mission to engage with a broader range of the population; leaving its more exclusive voluntary schools in place to meet the needs of the established Roman Catholic community.

Sixth form pupils are emancipated in matters of religious worship. Sixth formers can take their own decision to opt out of acts of collective worship, irrespective of the views of their parents; and those at boarding schools must also be allowed to attend religious worship according to their own conscience irrespective of the faith or secular status of the institution.

Impact on local authorities

As indicated above, the Act confers significant new functions on local authorities, schools, the LSC and further education colleges. Local authorities are given enhanced responsibilities in school place planning and admissions; and an important strategic role in coordinating schools' responsibility to ensure all pupils have access to the entitlement curriculum at key stage four. As the Regulatory Impact Assessment notes:

For local authorities it fits with their changing role as commissioners rather than deliverers of services. Making the full range of provision available is crucial to ensuring that all young people have access to the full range of opportunities. Only a local body sitting above the level of individual institutions can discharge these responsibilities effectively (paragraph 16.46).

In addition to the new duty to promote sustainable travel and other significant changes to school travel, there is an opportunity for LEAs to bid to adopt 'Pathfinder Schemes' to pilot much more extensive and innovatory local school transport arrangements. If these are successful, the Secretary of State could extend the opportunity to more authorities or even allow the more successful schemes to become mainstream, extending the changes beyond their initial scope using secondary legislation.

The changes in school transport arrangements have a distinctly green tinge and, particularly in larger counties, will impinge on wider transport policies. In socially challenging localities the involvement of police community support officers in the supervision of excluded pupils and headteachers' new power to issue fixed penalties to their parents will either provide enhanced joined-up working or a sinister extension of all embracing state power, according to the spectator's perspective.

Of the various changes to school discipline and behaviour, perhaps the most controversial area will be the new enforcement burden on LEAs arising from the power to impose fines where excluded pupils are found unsupervised in a public place during school hours. This, together with the requirement to make provision for excluded pupils from day six rather than 16 will represent a considerable test for many LEAs.

The Local Government and Public Involvement in Health Bill will pave the way for some new unitary authorities (described in the Bill as: 'responsible' local authorities) which will have children's services functions. The former 'best value' regime will be wound down, replacing some 1,200 national targets with 200 indicators and 35 generic targets to join the 35 existing targets for education and childcare. The new powers and expectations outlined in E&IA 2006, particularly those seeking to empower parents and the community to influence the shape and delivery of schooling, will sit alongside similar new approaches to community governance.

Conclusions

It is instructive to ask the question: will the Act work? Experience and the law of unintended consequences, suggests the answer 'yes, but not in the way its architects expect'. However the authors suggest that the reforms in this Act probably have a better chance of operating in the way intended than many of its predecessors, if only because in most areas they draw on a decade of experience and, in some, they refine two or three previous rounds of legislation. Policy development in several areas was supported by the reports of independent commissions and the scrutiny of the select committee. In the case of the Admissions Code, something like five different versions benefited from formal or informal consultation over a two-year period.

The trust school policy was subject to so much scrutiny from the government's own backbenches that the safeguards and concessions won will ensure there is little scope for difficulties to emerge. Lessons learned from the implementation of grant maintained schools in the 1990s mean that the complex area of land transfer may be better handled this time round.

There is anxiety amongst local authorities that the more generous school transport regime for less well off families and those seeking places at faith schools will not be properly funded. However, the more rigorous approach to admissions and outlawing some of the more 'creative' oversubscription criteria may mean that popular schools are even more likely to be filled by those who live closest. Thus, choice advisers notwithstanding, the one policy may cancel out the other; although new interest in the use of allocation of places by lot could increase mobility.

Perhaps one of the more difficult areas to predict is the progress of the Every Child Matters agenda. Local authorities will welcome the more explicit duty on school governors to promote the five outcomes, and these should be further promoted by the new Ofsted, building on the framework introduced by EA 2005. Local authorities themselves will need to embrace the revamped law and guidance on the youth service to promote positive experiences for young people outside school.

As we have noted, the two sections introducing 14–19 diplomas received little attention. However, curriculum control structures reside largely outside primary legislation so the Government will have considerable room for manoeuvre as this policy is developed.

Looking to the future, a further 'raising of the school leaving age to 18' has been floated as a possible enthusiasm of the putative incoming Prime Minister. We make no comment on that, but we would venture to suggest that no one should be surprised if a substantial Education/Children's Services Bill emerges in the parliamentary session following the next general election!

Part 1: Education functions of local authorities

Overview

Section 1 of the Education Act 1944 famously stated that LEAs were to operate under the 'control and direction' of the Minister of Education. At the time this was seen as centralist because previously the holder of that office had merely exercised 'superintendence'. But that formulation later came to be seen as enshrining local authorities' relative independence. It was subsequently replaced by s.1 of the Education Act 1993, introduced by way of an amendment unofficially christened 'clause zero', in a political atmosphere resonant with all the doomsday connotations of that phrase. That debate has now passed into obscurity and little of that Act remains on the statute book. What survives is now consolidated in the Education Act 1996 with the general responsibilities of LEAs residing at s.13. Two years later, s.5 of SSFA 1998 added a new section, 13A, setting out in no uncertain terms that LEAs were to have an explicit duty to use all their educational functions to promote high standards of education.

Part 1 of E&IA 2006 extends the duty to secure high standards to embrace the well-being of the whole child, to emphasise diversity and choice and to enshrine an enhanced role for parents. It covers School Improvement Partners as a key mechanism for implementing those duties. It also introduces a prominent focus on LEA duties in respect of children beyond school, through informal education and recreation and for individuals who have dropped out.

Section 1: Duties in relation to high standards and the fulfilment of potential

Section 13A of EA1996 is now recast in line with present concerns and particularly the Every Child Matters agenda. In addition to promoting high standards in a general sense, local authorities are required to promote the fulfilment of every child's 'educational potential'. It is also made clear that these duties apply to children of compulsory school age, whether or not they are attending maintained schools as well as those above or below that age who are in school. The section as a whole applies to both England and Wales, but English authorities only are additionally

required to 'ensure fair access to educational opportunity'. This duty is expected to come into force in May 2007.

Section 2: Duties in relation to diversity and choice

This also amends EA 1996 by adding an additional subsection (3A) into s.14, which deals with functions of local education authorities in relation to the provision of primary and secondary education. This requires LEAs in England to exercise their functions with a view to securing diversity in the provision of schools and increasing opportunities for parental choice. It also paves the way for the more detailed requirements set out in s.3. This duty is expected to come into force in May 2007.

Section 3: Duty to consider parental representations

This adds a new section (14A) after s.14 of EA 1996, enlarging on the general duties to secure diversity and choice. The main vehicle is a duty to consider and respond to any representations made by parents with children of, or below, compulsory school age living in the LEA's area. The LEA is absolved from this duty if representations appear to be frivolous or vexatious or substantially the same as any previously received from the same person. LEAs must have regard to guidance given by the Secretary of State in respect of these functions.

Outline draft guidance was made available during discussion on the Bill and a further version was published for consultation shortly after Royal Assent. The guidance is framed by a philosophy that local authorities should respond proactively and positively to parental concerns, providing technical advice and support to those who may not be well placed to articulate their ideas and needs. It presumes that the solution to parental demands will often involve a need for statutory proposals to reorganise schools in the area; whether by the creation of a completely new school of a particular type (notably faith schools), bringing an existing private school into the public sector or by modifying an existing school. The absence of any demographic need to change the existing pattern of schooling is not regarded as an obstacle to responding to parental needs. LEAs must therefore also consider how to remove any surplus places generated by the creation of new provision in response to parental demand.

This guidance feeds into the new arrangements for competitions (see pages 21 and page 28) and it is expected that there will be a continuum from dissatisfaction

amongst individual parents to the formation of active local groups, who can promote new provision and have a continuing role in its governance. Responding to initial parental representations should be the trigger for a local authority to support parents in resolving their concerns, whether via improving existing provision or creating new trust schools for the area. This duty (together with the final version of guidance) is expected to come into force in May 2007.

Section 4: Duty to identify children not receiving education

The new duty to identify children who are not receiving education fits in with the extension of the local authority's general duties under s.1. It operates by inserting a new section 436A, in part 6 of EA 1996, which is about school attendance. There are two consequential amendments, which shift the definition of 'suitable education' into this new section 436A from s.437.

Suitable education is defined as: 'efficient full-time education suitable to the age, ability and aptitude and to any special educational needs of the child' in question. Local authorities must make arrangements to enable them to identify, as far as possible, any children in their area who are of compulsory school age, but are not either at school or are otherwise receiving suitable education. In this context 'schools' include recognised private institutions and 'education otherwise' means children being appropriately taught at home by their parents or by any other informal means which is accepted by the LEA as being 'suitable'.

The background to this provision can be traced back to the inquiry into the death of Victoria Climbié where it became painfully obvious that, despite her contact with officialdom in several different areas, no one regarded it as their responsibility to check whether or not she was receiving education. The LEA is now unequivocally given this duty which builds on a number of earlier initiatives. In particular, sections 10 and 11 of the Children Act 2004 require collaboration between local authorities and other public agencies to safeguard and promote the welfare of children. The Information Sharing Index, which is intended to be implemented across England by the end of 2008, is expected to be a key tool in discharging this responsibility.

The new duty came into force on 27 February 2007. Accompanying statutory guidance issued by the Secretary of State is found at www.everychildmatters.gov.uk/resources/IG00202.

Section 5: School improvement partners

This section provides legal status for a policy that is already in place. It requires local education authorities to appoint a person to be known as a 'School Improvement Partner' (SIP) for each of the schools they maintain. Only people who have been accredited, either by the Secretary of State or someone authorised by him, can work as SIPs.

There are three separate regulation making powers in subsections (3) to (5). The first two of these enable the Secretary of State to impose other requirements relating to the employment of SIPs and confer functions on local education authorities and school governing bodies in relation to them. These have been put in place as a reserve power, in case schools and authorities fail to cooperate with the policy. Since the training, appointment and deployment of SIPs is well down the road to implementation, it seems unlikely that such regulations will ever be needed. The third regulation making power enables the Secretary of State to give retrospective effect to the provision, by deeming that anyone who has already been appointed as a SIP before this part of the Act comes into force is treated as having been appointed as a 'School Improvement Partner' under this legislation. *The Education (School Improvement Partner) (England) Regulations 2007* (SI 2007 / 25) came into force on 8 February 2007.

Subsection (6) covers definitions, which are generally unremarkable except to the extent that they confirm that local authorities' power to appoint SIPs as their main agents for promoting school improvement extends to all categories of school in their area apart from academies and CTCs.

Section 6: Functions in respect of youth work, recreation, etc.

This section contains the first comprehensive statement of the LEA's duty to secure educational and recreational provision for young people to supplement and reinforce school education since the Education Act 1944. In particular, the new s.507B inserted into the Education Act 1966 meets the policy objectives set out in the Green Paper *Youth Matters* (Cm 6629, July 2005) and confirmed in the DfES paper *Youth Matters: Next Steps* (June 2006). This work builds on the Every Child Matters programme and the cooperation duties for children's trusts in s.10 of the Children Act 2004 and the Children and Young People's Plan in s.17.

Despite the increased investment and strategic development of services for young people since the Transforming Youth Work programme was inaugurated in 2001, the Government has characterised services for young people as 'uncoordinated, unplanned, unsought after and highly variable' (para.4.5, Regulatory Impact Assessment). The Government wants local authorities to take the lead with partners in other statutory sectors and the private and voluntary sectors, for the strategic planning of the whole range of young people's out of school activities. Section 6 gives LEAs responsibility to secure access for young people to adequate positive activities and facilities. Essentially this means that authorities must try to secure better and more consistent opportunities for young people, but not necessarily by expanding their own direct services.

The section commenced on 8 January 2007. Further information on the implementation of the Youth Matters programme can be found at: www.everychildmatters. gov.uk/youthmatters.

Subsection (1) inserts two new sections: 507A and 507B into EA 1996. Subsection (2) introduces Schedule 1 (Amendments related to Section 6) to the Act. By virtue of para.3 of Schedule 1, s.508 (Functions in respect of facilities for recreation and social and physical training) of the 1996 Act is amended so that it only applies to Wales.

EA 1996: s.507A: LEAs in England: functions in respect of recreational and training facilities for children under 13

This re-enacts the existing s.508 so that it applies only to children under 13, thus providing the statutory basis for the LEA to continue to offer a range of out of school activities for younger children.

EA 1996: s.507B: LEAs in England: functions in respect of leisure-time activities, etc. for persons aged 13 to19 and certain persons aged 20 to 24

The key definition in s.507B is 'positive leisure-time activities' found in subsection (4). LEAs have to secure sufficient activities and facilities under subsection (1) for the improvement of the well-being of 'qualifying young persons' defined in subsection (2) as young people who have reached their 13th birthday but not their 20th. For young people with a learning difficulty, this is extended to their 25th birthday. Well-being is defined in subsection (13) using the five outcomes in the Every Child

Matters programme. Also under subsection (13) 'sufficient' means having regard to quantity, that is the mere existence of provision is not enough: it must relate to the number of young people wishing to participate.

Positive leisure-time activities, under subsection (1), comprise:

- educational leisure-time activities, which must include sufficient activities and facilities for personal and social development of young persons under subsection (3). This subsection was added by the Government during the passage of the Bill because of concerns that traditional youth work did not necessarily come within the definition of educational leisure-time activities

- recreational leisure-time activities, which according to subsection (13) includes 'physical training', a term first introduced by the Education Act 1918.

New LEA powers to secure positive leisure-time activities are found in subsection (5). LEAs may directly organise activities and provide facilities. Under local government legislation, this will include the power to employ staff to carry out such tasks. The provision of facilities, according to subsection (6)(a), includes the powers to establish, maintain and manage places, that is youth centres, sports centres, etc. LEAs can charge under subsection (8) for services provided. Such activities are not part of school education and the prohibition on charging young people for services does not apply. LEAs may assist others in the provision and organisation of facilities and help young people gain access to activities and facilities provided by others. Under subsection (6)(b) and (c), LEAs may provide funding to the organisation providing the activities or to the young person who will participate in the activity. LEAs may also provide transport and information.

Before taking 'any action' to secure activities and facilities, an LEA, under subsection (7)(a), must consider whether other organisations or individuals should provide the service. In other words, the LEA must not conclude that it should directly provide a service without first considering other options such as working with the private and voluntary sector. Subsection (8) requires the LEA to consult 'appropriate' persons on the action it determines. Under subsection (7)(b), if the LEA determines to secure facilities in the private and voluntary sector then the authority should enter into an 'agreement' with the provider, which leaves it open to the authority to decide whether a legally binding contract or a looser service level agreement is appropriate.

LEAs must, under subsection (9), ask young people what they think about the quality, quantity, range and accessibility of local activities and facilities. LEAs must then take the views of young people into account when deciding how to develop local services. Under subsection (10), LEAs must publicise and keep up to date information about positive leisure-time activities.

LEAs, under subsection (12), must have regard to guidance from the Secretary of State. Draft guidance was published on 5 January 2007: *Statutory Guidance on Section 6 Education & Inspections Act (Positive Activities for Young People)*. It is expected that the final statutory guidance will be published in summer 2007.

Schedule 1: Amendments relating to s.6

The Schedule updates statutory definitions in the Disability Discrimination Act 1995 and EA 1996 to take account of the new sections inserted by E&IA 2006. This:

- brings the new legislation within disability discrimination legislation
- makes clear that the definition of learning difficulty is that contained in LSA 2000 for young people aged 20–25
- enables LEAs to provide clothing for young people taking part in relevant activities
- empowers LEAs to remove people causing a nuisance or disturbance from premises where relevant activities are taking place.

Part 2: Establishment, discontinuance or alteration of schools

School organisation – overview

This part of the Act needs to be read in conjunction with s.2 *Duties in relation to diversity and choice* and s.3 *Duty to consider parental representations* (see above). It changes the way statutory proposals are determined by abolishing the school organisation committee (SOC) and builds further on EA 2002 and EA 2005, which introduced and extended the concept of inviting promoters to participate in a competition to decide the character of new schools.

Competitions

The changes introduced in 2002 were relatively modest. A competition was only required for 'additional' secondary schools, i.e. only those that were neither replacing an existing school nor created as a result of a merger. The idea has been progressively extended to encompass any new school, except nursery schools or those offering only post compulsory provision. Local authorities lose their dominance over the decision to initiate change. Although it was previously possible for anyone to propose the establishment of a new school, in practice this has rarely been done except by LEAs and the traditional providers of voluntary schools, predominantly the Churches. In future, there will be active encouragement for others to become involved. The desire of any organised group to promote new school provision, or the expression of generalised parental dissatisfaction with the status quo, can trigger procedures and attract the necessary resources to bring about change, whether or not there is an objective need to expand or contract existing provision.

In most circumstances a public competition will be held to decide the character and the promoter/operator of any new school. In all cases, whether the process has been initiated by the LEA or triggered by a group of parents, the local authority will have power to define the broad specification for new provision and the duty to secure appropriate premises and capital funding.

If the local authority itself is not involved in any of the proposals it can judge the competition, taking over the role set out for the school organisation committee under the 2005 Act. If, however, the local authority wishes to put forward its own proposals, or has a connection with one of the promoters, the competition will be judged by the Adjudicator.

Other statutory proposals

Where the question of a competition does not arise, for example closing or making certain alterations to existing schools, decisions will be made by the local authority or the governing body of the school in question. If the proposals are disputed 'specified bodies', which vary according to the circumstance but are broadly similar to those previously represented on the SOC, have a right to refer the decision to the Schools Adjudicator.

The diversification of the school system will also be promoted through the continuation of the academies programme and by encouraging existing community schools to become 'trust schools'. The process of change may be slightly less rapid than originally envisaged, because the White Paper proposal that no more community schools should be created was withdrawn following opposition from within the Labour Party. Nevertheless, a local authority must be in good standing by reference to its annual performance assessment (APA) and/or secure the permission of the Secretary of State before it is allowed to create any new community schools. In the meantime, a new office of the Schools Commissioner has been established within DfES, with a brief to assist the creation of trusts and encourage existing foundation and erstwhile community schools to embrace them.

Foundations and trusts

Despite the high profile of the political debate around the creation of 'trust schools' their legal status – technically a foundation school with a foundation – was already in place and a number of existing foundation schools already had the form, if not yet the title, of a trust school. It has long been the case that the provision of public education has been in the hands of independent charitable bodies. Indeed, the established Church's mission to educate the poor preceded the impulse to fund education from public taxation so this was originally the dominant form.

The 1944 settlement recognised the historic contribution of charitable bodies, predominantly but not exclusively Churches, through voluntary status. The charitable body, the 'foundation', had various functions including the power to nominate governors and, in the case of voluntary aided schools, as the employer of staff and owner of school premises with capital funding responsibilities. The position was complicated in 1988 by the creation of the grant-maintained sector, which allowed individual schools to 'opt out' of local authority control and to be financed nationally. By so doing, the governing bodies of former county schools acquired similar powers and responsibilities to voluntary aided schools. Where the opting out school was previously a voluntary school its foundation retained its historic powers with regard to school premises and the nomination of governors.

The School Standards and Framework Act 1998 (SSFA) changed the position once again. Grant maintained (GM) schools were abolished and had the option to revert to their former status or become one of the newly created 'foundation schools'. Section 21 of SSFA defined three kinds of foundation school.

- First: a school 'having a foundation established otherwise than under this act'. This definition covered former GM schools with a pre-existing relationship with a foundation, which were mostly former voluntary aided or controlled schools which had opted out but did not choose to revert to that status. (s.21(1)(a))

- Second: a school 'belonging to a group of schools for which a foundation body acts under this section'. These schools were similar to the first group except that the 'foundation' was specifically set up under the SSFA to have a relationship with three or more schools. (s.21(1)(b))

- Third: any school not covered by either of the first two definitions. These were the majority of former GM schools where the land and responsibility for appointing most new governors was vested in the governing body. Although they were renamed 'foundation schools' they did not 'have a foundation' and the governing body continued to do those things done by the 'foundations' associated with the other types of foundation and voluntary school (e.g. own the premises and identify replacement governors). (s.21(1)(c))

Table 1 sets this out with an indication of the numbers involved and their relationship to governance and religious character.

Table 1: Types of Foundation School set out in SSFA 1998

SSFA	Type	How many?	Governance	Religious affiliation
s.21(1)(a)	Foundation established otherwise than under SSFA	Former VA, VC and VSA schools which did not revert in 1999 and any that decided later to convert to foundation status. A Parliamentary answer indicated there were 96 at 15 March 2006 (Hansard col 2351)	Foundation nominates some governors. There must be a minimum one-third parent governors but if the foundation nominates a majority not all parent members will be elected	Formally 'religious character' is determined by regulations made under SSFA. Many of these schools will have an affiliation in accordance with the objectives of their foundation or 'trust deed'
s.21(1)(b)	Foundation body performs foundation function for three or more schools	This option was not widely adopted in 1999 but it is understood that there was at least one such foundation body. The form may become more prevalent if groups of schools adopt the same 'trust' under new arrangements	Similar to above	A foundation body could have a relationship with both faith and secular schools, but the religious designation of a school cannot be changed by adopting a foundation body
s.21(1)(c)	Not coming within (a) or (b)	600+ former GM schools adopted this status in 1999. A Parliamentary answer indicated that a further 55 had been created by 7 March 2006 (Hansard col 1431)	At least one-third elected parents. There is an element of 'self perpetuation' as the governing body appoints replacements to fill most vacancies	Could technically have a religious affiliation although this is uncommon. A religious character cannot be acquired by conversion to foundation status. School would have to publish proposals to close and reopen

VC = voluntary controlled school; VA = voluntary aided school; VSA = voluntary special agreement school

SSFA also defined three kinds of voluntary school, in a parallel structure.

- First, a school 'having a foundation established otherwise than under this Act'. This definition covered all voluntary aided or controlled schools with a pre-existing relationship with a foundation, e.g. most 'church schools' (s.21(2)(a)).

- Second, schools 'belonging to a group of schools for which a foundation body acts under this section'. There were no pre-existing schools of this type as 'foundation bodies' are creatures of the SSFA, but it provided for the possibility that voluntary and foundation schools could have a relationship with the same 'foundation' (s.21(2)(b)).

- Third, a school not covered by either of the first two definitions. This included any voluntary schools with no links to a 'foundation' and those former GM schools without foundations that wanted to opt for voluntary status under the SSFA (s.21(2)(c)).

Both foundation and voluntary schools 'have a foundation' if there is a body of persons other than the governing body which holds land or property on behalf of the school. The generic 'foundation' is known as a 'foundation body' if it was established as a corporate body under the SSFA to perform the functions of a foundation in relation to three or more schools (s. 21(4)(a)).

The SSFA, as well as allowing schools to opt into one of the newly defined statuses when the law came into force, provided for schools to be able to change status later. The route from community to foundation status was later simplified via the 'fast track'.

The present legislation leaves all of that in place, but promotes the further involvement of external bodies:

- the possibility of voluntary or foundation schools adopting community status is closed off

- new routes are created for foundation schools to acquire a foundation under either s.21(1)(a) or s.21(1)(b), i.e. to become a 'trust school'.

A foundation (trust) can have two levels of involvement depending on whether it nominates a minority or a majority of governors. There are also a number of differences, depending on the former status of the school, as to how it might go about changing its status and what it can subsequently do. These include whether the governing body must seek permission from existing trustees before it can publish proposals (s.20), whether the new arrangements in the E&IA 2006 allowing the governors to remove the foundation (s.25) apply and whether the Secretary of State has certain powers to appoint and remove trustees (s.33).

Table 2 sets out the different permutations of these various possibilities.

Table 2: Application of ss.20, 25 and 33 to Schools Changing Status to Acquire Trust Status

Type of school and action	Trustees' consent s.20	Trust removal s.25	Secretary of State powers s.33
Community school that converts to foundation school with minority foundation governors post commencement	n/a	Yes	Yes
Community school that converts to foundation school with majority foundation governors post commencement	n/a	Yes	Yes
Existing foundation school without a foundation that acquires a foundation and minority foundation governors post commencement	n/a	Yes	Yes
Existing foundation school without a foundation that acquires a foundation and majority foundation governors post commencement	n/a	Yes	Yes
Existing foundation school with foundation that acquires majority foundation governors post commencement	Yes	No[1]	Yes
Existing foundation school with foundation that makes no changes post commencement	n/a	No	No
VC (already has a foundation) that converts to foundation school with minority foundation governors post commencement	Yes	No	No
VC (already has a foundation) that converts to foundation school with majority foundation governors post commencement	Yes	No[2]	Yes
New foundation school established post commencement with a foundation and a minority of foundation governors	Yes	Yes	Yes
New foundation school established post commencement with a foundation and a majority of foundation governors	Yes	Yes	Yes
VA (already has a foundation) that converts to foundation with majority foundation post commencement	Yes	No	Yes
VA (already has a foundation) that converts to foundation with minority foundation post commencement	Yes	No	No

[1] In such cases, the majority cannot be reduced either, even though majority was acquired post commencement.

[2] In such cases, the majority will not be able to be reduced either, even though majority was acquired post commencement.

VC = voluntary controlled school; VA = voluntary aided school

NB 'community' and 'foundation' school includes community special and foundation special schools.

Education and Inspections Act 2006: the essential guide

Establishment of new schools ss.7–14

As far as England is concerned, these sections replace s.28 of SSFA 1998 as extended and modified by EA 2002 and EA 2005. Schedule 2 and regulations supplement this part of the Act with more detailed requirements.

The DfES aims to bring these school organisation and governance provisions into force at the end of May 2007. With effect from this date authorities must run a competition for a new primary school, or seek consent to publish proposals without a competition, for any proposals that have not been published when the regulations come into force. SOCs will also be abolished in May and the regulations will provide for any outstanding proposals to be decided under the new arrangements. This means that proposals initiated prior to the implementation date, in the expectation that they will be considered by the SOC, may fall to be determined by the LEA. However, since many of the interests previously represented on the SOC will have rights to refer proposals to the Schools Adjudicator this may not make a great deal of difference.

Section 67 and Schedule 11 of EA 2005, which allowed the Secretary of State to require local authorities to embark on a rationalisation of school places, are repealed (by Part 3 of Schedule 18). These powers were first created in the Education Act 1993 (ss.232–237) not long after the advent of grant-maintained schools, when a number of LEAs exhibited a reluctance to embark on reorganisation for fear that schools threatened with closure would seek to 'opt out'. They were subsequently consolidated into ss.500–505 of the 1996 Act and were recast as Schedule 7 of the SSFA 1998. No Secretary of State has ever invoked these powers and they have not been tested in the courts. When they were last re-enacted the then DfES Parliamentary Secretary (Derek Twigg MP) justified their retention as they 'have proved useful for demonstrating [the government's] commitment to the proper supply of certain school places and for requiring action if it is not taken voluntarily' (Commons Hansard, 22 March 2005).

A little less than a year later that view had changed. The prevailing philosophy is now that LEAs are sufficiently driven by their own performance assessments to initiate necessary rationalisation and in any event promoters will be stimulated to bring forward proposals to fill any gaps in provision and mechanisms for the accelerated closure of failing schools will weed out the surplus.

Section 7: Invitation for proposals for establishment of new schools

The default position for setting up new schools is that there will be a competition initiated by a local education authority inviting proposals from 'persons other than local education authorities'. This prevents local authorities responding to each other's competitions, although they are not precluded from setting up schools outside their own area (see s.13 below).

A notice under this section can invite proposals for a foundation, or voluntary school or for an academy but not for a nursery school or a maintained sixth form institution. This is a reference to 'year 12 and 13 schools' of the kind defined by LSA 2000, not sixth form colleges, which are independent corporations under the Further and Higher Education Act 1992. Proposals can be invited for a foundation special school, but only if the notice states that a special school is required. It is not possible to invite proposals for establishing community or community special schools under this section (see s.8 below).

The notice must:

- identify a possible site
- make clear whether the school should be a special or a mainstream school
- give a timescale for the submission of proposals.

The authority is required to publish all the proposals it receives in response to the notice together with any proposals of its own.

Schedule 2, which goes into considerably more detail on the consideration, approval and implementation of proposals published under this section, is brought into effect.

Draft regulations under this section, *The School Organisation (Establishment and Discontinuance of Maintained Schools) (England) Regulations 2007*, were published for consultation on 13 November 2006 and are expected to come into force at the end of May 2007.

This new set of regulations consolidates, replaces and updates the previous regulations dating from SSFA 1998 and a number of subsequent amending statutory instruments. It is organised in four parts covering respectively:

- proposals for establishing a new school via a competition

- proposals for establishing a new school with the consent of the Secretary of State or in special cases

- proposals for discontinuance (i.e. closure) of a school

- consideration of proposals by a local education authority or by the adjudicator.

There are five Schedules. The first three make detailed provisions about notices and proposals for new schools in different circumstances. The fourth concerns the discontinuance of schools and the fifth is about the unusual (but not unknown) circumstances of an LEA establishing a school outside its own area.

An innovation in the draft regulations is a reduction in the amount of information which must be included in the statutory notice published in a newspaper; but providing for fuller details to be made available on websites or in hard copy on request.

Section 8: Proposals under section 7 relating to community or community special schools

The White Paper envisaged a new role for local authorities as 'commissioners' rather than 'providers' of services. As a vehicle for divesting local authorities of school ownership, it was proposed that no new community schools should be created and that whenever provision was reorganised, existing community schools would be replaced by foundation or voluntary schools. The backlash against the idea of trust schools amongst Labour backbenchers forced the Government to retreat from this position. Section 8, therefore, allows LEAs to enter a new community school in competition alongside alternative proposals put forward by promoters; provided the authority can meet certain objective criteria and/or obtain the consent of the Secretary of State.

The first hurdle the authority must clear is to have achieved a prescribed standard in the annual review conducted by Ofsted (see s.138 below). Draft regulations set out these circumstances in more detail.

- An authority with an annual performance assessment (APA) rating of four will be allowed to publish proposals for community or community special schools without the consent of the Secretary of State.

- An authority with an APA rating of three will be allowed to seek the consent of the Secretary of State.

- An authority with an APA rating of two will be allowed to seek the consent of the Secretary of State, provided there are either (or both):

  - fewer than 15 per cent of schools in its area, subject to intervention ('special measures' or 'significant improvement')

  - more than 15 per cent of schools are already foundation, voluntary, CTCs or academies.

- An authority with a lower APA rating cannot publish proposals for a community school.

In considering whether or not to give consent, the Secretary of State must have regard to:

- the extent of diversity

- the range of curricula specialism

- the range of extended services

- general standards of attainment

- the range of special educational needs specialism

- the availability of boarding or respite provision

among relevant schools within the area.

Essentially, the Secretary of State would need to be persuaded, in all the circumstances of the case, that the inclusion of a community school option would be more likely to meet the general objectives of extending and maintaining parental choice and promoting high standards than ruling it out.

Section 9: Consultation and publicity in relation to notice and proposals under section 7

This requires the local authority to consult interested parties about the notice instigating a competition for a new school. The section creates a power to make regulations and also requires authorities to have regard to guidance from the Secretary of State.

This is broadly the same as current requirements for consultation to be undertaken before publication of statutory proposals. Similar considerations will apply, namely

that sufficient time and information are allowed for people to understand the proposals and express a view on the relevant issues. Essentially, this will be a consultation about the specification for the new school, which will define the invitation for promoters to bring forward proposals and against which competing proposals will be judged.

Section 10: Publication of proposals with consent of Secretary of State

The Secretary of State's 'consent' is required before proposals can be brought forward without the requirement for a competition. The mechanism for this is much the same as in previous legislation, but now reflects the assumption that this is the exception rather than the rule.

Such an exemption can apply either to local authorities or other people; but promoters who wish to avoid a competition must first submit their proposal to the LEA which would have to maintain the school if it was approved.

It is envisaged that exemptions will apply in similar circumstances to those articulated in 2005. These include:

- where a school with a religious character is proposed to replace a school without such a character (this is still a change that requires the legal process of replacing one school with another rather than changing the character of an existing one)

- where two (or more) existing church schools are merged

- where promoters propose to establish a new school to increase diversity rather than to meet a general need for places in the area

- where it is proposed an academy will replace an existing school.

In other respects, (with regard to consultation, publication, consideration, approval and implementation) such proposals are treated like any others and are governed by Schedule 2.

Section 11: Publication of proposals to establish maintained schools: special cases

It is intended that some statutory proposals for establishing new schools will automatically avoid triggering a competition. These include:

- proposals from a local education authority to establish institutions falling outside the compulsory years of schooling, i.e.:
  - maintained nursery schools or
  - foundation or foundation special sixth form institutions
- proposals from promoters to establish new foundation, voluntary or foundation special schools, which will be:
  - maintained sixth form institutions
  - replacing an independent school
  - where a foundation special school is to replace a non-maintained special school.

The meaning of 'replacement' in this context is tightly defined to avoid circumvention of the competition requirements. Indications were given during the passage of the Bill that there were up to 100 private Muslim schools that would be interested in joining the public sector via this route.

As before, promoters must summit their proposals to the LEA that would have to maintain the school, but in other respects they are treated like any others.

Section 12: Establishment of school as federated school

Any new school, or schools, set up under the preceding sections, can become part of a federation on establishment. This could be either by joining an existing federation or setting up new federated arrangements with other schools at the same time.

The term 'federation' is often used loosely to cover a range of arrangements, where schools which remain separate legal entities collaborate with each other and share management arrangements. It is here used in the strict sense where one or more schools come under the jurisdiction of a single governing body, sometimes referred to as a 'hard' federation, under s.24 of EA 2002. A 'soft' federation is, in legislative terms, 'collaboration between schools' under s.26 of EA 2002.

This section replaces s.68 in EA 2005, which itself replaced s.74 of the EA 2002, but otherwise represents no change to the status quo.

Section 13: Schools established outside area of relevant LEA

Under certain circumstances a local authority may wish to instigate a competition, or bring forward proposals without a competition, to establish a school on a site outside its geographical area. Although it is unusual, there are examples of this which arose from boundary changes or the creation of new authorities. This section creates a regulation making power to modify the previous sections and Schedule 2 to allow this to continue.

Section 14: LEA in England not to establish school in Wales

This section prevents the arrangements provided for in the previous section from extending to circumstances in which an English LEA might wish to establish a school in Wales. A Parliamentary answer established that no English LEA maintains a school in Wales (Lords Written Answer, col WA117, 9 February 2005).

Schedule 2: Proposals for establishment or discontinuance of schools in England

The overall approach to requirements for consultation, determination and implementation of proposals remains broadly similar to the current law. Changes revolve around the abolition of the SOC and the alternative arrangements for determining proposals. The abolition of the SOC also changes the manner and circumstances in which decisions are referred to the Schools Adjudicator. The Schedule includes powers for the Secretary of State to make regulations and issue guidance.

Introductory

The Schedule's application and key terms are defined.

'Relevant authority' applies to the local education authority that: either announces a competition; maintains a school named in the proposal; or, in the case of a new school, will be expected to maintain it.

A 'proposer' is anyone who publishes statutory proposals (unless they are a local education authority), either as a response to a competition or otherwise.

The power is created to make regulations governing objections to proposals and requiring local authorities to forward objections to the Adjudicator in relevant cases.

Part two: Consideration of proposals

This covers the new arrangements for deciding proposals in the absence of the SOC. The LEA is the decision maker of first instance in all cases where it is not the author of proposals and is not connected with any organisation or trust which is the promoter of a proposal. However, as now, the LEA is allowed to determine its own proposals in circumstances where it is has been exempted from the requirement to hold a competition and no objections have been received or all objections have been withdrawn.

In para.8, as before, the decision maker (except that this is now the LEA rather than SOC) is given power to make four decisions on proposals, namely to:

- reject the proposal (or all the proposals, where there is more than one as a result of a competition)

- approve a proposal (or any one of them in the case of a competition)

- approve a proposal, subject to certain conditions being met

- approve proposals with such modifications as the authority thinks desirable, after consulting such persons as may be prescribed.

Although this is not spelt out in detail, the power to modify is relatively limited. It is most frequently used when it is necessary to alter the proposed date of implementation. However, a modification can include changes beyond this provided they were contemplated as possibilities in prior consultation and are sufficiently minor as not to constitute a significantly different proposal.

Decision makers must have regard to guidance given by the Secretary of State and conditional approval may be given subject to specified events taking place or conditions being met. Draft regulations issued for consultation shortly after the passage of the Act indicate that previous circumstances giving rise to conditional approval will continue, namely: any requirement for planning permission, the conclusion of Private Finance Initiative (PFI) negotiations or the Secretary of State's decisions about academies. The list is expanded, however, to take account of the advent of 'trust schools'; so matters related to establishing charities and foundation bodies are now prescribed. Approval can also be given, subject to agreement, to changes in the admission arrangements, or linked proposals, relating to other schools.

Paragraph 9 replicates the existing provisions that proposals related to each other must be considered together. It also precludes relevant authorities determining any proposals relating to sixth form provision if they might conflict with separate FE sector proposals, before those matters are resolved. FE proposals are determined by the Secretary of State under s.113A of LSA 2000. Authorities are required to have regard to guidance on deciding when these rules apply.

Paragraph 10 concerns referral to the Adjudicator. The Adjudicator must judge the competition in all cases where an authority has made proposals under s.7, responding to its own invitation notice. The Adjudicator must also make the decision when proposals for a foundation school are put forward by a promoter with links to the LEA. This is defined as where the relevant authority, or any person appointed by it, is a member of the foundation, a charity trustee, or has any voting rights, either directly or through nominees, within the foundation.

Regulations can be made under para.11 requiring authorities to refer proposals to the Adjudicator. Paragraph 12 gives the Secretary of State power to direct a local education authority to refer proposals to the Adjudicator. Such a direction remains in force, with regard to any and all proposals that the LEA might otherwise have handled, until such time as it is revoked. These paragraphs effectively amount to a power for the Secretary of State to decide that a particular local authority cannot be trusted to take decisions of this nature.

Paragraph 13 provides for proposals to be referred to the Adjudicator if the relevant authority has failed to determine them within a specified time.

Paragraph 14 creates the power for certain 'aggrieved persons' to require the authority to refer a determination to the Adjudicator (except a determination following a competition). This right can be exercised by the Church of England or Roman Catholic diocese covered by, or included within, the area of the relevant authority; the promoter of unsuccessful proposals and the governing body of the school (or trustees of a foundation), which is the subject of proposals. The LSC also has a right of referral, where proposals relate to schools providing education for persons aged 14 years or over.

Paragraph 15 maintains the principle that linked proposals must be considered together. Once a proposal has been referred to the Adjudicator all other related proposals must be considered by the Adjudicator even if they were not subject to the circumstances which triggered the initial referral.

Paragraph 16 confirms that all proposers, including local authorities, have an absolute right to withdraw proposals up to the time they have been determined.

Paragraph 17 provides that the same requirements and limitations which apply to local education authorities in considering and determining proposals, apply to the Adjudicator. Where a referral relates to a determination that has already been made, the Adjudicator is required to consider the proposals afresh.

Paragraph 18 maintains the status quo on proposals to establish an academy. Any proposals to establish an academy have to be made subject to consultation with the Secretary of State and determination in favour does not bind the Secretary of State to conclude a funding agreement with the promoters of the academy.

Part three: Implementation of proposals

Paragraphs 21–27 broadly maintain the status quo whereby, once proposals are approved, the relevant authority acquires a duty to implement them. As now, there is a power to modify proposals after appropriate consultation, largely to allow the actual date of implementation to be different from that set out in the original proposal. It also continues to be possible, again after consultation, to determine that proposals should not be implemented because it would either be 'unreasonably difficult' or that 'circumstances have so altered' as to make the proposals no longer appropriate.

Where the initial decision was made by the authority the power to modify proposals remains with that authority, but if the Adjudicator has been involved, any such decisions have to go back to the Adjudicator to be considered again. The main changes relate to the apportionment of duties between the relevant authority and the promoter where a competition took place under the new arrangements. Separate paragraphs apply to community schools, voluntary controlled schools, voluntary aided schools, foundation schools, special or foundation special schools and academies.

Part four: Provision of premises and other assistance in connection with the establishment of new schools

Paragraphs 28–31 relate to the relationship between the local education authority and promoters on the site and buildings aspect of establishing a new institution. Even though a new school may be proposed and operated by a promoter, the local

---

authority still retains a duty to identify a suitable site, assist in the establishment of the new building and subsequently to transfer any interest in the land or buildings to the body which will operate the school once it is established.

Discontinuance of schools ss.15–17

These three sections bring together and re-enact the relevant sections of SSFA 1998, as modified by EA 2002 and EA 2005. They separate out closure from other statutory proposals, which were dealt with together in previous legislation.

The term 'closure' is not used and s.15(8) states that 'discontinuing' a school is the same as an authority 'ceasing to maintain' it. This may emphasise the fact that in law a 'school' is the human institution rather than the premises it occupies.

The wording of s.17 is identical to that of s.32 of SSFA 1998, except for the cross references to other sections in E&IA 2006 and the addition of the words 'in England' in s.17(1). This, with similar additions elsewhere, has the effect of leaving previous legislation in place for Wales.

Section 15: Proposals for discontinuance of schools maintained by local education authority

A local education authority has power to propose the closure of community, foundation, or voluntary schools, community or foundation special schools or nursery schools. The governing body of a foundation or voluntary ('aided' or 'controlled') school or foundation special school can also propose its closure.

Special considerations apply to rural primary schools. Previously, statutory guidance for decision makers stated that any proposal to close 'rural schools' (including secondary) could be made only after considering:

- the impact on the local community
- the transport implications – including both the cost of transport to alternative schools and the environmental impact of increased motor vehicle traffic
- whether there were any viable alternatives to closure, e.g. by federating the school with others.

Protection for rural primaries was promoted to the face of primary legislation by s.70 of EA 2005 following an amendment in the House of Lords which was felt to be unnecessary, rather than undesirable, by the Government but not strongly resisted for the same reason. See s.182 on the designation of rural primary schools.

Paragraphs 7 and 19 of Schedule 2 are applied to this section, allowing the relevant body to determine closure proposals where there have been no objections or all objections have been withdrawn and the proposals do not interfere with or are not dependent upon other proposals, which have been subject to objection, or relate to matters involving decisions by the LSC or the Secretary of State.

Section 16: Consultation in relation to proposals under section 15

The arrangements to be used for consultation on closure proposals, in common with those for most statutory proposals, require the relevant body to 'consult such persons as appear to them to be appropriate' and to have regard to relevant regulations and guidance from the Secretary of State. However, the section is more explicit in the case of proposals involving rural primary schools and community or foundation special schools. It requires consultation to include the parents of pupils at the school; other local authorities, i.e. the LEA if the relevant body is not the LEA that maintains the school; or, in the case of a county council, any district council for the area in which the school is situated and a parish or town council where there is one.

Section 17: Direction requiring discontinuance of community or foundation special school

Section 17 gives the Secretary of State a power to direct the closure of any community or foundation special school, if he considers it 'expedient to do so in the interests of the health, safety or welfare of pupils'. There is a requirement to consult the local education authority that maintains the school and any others that might be affected and any other persons, including the foundation if there is one, that the Secretary of State considers appropriate. He must also give a notice in writing to the governing body and the headteacher. When such a direction is made, the LEA must discontinue the school on the date required and all other normal procedures are disapplied.

Alterations to schools ss.18–24

These sections deal with statutory procedures for making significant changes to schools other than opening or closing them. Although other matters can also be 'alterations', the creation of 'trust schools' is at the heart of these seven sections and was a key focus of debate on the White Paper and during the passage of the Bill. Technically a 'trust school' is a 'foundation school with a foundation' which is a charity. As noted in the introduction to this part, voluntary schools usually have a 'foundation' which must also be a charitable trust. These matters are defined by ss.20 and 21 of the SSFA 1998, so a body of law defining the relationships between foundations and schools is already in place. The new legislation adds to that by defining in more detail the form such bodies can take and how new or existing schools can establish or break off a relationship with them.

For these reasons, the legislation does not use the words 'trust school' even though there is a clear expectation that the term will remain in popular use. Some of the complexity of the structure of these seven sections arises from the need to make special arrangements for the acquisition of 'trust school status', whilst broadly maintaining the status quo for schools with established relationships with charitable bodies (e.g. most voluntary schools) and with respect to other kinds of 'alteration' which may be necessary from time to time.

A formal consultation draft, *The School Organisation (Prescribed Alterations to Maintained Schools) (England) Regulations 2007* and the associated *Guidance on the Acquisition of a Trust and/or the Acquisition of a Majority of Governors Appointed by the Trust,* was published on 13 November 2006 shortly after Royal Assent. These regulations consolidate and update those covering similar ground dating from 2000. They set out, in nine paragraphs and five Schedules over 47 pages, the detailed requirements covered by these seven sections of the Act. One particularly helpful feature of the guidance is a table indicating which bodies could make which kind of proposal, by whom such proposals would be determined, whether a right of appeal exists and, if so, who can exercise it. A slightly modified version of this table is set out as Table 3.

Table 3 Publisher, Decision Maker and Appeals Process for Statutory Proposals

Who can publish?	School category and type of proposal	Decision Maker	Appeal to Adjudicator? (appeal by)
Local Education Authority	**Community & community special schools:**		
	New schools with the agreement of the Secretary of State: a) in competition (s.8); b) outside competition (s.10) [*NB consultation papers indicated this may be subject to change*]	Adjudicator	No
	Proposals to discontinue school (s.15)	LEA	Yes (CE or RC diocese, LSC)
	All other proposals except to remove selection from a grammar school or change category to foundation, VA or VC; or community special to foundation special (s.19)	LEA	Yes (diocese, LSC)
	Foundation and foundation special schools:		
	Proposals to establish a new school, a) in competition (s.7) b) outside competition with agreement of Secretary of State (s.10)	Adjudicator	No
	Proposals to discontinue a school (s.15)	LEA	Yes (CE or RC diocese, LSC, GB or trustees)
	Proposals for 'prescribed alteration' to: enlarge the premises of an existing school; add or remove SEN provision or add provision for children over compulsory school age (s.19)	LEA	Yes (CE or RC diocese, LSC, GB or trustees)
	Voluntary schools:		
	Proposals to discontinue a school (s.15)	LEA	Yes (CE or RC diocese, LSC, GB or trustees)
	Proposals for 'prescribed alteration' to: enlarge the premises of an existing school; add or remove SEN provision or add provision for children over compulsory school age (s.19)	LEA	Yes (CE or RC diocese, LSC, GB or trustees)
	Nursery school:		
	Proposals to establish a new nursery school (s.11)	Adjudicator	No
	Proposals to discontinue a school (s.15)	LEA	Yes (CE or RC diocese, LSC)

Table 3 Publisher, Decision Maker and Appeals Process for Statutory Proposals *cont'd.*

Who can publish?	School category and type of proposal	Decision Maker	Appeal to Adjudicator? (appeal by)
Governors of found-ation and foundation special schools	Proposals to discontinue the school (s.15)	LEA	Yes (CE or RC diocese, LSC, GB or trustees)
	'Prescribed alteration' for relevant change in instrument of government or to acquire a foundation, i.e. becoming a 'trust school' (s.19)	GB	Yes (LEA can refer if consultation inadequate. or concerns about standards)
	Proposals for other 'prescribed alteration' to the school (s.19)	LEA	Yes (CE or RC diocese, LSC, or GB)
Governors of voluntary schools	Proposals to discontinue the school (s.15)	LEA	Yes (CE or RC diocese, LSC, GB or trustees)
	'Prescribed alteration' to change the category of the school (s.19) N.B. Under s.20 governors of voluntary schools must obtain the consent of their foundation, if there is one, before publishing Trust School proposals. So, although trustees do not have a 'right of appeal', they effectively have a veto.	VC change to foundation GB	Yes (LEA can refer if acquiring foundation and consultation inadequate or concerns about standards)
		VA change to foundation GB	No
		Otherwise LEA	Yes (CE or RC diocese, LSC, or GB)
	Proposals for other 'prescribed alteration' to the school (s.19)	LEA	Yes (CE or RC diocese, LSC, or GB)
Governors of comm-unity or community special schools	'Prescribed alteration' (s.19) Community school: to enlarge school premises, increase the number of pupils in any relevant age group by 27 or more, add a sixth form or, where the school is a grammar school, to end selection	LEA	Yes (CE or RC diocese, LSC, or GB)
	Community special: increase in number of pupils by 10 per cent (or five pupils where school is just boarding and 20 in any other case, whichever is the lesser)	LEA	Yes (CE or RC diocese, LSC, or GB)

Table 3 Publisher, Decision Maker and Appeals Process for Statutory Proposals *cont'd.*

Who can publish?	School category and type of proposal	Decision Maker	Appeal to Adjudicator? (appeal by)
Governors of community or community special schools *cont'd*	'Prescribed alteration' to change the category of the school (s.19)	Change to foundation/ foundation special GB	Yes (LEA can refer if acquiring foundation & consultation inadequate or concerns about standards)
		Otherwise LEA	Yes (CE or RC diocese, LSC, or GB)
Proposers	Proposals to establish a new foundation school without a foundation, foundation special or voluntary school: a) in competition (s.7) or b) outside competition (with Secretary of State agreement) (s.10)	LEA	(a) No (b) Yes (CE or RC diocese, LSC, or proposer)
	Proposals to establish a foundation school with a foundation where: LEA, or their appointee, is a member of foundation; LEA. Appointee is trustee, or LEA, or their appointee, exercise appointing rights either in competition (s.7) or outside competition (with Secretary of State agreement) (s.10)	Adjudicator	No
	Other proposals to establish a foundation school with a foundation: a) in competition (s.7); or b) outside competition (with Secretary of State agreement) (s.10 or s.11)	LEA	(a) No (b) Yes (CE or RC diocese, LSC, or proposer)

The draft guidance makes it clear that the acquisition of a trust is to be made as easy as possible and the decision should be in the hands of the governing body of the school. In most cases, the governing body will first publish the proposal to acquire a trust and then be responsible for deciding that the proposal should be implemented. This differs from the position of a local education authority when it announces a competition to provide a new school. If the local education authority wants to make its own proposals for a community school, or even if it has a minority interest in a trust which proposes a foundation school, it is precluded from determining the outcome of the competition on the, not unreasonable, principle of natural justice that no one should be a judge in their own cause.

The distinction between the terms 'foundation', 'foundation body' and 'a foundation established otherwise than under SSFA 1998' are set out in the introduction (page 22 above).

Section 18: Alterations that may be made under section 19

This establishes the distinction between alterations related to 'trust schools' and other kinds of alteration and creates the regulation making power (subsection (1)) to define 'prescribed alterations'.

The framework of 'trust school' type alterations is set by subsection (2), which includes a school:

- becoming a foundation school

- which is already a foundation school, acquiring 'a foundation'

- which already has a foundation changing its instrument of government so that foundation governors achieve a majority.

Subsection (3) permits other kinds of alteration to be included (for example, a school changing premises or altering its age range or intake), but subsection (4) sets out explicitly those alterations that cannot be made under the same procedure. These include:

- the acquisition of a religious character by a school, or the loss of, or any changes to, a religious character it already has

- a change of category from foundation or voluntary school to become a community school including both mainstream and special schools

- any change of character as between mainstream and special schools

- turning a maintained nursery school into any other kind of school or vice versa.

Requiring closure and reopening as a new school in order to change religious character maintains the status quo, but preventing foundation or voluntary schools becoming community schools is new. Section 35 and Schedule 8 of SSFA 1998 allowed free movement between the various types of school. Effectively, there is now a one way street leading away from community schools.

Section 19: Publication of proposals for alteration of school

Local authorities and governing bodies can both make 'section 18' proposals to alter maintained schools within the parameters defined in regulations made under s.18(1).

Subsection (2) says that a local education authority can make any relevant proposals in relation to community schools, but in the case of foundation (including foundation special) or voluntary schools their powers are limited to proposals for:

- enlarging premises or transferring the school to a new site

- increasing the number of pupils in any relevant age group

- establishing or discontinuing provision for pupils with special educational needs and establishing sixth form provision.

This also represents a change. Previously, LEAs could decide to cease to maintain but could not propose an alteration to a voluntary aided school. They could propose to enlarge or add a sixth form to a foundation school but not reduce numbers or change its age range. The position is now more consistent in that LEAs can propose to increase the size of premises or expand pupil numbers but not seek reductions in either case. (Closure can, of course, still be proposed under s.15.)

Subsection (3) provides the power for governing bodies to make proposals but, in the case of community schools, the scope of the proposals governors can make is limited by regulations. The powers of foundation and voluntary school governors are limited by s.20 (see below).

The consultation draft for *The School Organisation (Prescribed Alterations to Maintained Schools) (England) Regulations 2007* also included new provisions:

- a temporary change, lasting no more than two years, can be made to a school's upper age limit

- a formal process is to be introduced when proposals are withdrawn before they are decided; in future, a notice must be placed at the entrance of the school and formal written notification given to the local authority, the school affected by the proposals, the Schools Adjudicator and the Secretary of State

- publication of proposals is not required in respect of nursery schools, except where it is intended to transfer the school to a new site more than two miles from its current location.

Subsection (4) creates a power for the governing body of a voluntary aided school that is unable or unwilling to continue to carry out its obligations, to publish proposals for the school to become either a voluntary controlled or a foundation school.

Section 20: Restriction on power of governing body to publish foundation proposals

The governing body of a foundation school with a foundation cannot make a proposal to change the instrument of government in a way which results in the majority of governors being foundation governors without first obtaining the consent of the trustees and anyone who appoints foundation governors to the school. The section also imposes a similar limitation on a voluntary controlled or voluntary aided school that wishes to become a foundation school.

This is because a school with a pre-existing foundation becoming a 'trust school' could require its foundation to reconstitute in order to meet requirements imposed by s.33 of the Act. If the trustees refused to do this the process would be frustrated and therefore the foundation's consent must be sought under s.20 before the governing body can publish proposals.

Section 21: Proposals under section 19: procedure

This section, with its associated regulations, controls procedures for s.19 proposals. These follow the normal pattern for statutory proposals regarding consultation, publication, allowing objections and comments and determination. Regulations cover the circumstances under which proposals may be referred to the adjudicator (including on the direction of the Secretary of State) and for approval of proposals, with or without modifications, or the imposition of conditions and the possibility of their withdrawal.

There is specific provision (subsection 5) for avoiding proposals relating to single sex institutions falling foul of s.27 of the Sex Discrimination Act 1975. This allows the LEA or the Adjudicator to make a 'transitional exemption order' which has the effect of delaying the application of the full effects of the SDA whilst a single-sex school is becoming co-educational.

As usual, regulations also require anyone exercising functions under them to have regard to guidance given by the Secretary of State.

Section 22: Right of governing body to determine own foundation proposals

Where the governors of a community (including community special) or a voluntary controlled school wish to change category to become a foundation school without acquiring a foundation, the governing body is allowed to determine its own proposals. Regulations cannot make provision for the proposals to be referred to the Adjudicator.

However, if the governing body of such a school wishes to adopt trust status, by seeking to acquire a foundation and/or give it the power to nominate a majority of governors, there is a right of reference to the Adjudicator. This can only be exercised by the LEA in accordance with s.23 (1) & (2).

Section 23: Rights of interested bodies in relation to proposals under section 21

Subsections (1) and (2) allow the LEA to refer trust school proposals to the Adjudicator where a school becomes a foundation school, acquires a foundation or gives it the right to nominate a majority of governors.

Regulations under subsection (3) restrict the scope of such referral decisions. Schedule 1, part 2, para.12 of *The School Organisation (Prescribed Alterations to Maintained Schools) (England) Regulations 2007* (issued in draft on 13 November 2006) provides that LEAs can only make such a referral if:

- the governing body has failed to fulfil the consultation requirements

- the governing body has not had regard to the responses to consultation

- the local authority consider the foundation will have a negative impact on standards.

Subsections (4) and (5) relate to any proposals for alterations, which are not about the acquisition of a foundation and govern the scope of regulations under s.21 about who can make referrals to the Adjudicator. In all cases where the initial determination can be made either by the governing body or the LEA, a right of referral to the Adjudicator is given to the relevant Church of England or Roman Catholic diocese. Where the proposals relate to the provision of education beyond 14 the LSC can also require a reference to the Adjudicator. Where the LEA is allowed to publish

proposals relating to a foundation (including foundation special) or voluntary school the governing body and the trustees of that school have the right to require proposals to be referred to the Adjudicator after the authority has made its initial determination.

Section 24: Proposals under section 19: implementation

The first two subsections provide, in general terms, that the regulations will approach the issue in much the same way as other statutory proposals. In other words, it makes clear that proposals under s.19 can be approved, or determined without requiring approval; with options not to implement, to implement with modifications or for issues to be referred to the Adjudicator. Regulations will also establish a framework governing the manner and time limits for implementing proposals.

More detailed requirements are set out for the regulations in respect of proposals relating to the acquisition of foundations (i.e. where trust schools are to be set up). Subsection (3) provides for regulations in these cases, to include provision with respect to making new instruments of government, transferring property rights and liabilities, transferring the employment of staff and transitional issues.

Subsections (4) and (5) go into even more detail on issues relating to the transfer or disposal of land, including the capacity to restrict the power of local authorities to dispose of land in advance of trust school proposals going through; and making detailed provision on the division of parcels of land, or the apportionment of property rights and liabilities, between various interested parties. The regulations can make provision for the resolution of disputes, the construction of agreements and mechanisms by which agreements should be recorded and certificated, to provide subsequent clear and unambiguous evidence of title and property rights.

The remaining subsections, as always, require relevant individuals to have regard to guidance on the exercise of their functions given by the Secretary of State. Regulations may make provision corresponding to paragraphs 21–31 of Schedule 2 about implementing proposals. Subsection (8) underlines the fact that a change of category under s.19 cannot involve, or be taken as authorising, any change in religious character including the acquisition or loss of a religious character.

Removal of foundation or reduction in foundation governors ss.25–27

These three sections provide a mechanism for dealing with circumstances in which a school wishes to reverse its decision to become a trust school, or reduce the influence of a trust with which it is associated.

Section 25: Proposals for removal of foundation or reduction in foundation governors

The first three subsections make it clear that the procedure applies only to schools, which were either set up, or acquired a foundation, under E&IA 2006. This means that the reversal procedure only applies to trust schools which acquired their foundation after the passage of this Act. It cannot be used retrospectively by former voluntary schools, which ended up as foundation schools by virtue of previously being grant-maintained schools, to sever their connection with the Church (see Table 2.) This is consistent with para.4 of Schedule 3, which amends the Diocesan Boards of Education Measure 1991, to require the governing body of a Church of England school to obtain the diocesan board's consent in writing before it can publish a proposal under s.19 to change a school's category from voluntary to foundation; or, where it is already a foundation school, to change the instrument resulting in a majority of governors being foundation governors.

Subsection (4) allows the governors of a relevant foundation or foundation special school to publish proposals, which either removes a foundation (s.25(4)(a)), or alters the instrument of government in such a way that foundation governors will cease to constitute the majority of governors (s.25(4)(b)) or both of those things. The 'either or both' formulation is potentially confusing here, clearly it will be possible to maintain a link with a foundation and to reduce its influence over the governing body, but it would be illogical to remove the foundation but leave it in a position where it nominated the majority of governors. However, whilst the correct construction of 'removing the foundation' is that this automatically removes its ability to nominate governors, subsection (4)(b) would not apply if the foundation did not appoint a majority of governors before the proposal to remove it.

Subsection (5) provides for a proportion of the governing body (to be defined in regulations made under s.25) to be able to require the governing body to publish

proposals for the removal or reduction of the influence of the foundation. A consultation draft was published under the title *The School Organisation (Removal of Foundation and Reduction in Number of Foundation Governors) (England) Regulations 2007* immediately after Royal Assent. This indicates that one third of the members of the governing body would be sufficient to require publication. The self-evident logic of this is that they would constitute the larger part of the minority of the governing body, who are not appointed by the foundation.

However, subsection (6) absolves the governing body from its duty to publish proposals at the behest of such a sub-group within a defined time period following specified events. These are:

- the establishment of the school

- the implementation of proposals for the acquisition of a foundation

- a change in the instrument of government giving a foundation the right to nominate a majority of governors

- a similar proposal having been made and subsequently rejected by the governing body.

The draft regulations indicate that the proposal is for that time period to be seven years. So (if the regulations are made un-amended) after any positive decision to establish a trust or give it control of the school, seven years must elapse before a minority on the governing body can initiate a process to reverse it. This would not, of course, prevent a similar decision being taken by a majority of the governing body under subsection (4) 'at any time'.

Section 26: Proposals under section 25: procedure

This section creates a regulation making power with the usual provisions about statutory proposals regarding: consultation, publication, objections, consideration withdrawal, approval or rejection. It also includes the usual requirement for anyone exercising relevant functions to have regard to guidance given by the Secretary of State.

It makes more explicit provision to enable the governing body to reject proposals that it was required to publish by a minority of its number under the previous section only by a decision made with 'the support of a prescribed proportion of governors'. The draft regulations mentioned above indicate that a two-thirds majority (of the

whole governing body, as opposed to those present and voting at a meeting) would be required to reject a proposal which had been requisitioned by the prescribed minority. It will be seen from this that if there is a solid consensus amongst the non-foundation governors on the governing body they would be able to prevail against the inbuilt simple majority controlled by the foundation.

Subsection (3) allows regulations to prescribe that issues related to land (under s.27(3) or (4) see below) including transferring title, or assessing the value of or apportioning rights and any consequential payments are sorted out prior to the publication of proposals. It also provides for these issues to be referred to the Adjudicator for 'determination' before the proposals are published if relevant parties cannot reach agreement. This envisages the possibility that the trust related to a school may have spent its own money improving the premises, or that the school may occupy premises that the trust also uses for other purposes in ways that would need to be disentangled before the separation of the school from the trust could be achieved.

Subsection (4) contains the usual power for the Secretary of State to issue guidance. Draft guidance published shortly after Royal Assent also applies to, and is summarised in, the next section

Section 27: Proposals under section 25: implementation

This provides for regulations to be made about the implementation of proposals under s.25 which have been approved in accordance with s.26. As with s.24 this refers in general terms to revising or replacing the school's instrument of government; the reconstitution of the governing body and making provision for the transfer of property rights and liabilities and prescribing the manner and timescales in which any necessary actions must be carried out. Relevant people are required to have regard to guidance given by the Secretary of State (s.27(6)) and it is emphasised that nothing in these sections allows the school to acquire a religious character, or lose or change a religious character it already has (s.27(7)). These provisions apply only to foundations established otherwise than under SSFA 1998 (s.27(8)).

Issues related to the transfer of land are, however, set out in more detail. Subsection (4) allows provision for the foundation to pay to the governing body, the LEA or another prescribed person, a sum equivalent to all or part of the value of land that forms part of the school premises, but is not subsequently transferred to the governing body.

Subsection (5) provides for the parallel circumstance in which the foundation body has incurred capital expenditure in relation to land or other assets, which forms part of, or has enhanced the value of, land which is to be transferred to the governing body. In these circumstances, the governing body may be required to pay the value, or any part of the value, of those assets to the foundation.

Draft versions of the regulations and guidance under ss.25–27 were issued for consultation on 13 November 2006. These are: *The School Organisation (Removal of Foundation and Reduction in Number of Foundation Governors) (England) Regulations 2007* and *Guidance on the Removal of a School's Trust and the Reduction in Number of Governors Appointed by the Trust.*

In addition to prescribing the seven-year period mentioned under s.26 above, they include the triggers, processes and arrangements for consulting, publishing and deciding upon proposals and issues consequential on the change of relationship between a school and a trust if proposals to remove the trust go through.

The guidance is quite lengthy, perhaps in recognition of the fact that the circumstances of these regulations coming into play may be quite unusual, but are likely to be highly contentious. Not only is the decision that a school and its foundation should part company likely to have been preceded by some difficulties in the relationship, but the necessary disentanglement of assets will themselves provide considerable scope for dispute.

The Office of the Schools Adjudicator will have a role in resolving such disputes and will also become the arbitrator where similar issues arise in respect of voluntary aided schools (this role was previously undertaken by the Secretary of State).

General ss.28–32

The remaining sections provide the usual tidying up provisions at the end of this part of the Act.

Section 28: Restriction on establishment, alteration or discontinuance of schools

This section applies only to England, leaving the SSFA 1998 provisions it replaces in force in Wales. It provides that, except where there is a separate explicit power, no

school can be opened or closed or altered in any of the prescribed ways without the publication and determination of statutory proposals.

The exceptions are:

- where Secretary of State's power to direct the local education authority to close a community or foundation special school (for example in the interests of health and safety) or to close a school in special measures is exercised

- where the governing body of a foundation or voluntary school give notice that they intend to close it.

Subsection (4) also prohibits alterations which involve the removal of a foundation or a reduction in the proportion of the governors it appoints such that they no longer constitute a majority, without the publication and determination of statutory proposals.

Section 29: Abolition of School Organisation Committees

School Organisation Committees are abolished. The draft regulations and guidance published on 13 November 2006 indicate that this is intended to come into effect at the end of May 2007.

Section 30: Amendments relating to school organisation

Schedule 3 is brought into effect. This lists minor and consequential amendments to other Acts of Parliament. Much of this arises from the fact that E&IA 2006 applies only to England and therefore sections of SSFA 1998, that otherwise might have been repealed, still remain in force but are amended to apply only to Wales. Other changes refer to redundant references to the School Organisation Committee in other Acts and consequential changes relating to voluntary schools affiliated to the Church of England, which are referred to in legislation about the established Church.

Section 31: Transitional provisions

This section provides the regulation making powers necessary to manage the process of dealing with any statutory proposals that may already be in train when the new arrangements are brought into force. These provisions may have been envisaged to accommodate the fact that statutory proposals take some time to work through the

system, particularly if they are contentious and are referred to the Schools Adjudicator. Transitional arrangements could prevent proposals that are under way at implementation needing to start again when new regulations come into force.

The draft regulations, published in November 2006, did not include any transitional arrangements and detailed arrangements had not been revealed by the start of April 2007. However, DfES signalled that any matters considered but not resolved by the SOC on abolition and any proposals for new schools made by LEAs should be passed to the Adjudicator. Any other kind of proposal published, but not decided by the SOC, should go to the LEA for decision, and the new arrangements for other bodies to appeal to the Adjudicator will apply. The regulations may need to be quite complex to provide for all eventualities, but since most of the interests previously represented on the SOC will have rights to refer proposals to the Schools Adjudicator this may not make a great deal of difference.

Section 32: Interpretation of Part 2

Confirms the interpretation of keywords and phrases in line with particular sections of this or previous legislation.

Part 3: Further provisions about maintained schools

General introduction

This part of the Act is something of a rag bag of different measures but is mainly about controlling the behaviour of governing bodies (and trusts where they exist) in the overall environment envisioned in the White Paper. Whilst the rhetoric surrounding trust schools was about 'liberating' them from state (or more particularly local authority) control and creating empowered, autonomous institutions, the Government has also sought to legislate for their good behaviour. Powers are taken in this part of the Act seeking to ensure that they operate in pursuit of the Government's vision of high quality public education for all.

It includes:

* controls on the formation and operation of trusts
* land and financial resources of schools
* staffing in faith schools
* significant changes to the regulation of school admissions
* some deregulation with regard to school forums and the removal of the Code of Practice on LEA School Relations.

Foundation, voluntary and foundation special schools ss.33–37

These sections can be understood as a response to anxieties about the possibilities of trust schools falling into the hands of unsuitable or unscrupulous people. The Secretary of State can exercise considerable control over the organisations or individuals who are members of foundations or trustees. During the debate it was suggested that organisations such as tobacco companies, arms manufacturers or the purveyors of fast food should not be allowed to form trusts. Although draft regulations do not go so far as to preclude particular kinds of company from involvement as 'trust part-

ners'; the Act provides the Secretary of State with sufficient powers to curtail the activities of any foundation which might give cause for concern.

In law a charity can take a number of different forms but there is a distinction between 'members' of the trust who can be organisations or individuals and who equate to company shareholders and 'trustees' who must be individuals and who have responsibilities similar to the directors of a limited company. All trusts must be charities and will be subject to regulation by the Charity Commission. At present, if the trust has no property other than the premises of the school, it will not be required to register with the Charity Commission.

However, when the provisions of the Charities Act 2006 come into force, there will be a number of changes. The income threshold for registration will change and trusts will only be required to register if their annual income exceeds £5,000.

The Charities Act 2006 also provides for a new type of incorporated charitable vehicle known as a Charitable Incorporated Organisation (CIO). CIOs will derive their existence from registration with the Charity Commission and trusts established in this way will always be registered charities, even if their annual income is less than £5,000. These provisions of the Charities Act 2006 are not expected to be in force until 2008.

In addition to control over the establishment of trusts, there is now a requirement for a trust school, where a majority of governors are nominated by the foundation, to have a Parent Council. This was introduced as an amendment following concerns that the number of elected parent representatives on governing bodies would be reduced by the adoption of trust school status.

Section 33: Requirements as to foundations

Two new sections (23A and 23B) are inserted in SSFA 1998. A consultation draft of *The School Organisation (Requirements as to Foundations) (England) Regulations 2007* was published on 13 November 2006. The regulations specify the legal form a foundation (trust) can take, categories of person disqualified from being a trustee and set out the powers of the Secretary of State to remove and appoint individual trustees in more detail.

SSFA 1998, s.23A: Foundation and foundation special schools: requirements as to foundations

This new section defines the form of body that can be the 'foundation' in respect of a trust school. The first four subsections make it clear that these limitations only apply to 'foundations' (trusts) that come into existence as a result of the present legislation. Thus foundations which pre-existed, both those associated with foundation schools and charitable trusts associated with voluntary schools, remain largely untouched.

Subsection (5) requires a foundation associated with a trust school to meet three criteria:

- 5(a) a foundation must be a corporate body of 'a prescribed description'. The draft regulations prescribe either:

  - an incorporated charity

  - a company limited by guarantee or by shares

  - a body incorporated by Royal Charter.

- 5(b) requires the body to be a charity 'whether by virtue of section23(3) or otherwise'. This is a reference to s.23(3) of SSFA, which provides that 'any foundation established otherwise than under the [SSF] Act which has no property other than the premises of any [foundation, voluntary or foundation special] school or schools' will automatically be a charity, without being required to be separately registered as such under the Charities Act.

- 5(c) says the foundation must have as its charitable purpose or one of its purposes: 'the advancement of the education of pupils at the school, or schools, in respect of which it acts as a foundation'.

It must meet all three criteria, so a body that is already a charity may need to reconstitute itself or adjust its charitable purposes to qualify.

Subsection (6) is an explicit requirement that a foundation should 'promote community cohesion'. The draft guidance on the acquisition of trusts links this phrase to the Government's desire to 'promote ethnic, religious and cultural tolerance and respect between different groups of people living together'. Trusts will therefore need to be able to demonstrate that they are committed to providing 'opportunities for young people from different backgrounds to learn from each other and encouraging an

---

understanding of and respect for, other cultures and faiths and by activities in the community, which help build bridges between different ethnic groups'. As well as these positive aspects, decision makers are guided to consider whether the involvement of trust partners in activities that may be 'inappropriate for children and young people e.g. tobacco, gambling, adult entertainment and alcohol' would work against their meeting this requirement.

Subsections (7) and (8) serve to ensure that the influence of a local education authority over a foundation, whether directly or through nominees, is limited to a maximum of 20 per cent of voting rights.

Subsection (9) creates a regulation making power to disqualify people from acting as charity trustees. The draft regulations indicate that the categories of people who will be excluded from acting as a charity trustee in respect of schools covered by the regulations will be people:

- on List 99 or teachers otherwise disqualified by the General Teaching Council

- who have been convicted of a criminal offence within a period of time (being longer for more serious offences) preceding their appointment

- under 18

- detained under the Mental Health Acts

- who are employees at any school associated with the foundation

- who are members or officers of any local education authority.

Consultation on the draft regulations drew attention to the fact that all trustees will be subject to a criminal record check and that the reference to members and officers of the authority would exclude all of them (not just those associated with the education function) and cases where the individual was acting in a purely personal capacity. The framing of the consultation implied that the Government might be amenable to arguments that the latter restriction should be relaxed.

SSFA 1998, s.23B: Powers of Secretary of State in relation to charity trustees of foundations

This new section creates a power to make regulations, defining circumstances in which the Secretary of State can remove a charity trustee from a foundation body or appoint somebody to join a foundation body associated with a school. Again, these

regulations will only apply to foundations created under the E&IA 2006. Such disqualifications and appointments will be made by direction and will have the same effect as similar orders that can be made by the Charity Commission, but will not otherwise interfere with the powers of the Charity Commission to act in respect of these or other bodies (s.23B(3)).

This section is made more complicated by the need to include a transitional arrangement (s.23B(2)) to take account of the fact that the Charities Act 2006 which was in the process of changing relevant parts of the legislation was not in force before enactment of E&IA 2006.

It is made explicit that the Secretary of State will have power to disqualify a particular individual from acting as a trustee, even if they would not be disqualified by virtue of subsection (9) of s.23A (see above).

The draft regulations indicate that the power to remove charity trustees can operate where the Secretary of State is satisfied that someone has been acting in a way which is incompatible with the object or purposes of the foundations or that they are likely to bring any school with which the foundation is associated into disrepute.

New appointments can be made if the Secretary of State is satisfied that such an appointment is necessary to improve the administration of a foundation, or the foundation has failed to appoint a replacement for someone that the Secretary of State has previously removed.

Section 34: Parent councils for certain foundation or foundation special schools

This provision was amended more than once during the progress of the Bill in response to concerns expressed about the reduction of the elected parental voice in trust schools where the foundation appoints a majority of the governors. It operates by inserting a new section 23A into EA 2002 where a number of other sections relate to the governance of maintained schools.

Subsections (2) and (3) require the governing body of any 'qualifying school' (i.e. a foundation school with a foundation where a majority of governors are appointed by the foundation) to appoint a Parent Council comprising parents who have registered pupils at the school. The purpose of the Parent Council is to advise the governing

body on matters relating to the conduct of the school and on any community activities that it is involved in (under powers defined in s.27 of EA 2002).

Subsection (4) is the power to make regulations defining how members will be elected or appointed, their eligibility, term of office and the proceedings and procedures for meetings. The regulations may confer specific functions on Parent Councils (subsection (5)) and the governing body must have regard to any guidance that may be given by the Secretary of State.

Drafts of *The School Governance (Parent Councils) (England) Regulations 2007* and *Guidance for Governing Bodies on Parent Councils*, which were produced shortly after the passage of the Bill, did not add greatly to what appears on its face.

The regulations require that the Parent Council must ensure that every year group is represented by at least one parent with a pupil in that year group and that there is representation from any distinctive group of parents or pupils, which may require 'special consideration'. Parent governors on the governing body are also ex officio members of the Parent Council. The governing body is, however, allowed to decide whether members should be elected or appointed and what procedure should be used. People who are not parents of children at the school can be members but only if they are appointed by the parent members (i.e. despite their ability to arrange the appointment process, governors cannot impose outsiders on the Parent Council). The Parent Council itself (in consultation with the governing body) can determine its quorum, manner of proceedings and place of meetings. The governing body is, however, required to provide such information and support as the Parent Council may 'reasonably require'.

The guidance fleshes this out in largely commonsense terms and concludes by pointing out that, whilst the requirement to have a Parent Council is only imposed on schools where a trust nominates the majority of governors, it is considered good practice for other schools to create one.

Section 35: Funding of voluntary aided schools: the meaning of 'capital expenditure'

This section amends part 2 of Schedule 3 of SSFA 1998, to modify the legal meaning of 'capital expenditure'. Subparagraph 3(3) of the Schedule is omitted, 'as it

applies to England' and two new paragraphs are added under the subheading 'meaning of "capital expenditure"'.

These two paragraphs recognise complexities under the new dispensation, where responsibility for capital expenditure on premises may rest with a governing body, 'promoters' of the school or others who are variously described as the 'appropriate body'. The section creates a regulation making power for the Secretary of State to define any particular category of expenditure, either as being deemed to be 'capital' or 'not capital' expenditure. Draft regulations show that the intention here is that expenditure on a voluntary aided school, amounting to less than £2,000 by an appropriate body will be deemed not to be capital expenditure.

This avoids providing an exhaustive list of what is, or is not, regarded as capital expenditure in the legislation by reference to general accounting practices and concepts. This reflects the approach taken in s.16 of the Local Government Act 2003 which defines capital expenditure in relation to an LEA. It is intended to ensure that the definition of capital expenditure reflects modern accounting practice and that optimal procurement arrangements are available to voluntary aided schools.

Section 36: Disposals and changes of use of land and Schedule 4: Disposals and changes of use of land

This section brings into effect Schedule 4 which contains amendments to s.77 and Schedule 22 to SSFA 1998, which refer to the disposal of school land and playing fields used by schools. The references are separate because, as a result of historical policy decisions, additional considerations apply to the disposal of open space that has been used as a playing field than to what may be loosely understood as 'brown field' school land.

This section is very short and its essential purpose is to govern the transfer of assets between various parties with an interest in the provision of schools. The Schedule, however, includes some 40 pages of very dense, if repetitive, provisions. This arises partly from the history of transfers of land between local authorities, school governing bodies and private individuals. It must also comprehend the various public and private funds that may have been used to acquire or enhance land and buildings, as well as the new arrangements which are even more complex than those that went before.

The new legislation attempts to put in place an interlocking network of rights, duties and responsibilities with fairness and equity between interested parties. It seeks to secure the appropriate reinvestment of any educational assets that are realised so that previous public expenditure is not lost. However, it recognises that where such resources originally derived from private or charitable sources, they should be allowed to revert to that source. Whilst the principle is straightforward, practical difficulties can arise from any given asset including elements of value derived from different original sources over a, possibly lengthy, period of time.

The legislation also allocates responsibility for the decision over how any realised assets might be reinvested for the public good. In any given situation, the governors of a particular school, the trustees of a foundation body which has a relationship with more than one school and the local authority which maintains the school in question, may have different views about reinvestment of the resources deriving from a redundant asset.

The structure of the legislation seeks to encourage resolution of these matters by agreement and provides for arbitration by the Schools Adjudicator where this cannot be achieved. A key feature requires the various parties to give notice to each other of any interests they consider they have when the question of a possible disposal arises. In support of reaching agreement, questions can be referred to the Schools Adjudicator for resolution in principle in advance of decisions to dispose of property being taken, or such disposals taking place.

As always, relevant parties are required to have regard to guidance issued by the Secretary of State. Early draft guidance was prepared to support debate on the Bill, and a revised version was issued ahead of regulations and the legislation coming into force at the end of May 2007.

The guidance summarises the legislation and procedures governing the transfer of land when a school changes category (and when a new foundation school is established) and also the disposal of surplus non-playing field land by foundation and voluntary schools and by foundations. It covers factors that the adjudicator must consider if asked to make a determination on land transfers or disposals and where an authority wishes to utilise surplus school land for another educational (or children's services) function. It does not include the disposal of playing field land, as the legal position is unchanged and is already covered by guidance *The Protection of*

School Playing Fields and Land for Academies (which can be found at www.teach-ernet.gov.uk/schoolslandandproperty).

Part two of Schedule 4 re-enacts s.77 of the SSFA and extends it to include the disposal of playing fields by the governing body, foundation body or trustees of a foundation of voluntary school. This extends the existing requirement on local authorities to seek the Secretary of State's consent before disposing of, or changing the use of, school playing fields to foundation and voluntary schools.

Schedule 22 of SSFA 1998 required any bodies (other than LEAs) which might wish to dispose of any school land previously provided or enhanced at public expense, to obtain the Secretary of State's consent. They were also required to notify the LEA of any such proposals and to reach agreement on what amount of the sale proceeds should be paid to it. In the event of a dispute over the division of sale proceeds the matter could be referred to the Secretary of State, who had powers of direction to approve (or not) the disposal and determine the destination of any sale proceeds and the uses to which they could be put.

Schedule 4 amends Schedule 22 to the SSFA to enable the governing body, foundation body or trustees of a foundation or voluntary school to dispose of non-playing field land without first having to obtain the Secretary of State's consent. Now, they simply have to notify their local authority that they are proposing to dispose of some land and reach agreement with it on the use of any sale proceeds. If they fail to agree, the dispute falls to be resolved by the Schools Adjudicator, rather than by the Secretary of State. Schedule 4 also transfers to the Schools Adjudicator a power previously exercised by the Secretary of State (under para. 4 of Schedule 22 of SSFA 1998) to require land that is needed as a site of a new school to be transferred to the local authority.

At the same time as making provision to take account of the new trust schools the opportunity has been taken to rationalise and streamline the arrangements that apply to all bodies that hold land on behalf of publicly funded schools.

There are echoes here of the vexed issue of 'reverter'. When, in the early 19th century, the Church sought to expand the availability of free education for the general population there was a great need for land to build schools. The School Sites Acts of 1841, 1844, 1849, 1851 and 1852, amongst other things, changed the law of property by allowing public spirited individuals to donate land for the charitable purpose of providing schools without losing permanent title. The incentive to encourage such

individuals was that, should the property ever cease to be used for education, the land should 'revert' to the original owners or their heirs and successors. This was no doubt a very effective strategy at the time, but it caused considerable problems rather more than a century later when such school sites needed to be disposed of and the identity and title of those who arguably had rights of 'reverter' became subject to legal dispute. In response to this, The Reverter of Sites Act 1987 was designed to solve some of these problems by making it possible to set up new charitable trust arrangements which would extinguish the rights of the former owners of the land. Although this did improve the situation, it did not entirely resolve it. The approach now is to recognise that certain parties have an interest, establish a mechanism for promoting agreement and identify a tribunal to arbitrate between them, if necessary. Only time (and possibly a considerable time) will tell whether this is a better solution to this 21st-century version of a 19th-century problem.

It also remains to be seen whether the Office of the Schools Adjudicator will prove a better arbitrator than the Secretary of State. Some observers have noted that recent land disputes have languished within Sanctuary Buildings for two years or more; whilst the Office of the Schools Adjudicator has set a target of six weeks for the resolution of cases. Time (and in this case quite a short time) will tell whether the OSA is able to rise to this new challenge.

Section 37: Staff at foundation or voluntary schools with religious character

This section amends SSFA1998 to make a minor adjustment to the powers of governors of faith schools. Voluntary controlled and foundation schools with a religious character can designate up to one-fifth of the teaching staff as 'reserved teachers', who are defined as people who can satisfy the foundation governors that they are fit and competent to provide religious education in accordance with the school's trust deed, or with the tenets of the school's specified religion or religious denomination. Hitherto, the headteacher of such a school could not be designated as a reserved teacher. The position now (by virtue of omitting subsection (4) of s.58 of SSFA 1998) is that the headteacher can, but is not required to be, designated by the governors as a reserved teacher.

Subsection (2) amends s.60 of SSFA 1998 in two ways. The amendment to subsection (4) is consequential on the change to the position of the appointment of headteachers and makes it clear that the ability of foundation and voluntary schools to have regard

to a potential headteacher's ability and fitness to 'preserve and develop a religious character of the school' remains in place if they choose not to make that post one which must be filled by 'a reserved teacher'.

The second change, which amends subsection (6) by inserting the words 'in Wales' has the effect, in England, of allowing all faith schools to refuse to employ someone as a member of the non-teaching staff 'by reason of his religious opinions, or of his attending or omitting to attend religious worship'. Their ability to do this is arguably tempered by *The Employment Equality (Religion or Belief) Regulations 2003* (S.I. 2003/1660) which prevent employers discriminating on religious grounds, unless there is 'a genuine occupational requirement' to do so.

These changes were introduced as government amendments at the House of Lords report stage following the issue being raised on behalf of the Church of England in committee. Lord Adonis explained that the Government agreed with the Church that:

> *it should not be necessary for a voluntary controlled school or a foundation school to convert to voluntary aided status simply to ensure that its headteacher is appointed with a view to promoting the ethos of the school.*

He also said that the second change was:

> *to reflect the changes brought about by workforce reform, particularly the much wider use of support staff in schools. It would be perverse, if faith schools were discouraged from appointing classroom assistants, rather than fully qualified teachers, for example, simply because they cannot extend the existing power in respect of a faith commitment for that particular post.*
> House of Lords Hansard 17 October 2006 col 737

When the amendment was considered by the Commons (House of Commons Hansard 2 November 2006 cols 510–532) objections were raised by both Liberal Democrat and backbench Labour MPs against the loss of employment rights and extension of religious discrimination within institutions which are wholly publicly funded. The amendment was agreed after a division (325–28), but the Minister, Jim Knight, confirmed that transitional arrangements would protect existing staff (cols 513 and 517).

General duties of governing body s.38

Section 38: General duties of governing body of maintained school

EA 2002 is amended to impose a new general duty on governing bodies to respond to the Every Child Matters agenda. Previously, s.21 required schools to promote 'high standards of educational achievement' and s.27 provided an additional power to provide charitable facilities for the benefit of school pupils, their families and other members of the local community.

Governors are now additionally required to conduct the school with regard to four new duties to:

- promote the well-being of pupils at the school, where well-being is defined as the 'five outcomes' (physical and mental health; protection from harm; enjoying and achieving; contribution to society and economic well-being)

- promote community cohesion

- have regard to any relevant Children and Young People's Plan (or an equivalent document, where an authority is not required to have a statutory CYPP)

- have regard to any views expressed by parents of registered pupils.

The first three of these duties also apply to maintained schools in Wales, but not the fourth. It is unclear why Welsh parents are not so favoured, although, as with much of this Act, the Welsh Assembly has sufficient powers to replicate aspects of the law in England for itself. In England, it could be seen as allowing schools a 'get out clause' if they can argue that parents do not agree with the school participating in particular activities or requirements that may be contained in the Children and Young People's Plan.

These changes go some way to address criticisms levelled during debate on the Children Act 2004, which imposed specific duties on all other public sector agencies which had dealings with children, but did not similarly constrain schools. This requirement now gives local authorities additional leverage in requiring the cooperation of schools in the implementation of the Every Child Matters agenda. The change in the Government's position was acknowledged by the Secretary of State, Alan Johnson, during Commons' considerations of Lords' amendments. He also

took the opportunity to confirm that these requirements would be imposed on academies, by virtue of their funding agreements even though they are not explicitly mentioned in the legislation (House of Commons Hansard 2 November 2006 at col 480).

The addition of a general duty to 'promote community cohesion' (see page 56) can be understood as the final outcome of a lively debate in the House of Lords over the possible imposition of an admission quota of 'non-believers' for new faith schools. This idea was first floated by the Government only to be dropped and then picked up by Lord Baker. That debate also led to a supplementary consultation on changes to the Admissions Code giving foundations the ability to restrict governors' powers to introduce a specific quota for those who do not share the same faith.

See also s.154 (below) on the inspection by Ofsted of the performance of schools in promoting community cohesion. The Home Office produced *Community Cohesion Education Standards for Schools* in 2004. A copy can be obtained from www.standards.dfes.gov.uk/pdf/commcohesion.pdf.

Placing these more explicit duties on the face of legislation, is also part of the justification for the removal of the Code of Practice on LEA/School Relations (see s.58 below). It is expected that s.38 will come into force in April 2007.

School admissions ss.39–53

This large group of sections is at the heart of measures to make the public education system fairer and more accessible to disadvantaged groups. Unlike some other measures, which apply only to trust schools, the rules on admissions apply equally to all admission authorities, be they the governors of voluntary aided or foundation schools (both of long-standing and of recent creation) or local education authorities. The most significant change is upgrading the status of the 'Code of Practice' on Admissions, to which admissions authorities were required to 'have regard', to a 'Code' (the loss of the reference to 'practice' is intended to be significant) with which admission authorities 'must act in accordance with'. In doing so, the Government has responded to recommendations of the Education and Skills Select Committee, which had called for the Code to be strengthened in more than one report in recent years. The strengthening of the Code can also be understood as a necessary price paid by the Government to secure the support of backbench MPs, who felt that the creation of trust schools was moving public sector education in the wrong direction.

A number of sections place particular issues of importance (e.g. the clear proscription on interviewing applicants for admission to maintained schools) on the face of the Act, partly to make it more difficult for a later government to weaken the effect of the Code and also explicitly to close loopholes opened up following judicial review of adjudicator decisions under the previous Code.

Academies are alluded to in the policy documents, but rarely mentioned on the face of legislation. It is clear, however, from ministerial statements and the Code itself, that the government requires academies to operate according to the same rules as all other publicly funded schools. Paragraph 7 of the introduction to the Code includes academies in the list of admission authorities to which it applies. A footnote reads:

Academies are independent, mixed ability schools, established with sponsors under s.482 of the Education Act 1996 (as substituted by s.65 of the Education Act 2002). The funding agreement between an academy's company and the Secretary of State requires the academy's admissions policy and arrangements to be consistent with admissions law and the school admissions code.

This makes it clear that academies are controlled by contractual arrangement rather than through the direct application of legislation, thus explaining why they are not directly mentioned. The mechanism for registering an objection to an academy's admissions policy, or seeking to place a pupil by direction, is by application to the Secretary of State rather than to the Schools Adjudicator.

The same is not true of City Technology Colleges (set up under the Education Reform Act 1988) which are not bound to comply with the Code and other arrangements, either directly or by contract. Many of the CTCs that were originally created have subsequently changed their status to become academies and so only a small number remain outside the mainstream. These are encouraged to comply voluntarily, but there is no mechanism through which they can be compelled.

Most of the sections in this group apply to both England and Wales, except for ss.42, 46, 48 and 50 which apply to England only and s.52, which applies exclusively to Wales. Generally, the code and the new law on admissions came into effect on 28 February 2007.

Section 39: General restriction on selection by ability

This section, which applies to both England and Wales, partly re-enacts and amends s.99 of SSFA 1998. Apart from changing the reference to 'maintained' schools in subsection 1 of s.99 of SSFA 1998, to become a reference to 'community, foundation or voluntary' schools in s.39, there are no material differences beyond those necessary to cross-reference the two sections that now coexist, saying essentially the same thing. The position therefore remains the same that the power to select by reference to ability is restricted to grammar schools and those schools that are explicitly allowed in legislation to select part of their intake by this means. The second category (s.99(2) SSFA 1998) exempts three kinds of selection:

- schools that select part of their intake by general ability, sometimes known as 'bilateral schools'

- selection necessary to implement banding arrangements

- allowing comprehensive schools to require a minimum performance at GCSE for admission to the sixth form.

Selection by reference to 'aptitude' for a designated subject is not regarded as selection by 'ability' and is covered by s.99(3) of SSFA 1998. Whether it is possible to maintain a clear distinction between aptitude and ability remains controversial; but for the purposes of the legislation it is deemed to exist. It can perhaps be illustrated by the example of Darren Gough. A man with proven *ability* as a cricketer was judged by the producers of the Strictly Come Dancing TV programme to have an *aptitude* to excel on the ballroom floor.

The decision to make these small changes by re-enactment of the whole of subsection (1) rather than consequential amendments reflects the importance of this element of policy.

Section 40: Code for school admissions

This section upgrades the previous Code of Practice for School Admissions and operates by amending ss.84, 85 and 85A of SSFA 1998. The key amendment to s.84 changes the wording from: 'a code of practice containing such practical guidance' to which admission authorities must 'have regard'; to 'a code for school admissions containing such provision' that admission authorities must 'act in accordance with'.

All references to 'code of practice' are changed to the simpler form 'code' to underline its new status.

Section 84 is also amended to include a specific reference to the 'Admission Forum' as a body which is bound by the Code alongside local education authorities, governing bodies of maintained schools, appeal panels and adjudicators who were referred to in 1988. Admission Forums were originally non-statutory bodies, intended merely as a convenient way of different admissions authorities fulfilling their duties of mutual consultation. EA 2002, by inserting a new section (85A), required LEAs to set up a forum with a defined structure and gave it a formal advisory function. E&IA 2006 and the new Code now invest the admissions forum with executive functions.

Subsection (9) retrospectively legitimises the consultation on the new Code, which was initiated in September 2006 before the Bill became this Act, so that it could apply to admissions in 2008. Consultation was undertaken in parallel with a revised version of the School Admission Appeals Code (which was not substantially altered) and 10 sets of draft regulations concerned with various aspects of admissions, appeals and adjudication. The new Code was laid before Parliament on 8 January 2007. *The School Admissions Code (Appointed Day) (England) Order 2005* (SI 2007/566) appointed 28 February 2007 for the day on which the Code came into force.

Overview of the Code

The Code runs to over 100 pages and, unlike Acts and regulations, is written in plain language. It is therefore unnecessary to paraphrase it here as it is accessible in the original. Its overall structure and some innovations are summarised below.

Typographical style is used to signal the status of different statements. Some elements of the Code will effectively be compulsory either by virtue of specific statutory requirements (helpfully referenced in footnotes) or because they are requirements imposed by the Code itself. These are flagged up with the words 'must' or 'must not' printed in bold red ink. Those aspects of the Code that retain a more advisory flavour are signalled with the words 'should' or 'should not' printed in bold blue ink.

There is a foreword by Alan Johnson, the Secretary of State and a short introduction sets out the legislative basis of the Code, to whom it applies and how it is to be monitored and enforced.

The first chapter, 'The Law: Equity and Fair Access in School Admission Arrangements', sets out the overall policy on admissions and the intentions of the Code.

The second chapter, 'Setting Fair Oversubscription Criteria', promotes admission arrangements that are fair to all children and families, whatever their background or circumstances and proscribes unfair oversubscription criteria. It is for admission authorities and Admission Forums, acting in accordance with the provisions and guidelines in the Code, to decide which criteria they will use and in what circumstances. Admission Forums should encourage all schools in their area to have arrangements that extend choice to parents whatever their social group. The scope of permissible criteria is considerably narrowed.

The third chapter, 'Admission Arrangements In-year and Outside the Normal Admissions Round and Fair Access Protocols', as the title indicates, covers a range of exceptional circumstances. Special consideration must be given to children who change school mid year or at times other than the normal age of transfer for whatever reasons – as a result of parents' employment, or because children themselves are vulnerable.

The fourth chapter, 'Ensuring a Fair Admission System' says local authorities and Admission Forums should object to the Adjudicator where admission authorities do not abide by the Code or disregard the advice of the Admission Forum.

The Code stresses the importance of admission arrangements that are clear and easily understood by parents, who now have an individual right to make an objection to the Adjudicator over partial selection, practices or criteria that they believe are unlawful or prohibited by the Code, or over an admission number lower than that indicated by the 'net capacity formula'. This has been secured by regulation 9 of *The School Admissions (Alteration and Variation of, and Objections to, Arrangements) (England) Regulations 2007* (SI 2007/496). *The Education (Determination of Admission Arrangements) (Amendment) (England) Regulations 2007* (SI 2007/497) require local authorities to publish annually in a newspaper circulating in the area, information about admission arrangements for all schools and inform parents that they may object to admission arrangements in certain circumstances.

The Code includes six appendices on:

1. other relevant legislation

2. Admission Forums

---

3. statutory requirements of coordinated admission schemes and model timetable for admission cycle

4. consultation and publication

5. choice advice – guidelines for local authorities

6. guidelines for boarding schools and a glossary.

Section 41: The role of Admission Forums

Forums are given enhanced powers and executive functions including:

- the ability to prepare and publish reports about the admission of pupils to maintained schools in the area (s.41(3))

- the power to demand information from the governing body of any school in the area, the local education authority for their own area and any adjacent authorities, in order to facilitate the production of such reports (s. 41(3))

- becoming an 'appropriate body' that must be consulted by all admission authorities in the area (s.41 (7))

- the power to make representations and refer objections to the Adjudicator, or to the Secretary of State (s.41(8))

- local authorities must defray the Admissions Forum's expenses (s.41(6)).

These changes are achieved by amendment to relevant sections of SSFA 1998 (s.85A, which was added by EA 2002, s.89 and s.90). Regulations can define and circumscribe them in more detail, including modifying them, where local authorities exercise their option to set up a joint Admission Forum.

There are changes to the constitution of Forums. *The Education (Admission Forums) (England) (Amendment) Regulations 2007* (SI 2007/192) indicate that the headteacher, or a governor, of every school will have a right to join their forum. They are identified as 'schools members' as distinct from the 'core' membership and the Code says it will 'not be necessary for them to actively take part in all the work of the forum and attend all its meetings'. The Code and regulations are, however, silent on the practical consequences of differing levels of participation of the two categories of member and issues arising from the fact that, in larger authorities, there may be up to 30 'core' members, but several hundred 'school' members.

The regulations do, however, make it clear that a simple majority of those present at a meeting will be sufficient for the Forum to exercise its power to refer an objection to the Adjudicator. They also list the issues that may be covered by the Forum's 'Report':

- the extent to which preferences are met

- numbers of appeals

- the social and ethnic mix of pupils attending schools

- the working of hard to place pupil protocols and infant class size limitation

- anything that might affect the admissions process and the extent to which it operates fairly and promotes parental choice and access to education.

Publication of such reports is the main vehicle by which Admission Forums can discharge their duty to monitor compliance with the Code and the overall impact of an area's admission arrangements on fair access.

Section 42: Support for parental preferences

This is the legislative expression of the White Paper commitment to establish a network of 'choice advisers' to assist parents, particularly those from disadvantaged sections of the community, to identify and secure places for their children at 'good' schools.

A new subsection, s.86(1A), requiring LEAs in England to 'provide advice and assistance to parents of children in their area in connection with the preferences expressed, or to be expressed, by them' is inserted in s.86 of SSFA 1998 (the LEA duty to allow parents to 'express a preference for a school ... with reasons', loosely termed the right of 'parental choice').

The Explanatory Notes suggest that this advice and assistance might include providing parents with good, easy to understand information about schools in the area and neighbouring areas and whether schools have any special features which may be of interest to parents. They also suggest that authorities should explain how admission arrangements work, the level of priority children might have for a particular school and their possible entitlement to free transport.

Separate non-statutory guidance has been produced on the subject and appendix 5 of the draft Code elaborated further. Although this is not explored in the legislation,

authorities will wish to consider how this new duty relates to the Connexions service, the provision of independent advocacy for parents of children with SEN and LEAs' new and more general duty to act as advocates for parents.

Section 43: Duty of governing body to implement decisions relating to admissions

This section is about helping LEAs to secure the admission of hard to place pupils. Schools sometimes appear to believe they can resist accepting a pupil which the LEA, in its role as admissions authority, has decided to admit. It amends s.88 of SSFA 1998 to make it clear that the governing body of a community or voluntary controlled school must implement any decision taken by the admissions authority, except in a limited number of circumstances, e.g. where there is a right of appeal against a decision to admit twice excluded pupils under previous legislation.

The LEA normally acts as the admissions authority for community and voluntary controlled schools, but it can delegate some of its admissions functions to school governors. Governors are always the admissions authority for foundation and voluntary aided schools, but there are some circumstances in which the local authority can direct admission and the ability to do so in respect of looked after children is featured elsewhere in this Act (see ss.48–52 below).

Subsection (3) amends s.89C of SSFA 1998 to make it clear that the governing body of any maintained school (whether it is its own admissions authority or otherwise), must comply with the LEA's determination that a child should be admitted in its role as the administrator of the area's coordinated admissions scheme.

Section 44: Prohibition on interviews

This outlaws interviewing either parents or pupils for the purposes of influencing a decision on admission to school. A new section (s.88A) is added to SSFA 1998 putting the Government's opposition to interviewing unambiguously on the face of the Act.

SSFA 1998, s.88A: Prohibition on interviews

Boarding schools are permitted to interview pupils in order to assess a child's suitability for a boarding place. But such interviews should only take place after an initial decision has been made that the individual can be offered a place at the school.

Schools which are allowed to use a permitted form of selection by aptitude can undertake auditions or other oral practical tests, solely in order to ascertain an applicant's aptitude relevant to a permitted form of selection, without this being construed as an unlawful form of interview.

The new Admissions Code sets out these matters in more detail and, now it has virtually the force of regulations, it could be questioned as to why this needs to appear on the face of the Act. It is likely that this follows from a judicial review case brought by the London Oratory School which overturned the Adjudicator's decision to uphold an objection against its interviewing practice in 2005 *The Queen on the application of 1) The Governing Body of The London Oratory 2) Richard John Adams 3) Harvey Kaye Goodliffe 4) Peter Charles John Lindsay – and – The Schools Adjudicator – 17 December 2004* and by the Secretary of State's decision not to accept the advice of the Adjudicator to rule it out following a subsequent objection in 2006 (Adjudication reference ADA/000773 downloadable form, www.schoolsadjudicator.gov.uk).

Section 45: Admission arrangements for schools with religious character: consultation and objections

Any foundation or voluntary school with a religious character must seek views on its draft admissions policy from the local representative body for the religion or religious denomination that corresponds to the school's faith designation. This is effected by adding to s.89(2) of SSFA 1998.

Prior to this Act being passed, all voluntary aided Church of England schools were legally required to consult the Church of England diocese for the area in which they are located before proceeding to wider consultation with other bodies. Because the Church of England is the established Church this duty exists by virtue of church legislation (Diocesan Boards of Education Measure 1991, s.3.1 (cc) as amended by EA 2002). However, no similar requirement was imposed by law on other kinds of faith school. In practice many Roman Catholic schools take heed of the advice offered by their own diocese although certain RC schools set up by religious orders have pointedly refused to regard the local diocese as having any jurisdiction over them.

The effect of this section is to place a similar obligation on all faith schools to consult local religious authorities, although not the duty of prior consultation still enjoyed by the Church of England. This would seem to be sensible, particularly

bearing in mind the increasing number of faith schools sponsored by different faiths groups. There is provision to define the bodies to be consulted in regulations, but the consultation draft simply offered a framework for defining particular bodies in relation to particular kinds of school without providing any detail.

Section 46: Restrictions on alteration of admission arrangements

This implements the White Paper commitments to prevent new and expanded schools from amending their admission arrangements for three years from the date on which they open; and to prevent admission authorities which have had an objection against their admission arrangements upheld by the Schools Adjudicator or Secretary of State from amending that aspect of their admission arrangements for three years. It operates by amending s.89 of SSFA 1998, adding two new sections (89D and 90A) and creating regulation making powers. It applies only to England.

SSFA 1998, s.89D: Power to restrict alteration of admission arrangements following establishment or expansion

The admission arrangements of a new or expanded school are frozen for a period of time after it is established or expansion takes effect. Regulation 4 of *The School Admissions (Alteration and Variation of, and Objections to, Arrangements) (England) Regulations 2007* (SI 2007/496), indicates that the freeze is intended to last for two school years after the first year (i.e. three years in total) from the start date defined in the Act. Whilst a freeze is in force the admission arrangements are deemed to have been determined by the governing body for each relevant year; although the governing body is allowed to apply to the Adjudicator for permission to modify the admission arrangements at an earlier date. The regulations indicate that the Adjudicator must be satisfied that there has been a 'major change of circumstances' since the admission arrangements were determined before agreeing a change.

SSFA 1998, s.90A: Restriction on alteration of admission arrangements following Adjudicator's decision

The Adjudicator, or the Secretary of State, can now fix a school's admission arrangements for more than one year following the determination of an objection.

Under previous arrangements, decisions following an objection were only binding for the year in question and an admission authority could revert to its previous arrangements for the following admissions round. Although a further objection could be made, with some expectation of the same result, the process of objection is more arduous than the procedure for determining arrangements in the first place. This meant that a determined admissions authority might eventually win a war of attrition against an objector.

The formulation of this section is made more complex because it interacts with changes to the scope of Adjudicators' action in respect of an objection (see s.47 below) and, like the previous section, the actual period of years by which a decision can be extended is made subject to regulations. The regulations provide for the Secretary of State and Adjudicators to enforce a decision for up to three years.

However, unlike the previous section, this does not freeze the admission arrangements as a whole, but merely 'protects' the changes made by the Adjudicator or the Secretary of State. An admissions authority is therefore free to change other aspects of their policy during the three-year period. But, as before, an admissions authority may apply to the Adjudicator to be allowed to vary protected aspects of the arrangements during the period of restriction if there is a 'major change of circumstances'.

Section 47: Objections to admission arrangements

This introduces some major extensions to the powers the Schools Adjudicator. The changes are effected by amending s.90 of SSFA 1998. The provision applies to both England and Wales, where the adjudication function is undertaken by the National Assembly in accordance with the *Transfer of Functions Order* (SI 1999/672). In respect of Wales therefore, references to 'the Adjudicator or the Secretary of State' need to be read as 'the National Assembly'.

Adjudicators have greater scope to change admissions policies referred to them. Under previous arrangements it was generally accepted that an adjudicator could only change the particular aspect of a school's admissions policy which was identified as problematic by an objector. In the past adjudicators frequently identified unsatisfactory aspects of admissions policies, notably with reference to looked after children, which had not been alluded to in the objection; but could do little more than draw attention to them in the hope that either the admissions authority would deal with the problem, or another objection would emerge during the next round.

Subsections (2) and (3) delete the existing SSFA s.90(6) and s.90(7) and insert three new subsections s.90(5A), s.90(5B) and s.90(5C). The new subsection (5A) gives the Adjudicator power to 'consider whether it would be appropriate for changes to be made to any aspect of the admission arrangements, whether or not he would be required to do so for the purposes of determining the objection'.

New subsections (5B) and (5C) require the Adjudicator to:

- decide whether it would be appropriate to make changes to the admission arrangements
- specify exactly what they should be
- publish a 'report' (which replaces the term 'decision') setting out separately:
  - his decision on the objection
  - any further decisions about the arrangements not related directly to the objection
  - the length of time (up to the maximum prescribed in regulations) that any or all of those changes should be 'protected' (see previous section).

It is now made explicit, by s. 47(5), that adjudicators can require an admissions authority to provide information in order to assist them in carrying out their duties under this section. The absence of this power did not previously act as a serious inhibition to the functions of the Adjudicator; as objectors have a vested interest in providing information and an admissions authority which refuses to cooperate self-evidently runs the risk of suffering an adverse decision.

Subsection (6) gives the Adjudicator full jurisdiction over objections to the admissions arrangements of faith schools. SSFA s.90(10), which is now omitted, previously required the Adjudicator, via regulations, to refer cases to the Secretary of State where they were 'concerned with admissions criteria relating to a person's religion or religious denomination'. This provision has proved practically difficult to operate because it has been hard to distinguish, where faith schools are concerned, which aspects of their admissions policy relate to the individual's religion and which do not; and how a single objection which contains elements of both should be handled. The result has been some disputed cases where schools have complained that a decision by the Adjudicator should, or should not, have been referred to the Secretary of State and others where separate determinations have been issued in parallel

by the Adjudicator and by the Secretary of State to deal with different aspects of the same objection.

The effect of this change is that, in future, all objections to the admissions arrangements of maintained schools will be dealt with by the Adjudicator. References throughout the section to both the Adjudicator and the Secretary of State now arise because there remains (in s.90(3) of SSFA 1998) the power to make regulations prescribing cases which the Adjudicator must refer to the Secretary of State. However, the Explanatory Notes indicate that the DfES has no current intention to make any such regulations. The Secretary of State still has jurisdiction over any complaints relating to academies but, as previously indicated, this power is exercised via the contractual arrangement of the 'funding agreement' and is therefore not prescribed on the face of the Act.

Section 48: Looked after children to whom s.87(2) of SSFA 1998 applies

This is the first of a group of sections dealing with the enhanced powers of local authorities, backed up by the Adjudicator, to secure appropriate schooling for looked after children.

Section 87(2) of SSFA 1998 removes parents' right of appeal against refusal to admit a pupil who has been excluded twice. But S.95(2) of SSFA gives the governing body of a community or VC school a right of appeal against an LEA's decision that such an individual *should* be admitted to their school. That section is now amended (by s.48(1)) so that it does not apply to looked after children because they are covered by the new section.

SSFA 1998, s.95A: References relating to looked after children to whom s.87 (2) applies

Normally where the admissions authority for a community or VC school (usually the LEA) decides to admit a child who has previously been excluded twice or more times the governing body has a right of appeal to an independent appeal committee. Where, however, that child is looked after, the right of appeal is now to the Adjudicator. The Adjudicator can uphold the appeal, only if admission would 'seriously prejudice the provision of efficient education or the efficient use of

resources', a more stringent requirement than the normal 'prejudice' test applied by appeal committees.

If adjudicators decide to uphold the appeal, they nevertheless have a power to direct that the pupil should be admitted to an alternative school, provided that:

- the child has not previously been excluded from that school

- the governors have been consulted

- the Adjudicator is satisfied that serious prejudice would not arise from that admission

- the local authority, who look after the child, agree to the placement.

Regulations can be made with more detailed provisions on consultation and the provision of information. *The School Admissions (Adjudicator Determinations Relating to Looked After and Certain Other Children) (England) Regulations 2007* (SI 2007/105), came into force on 27 February 2007.

Section 49: Procedure for giving directions under s.96 of SSFA 1998

Section 96 of SSFA 1998 is the power of a local authority (with certain limitations) to direct a school, for which it is not the admissions authority, to admit a particular child. The power of direction is used where a child has been permanently excluded from another school or is otherwise hard to place. The school must be a reasonable distance from the child's home and be capable of providing suitable education. The power cannot be used to require re-admission to a school from which the child has been permanently excluded, or if it would cause the school to exceed class size limits in key stage one.

Amendments to s.97 of SSFA 1998 set out the new procedure to be followed. Previously a governing body that did not wish to accept the LEA's direction could appeal to the Secretary of State. In future, such appeals will be heard in England by the Adjudicator and in Wales by the National Assembly.

Section 50: Direction to admit looked after child to specified school

This section creates a new explicit power of direction for local authorities to require that schools admit looked after children. The structure parallels the changes made in the previous two sections. They are kept separate, perhaps partly for emphasis but mainly because the power is more open-ended and because more stringent requirements and shorter timescales are specified where directions relate to looked after children.

These powers do not apply directly to academies, but authorities can access a parallel mechanism to the same effect via the Secretary of State.

Subsection (1) introduces two new sections after s.97 of SSFA 1998.

SSFA 1998, s.97A: Direction to admit looked after child to specified school

This creates a power for LEAs to direct any school for which they are not the admission authority (including one outside their own area) to admit a looked after child for whom they are responsible. The only limitation is that the power cannot be used to direct re-admission to a school which has excluded the child, or to forestall exclusion. Provided the proper procedures are followed, the admissions authority for a school in receipt of such a direction must admit the child.

SSFA 1998, s.97B: Procedure for giving directions under s.97A

This new section specifies that, prior to issuing the direction, the authority that wishes to secure admission must give the admissions authority for the school a period of seven days in which to admit the child voluntarily. If the school does not respond positively, the directing authority must serve a notice on the headteacher, the admission authority for the school, the governing body (where it is not the admissions authority) and the LEA where they intend to make that direction outside their own area and the LEA is not the admissions authority for the school.

The admissions authority (and the governors if they are not the admissions authority and the child in question has previously been twice excluded) then has seven days to appeal to the Adjudicator against the direction. If there is no reference to the Adjudicator or a reference is rejected, the local authority can issue the formal direction

under s.97A by notice in writing to the headteacher of the school, after which the pupil must be admitted.

An appeal can only be properly made and upheld if the Adjudicator is satisfied that 'serious prejudice to the provision of efficient education or efficient use of resources' will ensue. This, once again, sets a higher threshold for resisting an admission decision.

As before, if an appeal is upheld the Adjudicator has power to direct admission to an alternative school provided exclusions, similar to those specified for the original local authority direction, do not apply. However, the process is short-circuited as the Adjudicator is required only to 'consult' the alternative school (and its admissions authority where different) and secure the consent of the authority that is responsible for looking after the child. The Adjudicator does not have to go through a formal process of issuing notices and waiting a specified time for responses.

Subsections (2), (3) and (4) make minor consequential amendments to other sections of SSFA 1998.

Section 51: Directions to admit child to specified school: supplementary provisions

Subsection (1) removes the parents' right of appeal against the admissions decision embodied in a direction made under s. 50(1) above. By definition, the local authority making the direction will be acting as the 'corporate parent' of the child in question. It would therefore be perverse if the natural parent could delay the child's swift integration into the chosen school once the direction had been made.

Subsection (2) makes technical amendments to SSFA 1998 consequential on the previous changes to ensure that cross references elsewhere in the Act are correct.

Subsection (3) inserts a further new section.

SSFA 1998, s.97C: Determinations under 97 or 97B: supplemental

This creates the power to make regulations dealing with consultation by, and provision of information to, the Adjudicator in connection with directions. These are *The School Admissions (Adjudicator Determinations Relating to Looked After and Certain Other Children) (England) Regulations 2007I* (SI 2007/105), which came into force on 27 February 2007 and are the same as those relating to s.48 above.

Section 52: Power of Assembly to make regulations about looked after children

This section has the effect of separating out the arrangements relating to looked after children as between England and Wales and, for technical reasons, has to be made more explicit than in other parts of this Act.

Subsection (1) inserts into SSFA 1998 a new section under a new heading *'looked after children in Wales'*.

Section 97D: Power of Assembly to make regulations about admission of looked after children

This gives a power to the Welsh Assembly to make regulations about the admission of looked after children to maintained schools in Wales. The Welsh Assembly is thereby empowered to adopt similar arrangements to those that apply in England, to adopt some and not others, or modify them, or to draft their own regulations covering the same issue.

Subsection (2) effects the separation by specifying that the regulation making power defined in subsection (1A) of s.89 (which was itself inserted by s.106 of EA 2005) applies only to England.

Section 53: Schools with pre-1998 arrangements for selection by ability or aptitude

The Adjudicator can make a permanent reduction to the proportion of children admitted under 'permitted partial selection' arrangements at a school covered by s.100 of SSFA 1998. This allows schools which previously had arrangements for partial selection exceeding the limits imposed by that Act to continue to select to the same extent and on the same basis. Before the passage of E&IA 2006 such arrangements could be challenged by other admission authorities or groups of parents and changed if the Adjudicator agreed. However, such determinations only held good for the year in which they were made and it was established, following a judicial review case (*The Queen on the Application of 1) Watford Grammar School for Girls 2) Watford Grammar School for Boys – and – The Adjudicator of Schools, 8 October 2003 [2004] ELR 40, QBD*), that the admissions authority for the school could revert to its previous arrangements thereafter. However, the schools involved tended to be seri-

ously attached to their arrangements and showed that they were willing to engage in a 'war of attrition' as described under s.46 above and the Government's intention that these anomalous arrangements would be removed over time by objections from parents and others had been frustrated.

The effect of the amendments introduced by this section therefore, is to create a ratchet effect whereby, once the proportion of the intake admitted by selection has been reduced, it cannot thereafter be increased beyond the normal permitted levels.

Section 54: Pupil banding

The scope of arrangements for seeking to ensure that a comprehensive school receives a balanced intake is extended. Historically, a number of LEAs, notably the Inner London Education Authority (ILEA), had admission arrangements which tested all pupils prior to secondary transfer and sought to achieve school allocations which secured a distribution of pupils of different levels of ability between each school reflecting that of the general population. Later, following the abolition of ILEA, local education authorities lost the power to introduce such arrangements, but were allowed to retain them if they were already in place.

However, subsequent legislation allowed a similar approach to be adopted by an individual school. It was felt to be particularly appropriate for CTCs which, whilst seeking to select their intake on the basis of aptitude for the subject, were nevertheless encouraged to recruit pupils with a range of general ability. This power, which persists in s.101 of SSFA 1998, was formulated to refer to

admission arrangements designed to secure that in any year the pupils admitted to the school in any relevant age group are representative of all levels of ability among applicants for admission to the school in that age group.

Any proposal to change admission arrangements to adopt such an approach was deemed to be an alteration which required a statutory proposal rather than one that could be made simply by virtue of the admissions authority determining its arrangements from year to year.

This approach was criticised by the Education Select Committee (House of Commons Education and Skills Select Committee, Secondary Education: School Admissions, Fourth report session 2003–04 Vol. 1, 14 July 2004 HC 58–1) because sharing out places based on only that subsection of the general population who chose

to apply to the school could skew the outcome and would not be representative of the population at large.

The section applies to both England and Wales, but its effect is to put in place new arrangements for England but leave the status quo in Wales. In England individual schools can continue to operate banding arrangements based on their own intake as before, but a new subsection (s.101(1A)) is added, which provides for 'the reference group' by which the bands are determined to be based on one of three further categories. These are:

- all the applicants for a group of schools
- children within the area of a local education authority
- those throughout England.

The decision to introduce a banding approach to admissions ceases to be a statutory proposal in England but continues to apply in Wales. If an English LEA wishes to introduce any such arrangements in schools for which it is the admissions authority, it must secure the consent of the governing bodies of all the schools involved.

The status quo is maintained where a school wishes to band as well as selecting up to 10 per cent on aptitude for a particular subject. Such a school can choose whether or not to leave the 10 per cent so selected outside the arrangements for banding. This exemption does not apply to any other form of selection by ability.

Section 54(3) contains minor amendments consequential on the above.

Two distinct strands of policy arising from the White Paper are evident in this section. First, the ability for a group of schools to work together through a set of common admissions arrangements using banding, clearly relates to facilitating common arrangements by a foundation body which has a relationship with a number of trust schools.

Second, the reintroduction of the possibility of a local authority adopting banding arrangements, which might apply across the whole of their area, can be related to the idea of LEAs now acting as the champion of parents and pursuing policies designed to aid and support disadvantaged groups.

Miscellaneous ss.55–58

Section 55: Right of sixth form pupils to be excused from attendance at religious worship

The amendment which brought about the inclusion of this section in the Act attracted substantial publicity at the time and does exactly what it says in the title. The existing right of parents to withdraw their children from religious education and worship is modified, by amending s.71 of SSFA 1998, so that young people beyond compulsory school age can make their own decision to absent themselves from acts of worship.

An interesting feature is that this right is only exercisable once a pupil is attending the sixth form ('is receiving education suitable to the requirements of pupils over compulsory school age') rather than from their 16th birthday and that the right does not extend to avoiding compulsory religious education. So, sixth formers would still have to rely on their parents if they wished to be excused lessons (although it has to be said that this aspect of the basic curriculum may be more honoured in the breach than the observance).

Subsection (6), inserts a new requirement for the governors of maintained boarding schools to provide opportunities for pupils to participate in religious education or worship in accordance with the tenets of any particular religion. This right, which is exercisable by parents of younger children or directly by sixth formers, allows them to go off site and applies irrespective of the faith or secular status of the school.

Subsection (8) provides for parallel circumstances in special schools to allow sixth formers to make their own 'opt in or out' decisions. Subsection (9) defines 'sixth form pupil'.

Section 56: Charges for music tuition

The current law defining circumstances under which charges may be made for musical tuition is contained in ss. 451 and 456 of EA 1996. These sections provided that no charge may be made for any musical tuition which is required as part of the syllabus for prescribed public examinations or as part of the National Curriculum. However, in other circumstances, a charge could be made for tuition in playing a

musical instrument given either to individuals or groups of not more than four, but no charge could be made for vocal tuition provided during school hours.

Section 56(1) replaces the above arrangements (s.451(3) EA 1996) with a power to make regulations prescribing circumstances in which tuition in singing or playing a musical instrument may attract a charge.

Section 56(2) amends the reference to permitted charges (s.456(6) EA 1996) to include singing alongside teaching a musical instrument.

This clause was added to the Bill in late October as an amendment proposed by Lord Moser in support of the 'Music Manifesto' campaign for extending and improving school music. On Commons' consideration of Lords' amendments the Secretary of State, Alan Johnson, said:

> *We have been told that one of the barriers to meet our pledge for every primary school child to be able to learn an instrument is the current charging regime. The school music community and parents will welcome this more flexible system. Music can improve attainment because children who read music often have better memories. Playing in groups also helps build team-working skills and can be great fun.*

The position now is that musical education necessary to fulfil the National Curriculum and prepare for public examinations must be provided free; but other tuition, including singing, can attract a charge within the constraints set out in regulations.

Section 57: School funding and Schedule 5

This section applies Schedule 5, which contains a series of amendments to previous legislation relating to the financing of maintained schools. These amendments are individually relatively minor, but are quite complex, as the law has been changed twice since 1998. The changes of substance are set out below.

Obligations concerning School Forums are simplified and localised by para.2. The current power of the Secretary of State (or Welsh Assembly) to set out the constitution and function of School Forums in regulations is replaced by a more general requirement for School Forums to exercise any function imposed on them by legislation. The Secretary of State (and Welsh Assembly) loses the power to remove a non-schools member of a School Forum.

The current duty of LEAs to establish a scheme for financing maintained schools (found in s.48 and Schedule 14 of SSFA 1998) is amended by paragraphs 3 and 5 to 'maintain' the schemes they now all have. A new regulation making power for the approval and revision of such schemes includes some delegation to School Forums themselves to approve revisions. The Secretary of State or National Assembly for Wales will no longer have the power to impose a scheme on a local education authority.

Paragraph 4 shifts the requirements for providing a delegated budget to a new school, from the face of SSFA 998 (s.49 (2) and (3)) to a regulation making power. The increased flexibility this provides is no doubt felt to be necessary in the light of the more complex process of bringing a new school into being through competitions. The first use of this is in the *School Finance (Amendment) (England) Regulations 2007* (SI 2007/365).

Paragraph 6, by deleting the relevant paragraphs from Schedule 15 to SSFA 1998, removes the right of a governing body to appeal to the Secretary of State (or the Welsh Assembly) against a decision by the LEA to withdraw its delegated budget responsibility. This is consistent with the realignment of the interrelationship between central government, local authorities and individual schools, which seeks to give a more decisive strategic role for local authorities and less central interference on individual cases.

Section 58: Removal of requirements to issue code of practice as to relationships between LEAs and maintained schools in England, etc

This section does exactly what it says in the title. SSFA 1998 is amended so that the relevant section (s.127) applies only in Wales. The existing code of practice is therefore withdrawn. The rationale for this, as set out in the White Paper, is identified by the general title of 'the New Relationship with Schools'. A number of measures, including the introduction of the Every Child Matters agenda, school improvement partners and the 'single conversation with schools', set out the respective roles and responsibilities of local authorities and schools with sufficient clarity as to make a separate code of practice redundant. Abolishing it therefore removes legislative clutter and will help to reduce the impact of unnecessary bureaucracy on schools and authorities. This section came into force on 8 January 2007.

Part 4: Schools causing concern: England

This part of the Act builds on previous legislation in SSFA 1998 and EA 2002 to both enhance and clarify LEAs' duties, powers and responsibilities to intervene in schools causing concern. It continues to reflect the earlier principle that LEAs should support schools in 'inverse proportion to success', but reflects the *New Relationship with Schools* (NRwS) characterised by the introduction of School Improvement Partners (SIPs), the importance of robust school self-evaluation and the new Ofsted inspection system, which seeks to provide more timely and focused information on schools' capacity to improve. Crucially, it gives LEAs new tools to enable earlier and more decisive action and support to be brought to bear to address school underperformance as well as outright failure – consistent with the emphasis in the White Paper on the LEA's strategic role as commissioner of support services to schools, rather than necessarily direct service provider.

Taken together, these changes supersede the Code of Practice on LEA School Relations introduced under s.127 of the SSFA 1998, so the Secretary of State's duty to issue it is repealed (see s.58 above) in England, although it will continue to apply in Wales under the control of the Assembly. The Act also builds on earlier initiatives and provisions in EA 2002 to encourage greater collaboration between schools. LEAs have new powers to broker collaborative arrangements to secure more sustainable, effective and cost efficient support to weak schools by partnering with strong schools through formal collaboration and federation and with third party external consultants. Draft guidance emphasises the need for authorities to be 'vigilant and proactive' and to tailor interventions to the needs of a school and its pupils. For the first time, LEAs must involve parents in preparing the statement of action for schools that require special measures or significant improvement. This may extend to the appointment by the LEA of a specified person, a Parent Champion, to facilitate communication with parents in anticipation of, or following, an adverse Ofsted inspection report. The Parent Champion will also be expected to articulate the views and interests of parents in order to influence decisions about the future of the school.

In keeping with most of the rest of E&IA 2006 all the sections in this Part apply only to England. The status quo remains in Wales until such time as the Assembly exercises its powers to make separate changes.

The DfES published a consultation document on the statutory guidance on schools causing concern on 4 January 2007. The provisions in Part 4 of the Act came into force on 1 April 2007.

Introduction

Section 59: Meaning of eligible for intervention

Subsection (2) provides a definition for the new expression 'eligible for intervention', which is used as an umbrella term in the Act to denote schools subject to the spectrum of intervention powers set out in ss.60–62. Table 4 shows, in summary form, the process for issuing warning notices.

Schools that are eligible for intervention ss.60–62

Section 60: Warning notice by local education authority

Earlier provisions set out in s.15 of SSFA1998 concerning formal warning notices to schools by LEAs are amended. A school becomes eligible for intervention if the governing body has received a formal warning and has failed to comply with it to the LEA's satisfaction.

The LEA must have provided reasonable written notice to the governing body that intervention is being contemplated and, when a notice is issued, must inform them of their right to appeal to Ofsted within the 'initial period' of 15 working days. The school can avoid intervention if HMCI decides not to confirm the warning notice following representations from the governing body. The governing body has a further period of 15 working days 'the compliance period' to respond appropriately to the warning notice starting immediately after the 'initial period' or when HMCI confirms the notice if an appeal has been made.

An LEA may issue a warning notice when:

- standards of pupil performance are unacceptably low (s 60(3) (a))
- there is a serious breakdown in management or governance such as to put standards at risk (s 60(2) (6))
- the safety of pupils or staff is threatened. (s 60(2) (a), (b) & (c))

Table 4   Flow chart showing process of issuing warning notice leading to compliance or intervention

Local Authority Action	Governing Body Action	HMCI Action
Issue warning to Governing Body setting out: – Evidence for decision – Action required by Governing Body – Period of notice (15 working days) – Action Local Authority is minded to take (ss.63–66) – Governing Body right to make representation to HMCI To be sent to: – Governing Body – HMCI – Headteacher – Diocesan authority – Person who appoints foundation governors		
No further action ◄	Governing Body complies within 15 days	
	or	
	Governing Body makes representation to HMCI (copy to Local Authority within 15 days) ──►	Ofsted decides to confirm notice (copy to Local Authority)
No further action ◄	Governing Body complies within 15 days of HMCI letter ◄	
	or	
	Governing Body does not comply within 15 days of HMCI letter ──►	HMCI Action (ss.67–69)
	or	*or*
Local Authority Intervention ◄ (ss.63–66)	Governing Body does not comply with Local Authority warning within 15 days	
	Governing Body prepares ◄ for inspection	Ofsted to visit school (copy to Local Authority)
		or
No further action ◄		HMCI disagrees with warning notice (copy to Local Authority)

An innovation of E&IA 2006, in subsection (3), expands the definition of 'low standards' to include underperformance in relation to pupils' expected achievement or the school's general context, as well as those at which absolute standards (attainment rates) are generally low. This new approach partly reflects the recommendations of the Education and Skills Select Committee that ministers and educationalists should distinguish clearly between low performance and underperformance. (7th Report, paras. 50–52, December 2003 http://www.publications.parliament.uk/pa/cm200203/cmselect/cmeduski/513/51306.htm).

A warning notice must specify:

- which of the s.60(2) grounds for intervention is being invoked
- the action the governing body is expected to take 60(4) (b)
- the 'initial period' during which they can appeal 60(4) (c)
- action that might be taken under ss.63–66, if the governing body fails to comply 60(4) (d).

As well as being issued to the governing body, copies of the formal warning notice must be given to:

- HMCI
- the headteacher
- the appropriate diocesan authority of a Church of England or Roman Catholic school or any foundation that appoints school governors.

A governing body that decides to appeal to HMCI must copy their representations to the LEA. HMCI must consider and may confirm or reject the representations on the basis of the written information submitted. If that written evidence is inconclusive, Ofsted may visit the school using general powers to determine whether the warning notice has been issued correctly under the criteria set out in guidance. HMCI must then give written notice to the governing body of her decision whether or not the warning notice is justified. This notice should also be copied to the LEA and other individuals specified by the Secretary of State in guidance issued under s.72.

Section 61: Schools requiring significant improvement

A school that is given a notice by Ofsted under subsection (3)(a) of s.13 of EA 2005 that the school requires significant improvement (as defined by s.44 of that Act) is

Table 5 Intervention available to LEAs and the Secretary of State

	Section 60 Warning Notice	Section 61 Significant Improvement	Section 62 Special Measures
Intervention by Local Authority			
Section 63 Require Governing Body to enter into arrangement to: – Obtain services of an advisory nature from specified body; or – Collaborate with another school (S26 EA 2002); or – Collaborate with an FE college (S166 E&IA 2006); or – Federate with existing federation or create new federation (S24(2) EA 2002).	✔ Within 2 months following end of compliance period	✔ Must consult	✔ Must consult
Section 64 Appoint additional governors (any number)	✔ Within 2 months following end of compliance period (voluntary aided schools may also appoint equal number of additional foundation governors)	✔	✔
Section 65 Governing Body to be re-placed by Interim Executive Board (consent of Secretary of State required)	✔	✔ Must consult	✔ Must consult
Section 66 Suspend right to delegated budget	Within 2 months following end of compliance period	✔	✔
Intervention by Secretary of State			
Section 67 Appoint additional governors (any number) Nominate Chair/Pay Chair		✔ Must consult	✔ Must consult
Section 68 Direct closure			✔ Must consult
Section 69 Governing Body to be replaced by Interim Executive Board		✔ Must consult	✔ Must consult

Education and Inspections Act 2006: the essential guide

automatically 'eligible for intervention'. It remains subject to intervention unless or until the original judgment is superseded by a report that the school no longer requires significant improvement. This section does not apply if an additional notice has been given to the Secretary of State that the school requires special measures; but only because the following section applies.

Section 62: Schools requiring special measures

Section 62 covers schools requiring special measures following an inspection when Ofsted has given a notice under subsection (3)(a) of s.13 of EA 2005 that the school requires special measures (as defined by s.44 of that Act). A school in special measures remains eligible for intervention until it is reprieved by Ofsted.

Intervention by local education authority ss.63–66

The term 'eligible for intervention' is used generically in the preceding three sections but they are separate because there are some differences in the interventions that can take place under the following sections. The powers and the approaches are broadly similar but the nomenclature is different and there are some changes, extending the range of intervention strategies and seeking to streamline processes associated with the existing ones. Table 5 sets this out diagrammatically.

Section 63: Power of LEA to require governing body to enter into arrangements

LEAs are given a new power of intervention allowing them to direct the governing body of a maintained school to take certain steps if the school is eligible for intervention. Subsection (1) sets out what sort of arrangements a governing body might be instructed to enter into:

- contracting with another party for the provision of advisory services to the governing body
- collaborating with the governing body of another school
- collaborating with a further education college or creating or joining a federation.

Before using the power, the LEA must consult the governing body of the school. In the case of a church school, foundation or voluntary, the appropriate diocesan

authority and in the case of other foundation or voluntary schools, the body that appoints the foundation governors must also be consulted.

If a school becomes eligible for intervention because it has failed to comply with a warning notice issued by the LEA under s.60, this power can only be exercised within two months of the end of the compliance period by virtue of subsection (3). If the school is in special measures or requires significant improvement the power is available as long as that status pertains.

Section 64: Power of LEA etc. to appoint additional governors

This section re-enacts with modifications s.16 of SSFA 1998 (in its application to England), giving LEAs the power to appoint additional governors at a maintained school which is subject to special measures, in need of significant improvement or to a governing body that has failed to comply with a formal warning.

As above, a 'section 60' intervention is time-limited to two months after the elapse of the compliance period; but powers under ss.61 and 62 are not. The LEA is also no longer required to have received a notice of receipt of the inspection report from the Secretary of State, or for a 10 day period to have elapsed once that notice has been received, before the LEA can appoint additional governors. In other words, bureaucracy is reduced and the authority can act with expedition as soon as an adverse inspection report is published.

Otherwise, the appointment of additional governors remains the same as before. For example the 'appropriate appointing authority' can match additional LEA governor appointments to a VA school with an equal number of its own.

Section 65: Power of LEA to provide for governing body to consist of interim executive members

LEAs can appoint a specially constituted governing body in place of the existing governors at a school that is eligible for intervention. The specially constituted governing body is known as an Interim Executive Board (IEB). The power may only be exercised with the consent of the Secretary of State and the governing body must be given written notice of the exercise of the power. LEAs must consult the governing body of the school; in the case of a church school, foundation or voluntary, the appropriate diocesan authority and in the case of other foundation or voluntary

schools, the body that appoints the foundation governors. This is achieved by re-enacting s.16A of SSFA 1998 (as inserted by s.57 of EA 2002) with amendments; again, this only applies to England.

As in the previous section, the LEA is no longer required to have received a notice of receipt of the inspection report from the Secretary of State, or to wait ten days before the LEA seeks consent to appoint IEB members.

Section 66: Power of LEA to suspend right to delegated budget

This section re-enacts s.17 of SSFA 1998 (in its application to England). It confers power on LEAs to suspend a school's right to a delegated budget if a school is eligible for intervention.

Again the power to withdraw delegation remains the same but without having to wait ten days after receipt of a formal notice from the Secretary of State.

Intervention by Secretary of State ss.67–69

As with the sections on LEA intervention powers, the Secretary of State's power to intervene remains broadly the same but relevant sections are re-enacted to take account of the new terminology. These powers are shown diagrammatically in Table 5 on page 92.

Section 67: Power of Secretary of State to appoint additional governors

The power of the Secretary of State to appoint additional governors to the governing body of a school that is eligible for intervention is re-enacted but remains very similar to s.18 of SSFA 1998 which it replaces (in England).

It applies only to schools eligible for intervention following Ofsted reports and not to those which have not complied with a formal warning issued by the LEA. Subsections (2) to (7) simply re-enact subsections (2) to (7) of s.18 of that Act. It therefore remains the case that if the Secretary of State chooses to use this power it overrides the LEA's power to intervene and the rights of those who appoint foundation governors.

Section 68: Power of Secretary of State to direct closure of school

This section re-enacts s.19 of SSFA 1998 (in its application to England). It gives the Secretary of State the power to direct the closure of a school if that school requires special measures.

Section 69: Power of Secretary of State to provide for governing body to consist of interim executive members

The Secretary of State can appoint a specially constituted governing body, called an Interim Executive Board (IEB), to conduct the school in place of the normal governing body, mirroring the LEA's ability to do this under s.65. However, unlike the LEA's power, it is applicable only if a school requires significant improvement or special measures and not when the school has failed to comply with a formal warning issued by the LEA under s.60. It operates by re-enacting s.18A of SSFA 1998 (as inserted by s.58 of EA 2002) and applies only to England.

Governing bodies consisting of interim executive bodies: further provisions

Section 70: Governing bodies consisting of interim executive members

This section introduces Schedule 6, re-enacts s.19A of SSFA 1998 (as inserted by s.59 of EA 2002) and provides for various matters relating to IEBs. The Schedule applies to all boards, whether they were appointed by the LEA or the Secretary of State and sets out arrangements for setting up the IEB, the number of members, the duties of the IEB and the transition from the IEB to a normally constituted governing body after it has completed its work.

Schedule 6: Governing bodies consisting of interim executive members

Schedule 6 simply re-enacts Schedule 1A to SSFA 1998 (as inserted by s.59 of EA 2002) and provides for the various technical matters relating to IEBs appointed by the LEA or the Secretary of State referred to above in relation to s.70. The draft

guidance provided to accompany the Bill during its consideration by Parliament suggested there was no intention to make substantive changes to the regulations originally made in 2002. This was subsequently confirmed when the draft guidance on schools causing concern was published for consultation early in January 2007.

Amendments relating to schools causing concern

Section 71: Amendments relating to schools causing concern

This section introduces Schedule 7, Part 1 of which makes amendments to s.15 and s.17 of EA 2005, dealing with measures that need to be taken by LEAs following the receipt of an inspection report stating that schools require special measures or significant improvement. Part 2 of the same Schedule makes minor and consequential amendments to existing legislation, including amendments that arise from re-enacting certain existing provisions for England only.

Schedule 7: Amendments relating to schools causing concern

The new arrangements are broadly similar to the existing ones, but there are some substantive changes to what an LEA has to do when a school goes into special measures or requires significant improvement. These flow from the greater expectations of parental involvement and need for urgency in securing school improvement central to this Act. LEAs must now 'consider' involving parents in action planning and the appointment of a Champion to represent them. Parental views should be taken into account in preparing the LEA's written statement following receipt of an inspection report. This is tantamount to a requirement as they have to explain themselves to the Secretary of State and HMCI if their 'consideration' does not translate into action. The Secretary of State acquires new powers to demand additional responses from the LEA if he considers that 'the case has become urgent', which can be understood as the school is not improving sufficiently quickly. There is a new duty on LEAs to have regard to guidance issued by the Secretary of State in performing their functions under new subsections (2) and (2B).

Paragraph 2 of Schedule 7 amends s.17 of EA 2005, referring to the statement required to be prepared by a proprietor following an adverse report on a non-maintained school. This provision for non-maintained schools mirrors the provision for

maintained schools discussed above. (N.B. there is an error in the Explanatory Notes that attributes this to Schedule 6.)

Part 2 of this Schedule makes minor and consequential amendments to SSFA 1998, LSA 2000, EA 2002 and EA 2005.

Supplementary ss.72–73

Section 72: Duty of LEA to have regard to guidance

This section requires LEAs to have regard to guidance issued by the Secretary of State.

Section 73: Interpretation of Part 4

Section 73 confirms the interpretation of keywords and phrases in line with particular sections of this or previous legislation.

Part 5: Curriculum and entitlements

The new entitlement to rich and varied opportunities for 14–19 year olds has been hailed as 'the most important reform of curriculum and qualifications since the introduction of the National Curriculum' (*A short Guide to the Education and Inspections Act 2006*, DfES, p.8). At just two sections this Part of the Act therefore has a significance way beyond its size.

The aim is to improve participation of young people in education and training from the current 75 per cent to at least 90 per cent at the age of 17. This derives from Public Service Agreement Targets 11 and 12 on increasing the proportion of 19 year olds who achieve NVQ level 2 qualifications and reducing the proportion of young people not in education, employment or training (NEETs). The Government announced its intention of reforming 14–19 education in 2001 and established a 14–19 working group, chaired by Sir Mike Tomlinson. Its final report recommended overarching diplomas covering all existing qualifications.

The DfES proposals, trailed in the White Paper *14–19 Education and Skills* (Cm 6476) in 2005 and confirmed later in the year in the White Paper announcing E&IA 2006, are to retain the current academic options post 14 but to offer additional vocational routes alongside them. All young people aged 14–19, wherever they live, will have access to one of 14 specialised diplomas enabling them to learn through practical experience. The Act legislates for the curriculum of 14–16 (s.74) and 16–19 year olds (s.76) separately because of the separate funding and responsibilities of the LEA for pre-16 education and the LSC for post-16 education. There is, of course as yet, no requirement for young people over the age of 16 to remain in education.

The diplomas are expected to be available at three levels with level 3 being equivalent to GCE A level standard. It is intended that young people will study at an appropriate level and that success will prepare them for progression to the next. Specifications for the diplomas are being developed by employer-led and education-led partnerships.

In addition, the Government has used the legislation to require schools to provide an entitlement to a science course which leads to a double award GCSE.

Implementation

The Government intends to introduce the new national entitlement from 2013. Prior to that the new diplomas will be introduced progressively and will be evaluated over a three-year period from introduction. The intention is to introduce five diploma courses for the first year of key stage 4 in September 2008: Engineering; Creative and Media; Society, Health and Development; Information Technology; and Construction and Built Environment.

The Government has supported the strategic planning role of the local authority and LSC by helping to meet additional costs of collaboration and partnership management, using the Increased Flexibility Programme (IFP) and 14–19 Pathfinders.

Section 74: Curriculum requirements for the fourth key stage

Subsection (1) inserts new ss.85 and 85A into EA 2002 replacing the existing s.85. This was inserted by *The Education (Amendment of the Curriculum Requirements for the Fourth Key Stage) (England) Order 2003* (SI 2003/2946) and removed 'design and technology' and 'modern foreign language' as compulsory subjects, introduced work-based learning as a requirement and introduced the category of entitlement subjects for students starting key stage 4 courses in September 2004.

EA 2002, s.85: Curriculum requirements of the fourth key stage

The fourth key stage comprises three elements:

- the 'core' and 'foundation' subjects
- opportunities for work-related learning
- the 'entitlement' courses of study.

The core (mathematics, English and science) and foundation (ICT, PE and citizenship) subjects have not changed and the work-related learning and entitlement subjects are now specified in the new s.85A. This 'required curriculum' remains the same except subsection (5) enables the Secretary of State, by order, to require all schools to provide courses leading to at least two science GCSEs. The Explanatory Notes (para.327) record that it is intended to specify 'combinations of GCSEs ... that will adequately prepare students for physics, chemistry and biology "AS" and "A" levels'. Subsection (4) of s.74 allows the science requirement to be brought in ahead of the new key stage 4 curriculum.

EA 2002, s.85A: Entitlement area for the fourth key stage

The new s.85A legislates for the 'entitlement curriculum'. Young people will be able to pursue roughly the current arrangements or one of the new diploma courses.

Subsection (1) offers students a choice between:

- the existing key stage 4 entitlement to the arts, design & technology, the humanities and modern foreign languages
- a course of study in an entitlement area specified by the Secretary of State, that is, one of the 14 new specialised diplomas.

The remainder of the new s.85A repeats existing legislation. Subsections (4) and (6) give schools a duty to make available courses which lead to appropriate qualifications in order to meet the entitlement. A school does not have to offer the full range of courses to all pupils. Subsection (5) is new: LEAs, governing bodies and head-teachers have to have regard to guidance from the Secretary of State and the QCA.

Subsection (2) of s.74 of E&IA 2006 confirms that the Secretary of State can, by order, amend the key stage 4 curriculum requirements using the affirmative resolution procedure EA 2002 (see s.182).

Subsection (3) of s.74 inserts seven new subsections into s.88 (Implementation of the National Curriculum) of EA 2002. New subsection (2) of s.88 places duties on LEAs, governing bodies and headteachers to secure as best they can that all the new diploma courses are available. However, the LEA acquires a specific power to relieve a school of this duty if providing the course would lead to 'disproportionate expenditure'. New subsection (3) makes clear that a pupil is not entitled to follow just a particular course leading to a particular diploma or to follow more than one course leading to one or more diplomas. The pupil has to do the whole diploma course.

In meeting their duty to deliver all the diplomas, schools must, under new subsections (4) and (5), consider collaborating with other schools (under s.26 of EA 2002) and further education colleges (under s.166 of E&IA 2006). The LEA under new subsection (6) may make arrangements with an FE college for the college to provide a diploma course which is then available to pupils at local schools. New subsection (7) requires the LSC to cooperate with such arrangements.

The combined effect of the amendments to s.88 of EA 2002 is to give 'local author
ities the strategic lead for securing the entitlement for these young people, with the
essential role of making sure that schools and colleges between them make the full
range' of diplomas available (*A short Guide to the Education and Inspections Act
2006*, DfES, p.8). The LSC is required to cooperate under s.88 but also under the
plans to improve the well-being of young people under s.10 of the Children Act
2004. Plans to develop 14–19 provision will be set out in the Children and Young
People's Plan under s.17 of the CA 2004 to which schools must now have regard, by
virtue of s.38 of E&IA 2006.

Parliamentary debate

The only Parliamentary debate on Part 5 was on the changes to the school curriculum. Inevitably, there were calls for additional subjects. Ministers had to explain
why the three science GCSEs could not be available for all schools, a modern foreign language was not compulsory, why non-European modern foreign languages
were not included and why history and geography were grouped as part of humanities. The Minister said that dropping the compulsory language requirement was 'one
of the most difficult decisions' the Government had taken but that it avoided the
'massively bureaucratic process' of disapplying the requirement from many young
people each year in order to allow them to follow a vocational programme. The
Minister described this and other choices as 'trade-offs', for example, dropping separate history and geography at key stage 4 allowed the three separate science
subjects to be taught (Lord Adonis, Lords Hansard, 20 July 2006, cols 1512–1514).

Later in the debate the Minister was asked whether pupils could study both an entitlement subject and a diploma. This was ruled out on practical grounds in that the
entry level (level 1) diploma would be the equivalent to about four or five GCSEs
and level 2 would equate to five or six GCSEs. 'In addition to their specialist diplomas, students will be required to study the core subjects of English, maths and
science and the foundation subjects of ICT, PE and citizenship. Although some of
these subjects will be covered as part of the specialised diploma, most will be studied as an additional course' said the Minister. In other words such decisions are best
left to schools: schools will have the freedom to allow additional studies but there
will be no mixing and matching of courses from different diplomas (Lord Adonis,
Lords Hansard, 20 July 2006, col 1522).

Section 75: Education and training to satisfy entitlements

Four new sections are inserted into the Learning and Skills Act 2000 (LSA 2000) by subsection (1).

LSA 2000, s.3A: Entitlement to education and training for person aged 16 to 19

A person who is above compulsory school age, but has not yet reached his/her 19th birthday, has a right to study either or both:

- the core entitlement in new s.3B and

- the additional entitlement in new s.3C.

They must begin the course of study before their 19th birthday.

LSA 2000, s.3B: The core entitlement

This is a course of study in one or more of the following: mathematics, English and ICT.

LSA 2000, s.3C: The additional entitlement

This is a course of study leading to a diploma as specified by the Secretary of State.

LSA 2000, s.3D: The core and additional entitlement: duties of the Council

Subsection (2) places a target duty on the LSC to secure that all diploma courses are available in each local learning and skills area unless this would lead to disproportionate expenditure. Note: the Further Education and Training Bill as published on 20 November 2006 proposes abolishing the statutory local learning and skills areas but does not include consequential amendments to this provision.

Section 75(2) amends s.13 of LSA 2000 to require the LSC to have regard to the needs of persons with learning difficulties when provision for diploma courses is secured.

Part 6: School travel and school food

This Part of the Act covers LEAs' duties and powers relating to school travel for children of compulsory school age and below, as well as for post-16 travel. It builds on proposals for a significant change to the law on home to school transport first proposed in a draft School Transport Bill published in March 2004. A substantive Bill, which was introduced in November, but ran out of Parliamentary time in May 2005, would have given LEAs new powers to operate school travel schemes intended to address the social, environmental and health problems arising from the increased use of cars on the school run.

The present Act, E&IA 2006, goes further, however. It introduces a new duty to promote sustainable travel whereby LEAs are now required to assess school travel needs, prepare and publish a sustainable school travel strategy. It reduces the current 'walking distances' expected of school pupils, significantly extends the right to free transport for low income groups and strengthens the duty on LEAs to have regard to parents' preferences for children to attend a particular school on the grounds of 'religion or belief'. The Act also provides for Pathfinder school travel schemes and restrictions in previous school transport legislation are removed; allowing LEAs to pilot new approaches to school travel meeting local priorities.

The duty to publish a sustainable school travel strategy came into force on 1 April 2007. The remaining changes are expected to come into force as follows:

- the extended right to free transport for low income groups and the reduced 'walking distances' – for primary pupils from September 2007 and for secondary pupils from September 2008

- the Pathfinder school travel schemes – in the latter half of 2008, with the first schemes coming on line for September 2009.

This part also extends the Secretary of State's powers to make regulations governing nutritional standards for school meals. It echoes the reformist intentions behind the Liberal Government's introduction of school meals for needy children in the Education (Provision of Meals) Act 1906. However, it restores the universal service approach adopted subsequently in the Education Act 1944, by reversing the decision to deregulate the school meals service and to remove nutritional standards

made in EA 1980. LEAs are again expected to take the lead role in securing the new standards in conjunction with schools and caterers. A wide range of advice, guidance and support is also available from the School Food Trust, which was set up in 2005 with £15 million of funding from the DfES to promote the education and health of children and young people by improving the quality of food supplied and consumed in schools. These measures have a clear focus on the delivery of the five outcomes in the ECM agenda. The improvements to school food are being introduced progressively over a three-year period and are expected to be fully in force from September 2009.

Travel to schools, etc. ss. 76–87

Section 76: LEAs in England – duty to promote sustainable modes of travel and Schedule 8

A new s.508A is inserted in EA 1996, placing a general duty on LEAs to promote the use of sustainable travel and transport.

EA 1996 s.508A LEAs in England: duty to promote sustainable modes of travel etc.

There are four main elements to the duty:

- to assess the travel and transport needs of children and young people
- to conduct an audit of the sustainable travel and transport infrastructure
- to prepare each year a strategy to promote the use of sustainable modes of travel to meet the school travel needs of the area
- to publish the strategy as required by regulations.

Regulations require LEAs to publish their general arrangements and policies on home to school transport for pupils of compulsory age and below; and for older students including those studying at institutions in the FE sector. LEAs are also required to publish details in relation to transport for pupils with SEN. The draft guidance issued for consultation by the DfES encourages LEAs to integrate their sustainable school travel strategies into these existing policy statements and publish them together.

Section 77: LEAs in England — provision of travel arrangements, etc. for children and Schedule 8: Travel to schools, etc.: meaning of 'eligible child'

Three new sections are inserted in EA 1996.

EA 1996, s. 508B LEAs in England: travel arrangements for eligible children

This new section requires LEAs to ensure that suitable free travel arrangements for 'eligible children' facilitate their attendance at relevant educational establishments.

EA 1996, s. 508C LEAs in England: travel arrangements etc. for other children

This new section also provides LEAs with discretionary powers to make arrangements for those children not covered by s.508B.

EA 1996, s. 508D Guidance in relation to sections 508B and 508C

A further new section is inserted under which the Secretary of State may issue and revise guidance on the discharge of LEAs' functions in relation to school travel.

Schedule 8: Travel to schools etc. Meaning of 'eligible child'

Schedule 8 inserts Schedule 35B in EA 1996 and defines 'eligible child' for the purposes of this section. Essentially those who qualify by virtue of living beyond the walking distance and those for whom special arrangements apply, e.g. SEN, free schools meals or where safe routes are an issue.

The draft guidance issued for consultation by the DfES emphasises that every feature of the travel arrangements must be free, e.g. LEAs may not levy a charge for issuing a pass that entitles the pupil to a seat free of charge – although a refundable deposit could be charged to cover the potential cost of replacing lost or damaged passes. Other examples included in the draft guidance are:

- mileage allowances paid to parents driving 'eligible' children to school in lieu of LEAs arranging for taxis

- cycling allowances paid where parents consent to 'eligible' children cycling to and from school instead of catching a bus for, say, a three mile journey

- LEA provision of escorts to enable 'eligible' children with SEN or a disability to walk a short distance to school in reasonable safety, or where a child is unable to travel independently on a public service bus, instead of LEAs arranging for taxis.

The draft guidance states that for LEAs to consider arrangements 'suitable' they must enable 'eligible' children to travel without such stress, strain or difficulty that they would be prevented from benefiting from the education provided. This includes reasonable journey times, and factors such as the age and individual needs of children. It is still suggested the maximum length of journey should be 45 minutes for primary pupils and 75 minutes for secondary pupils. It remains to be seen if these guidelines will be retained as absolute limits or whether some explicit leeway will be given to rural LEAs.

The safety of walking routes to children's nearest suitable school should also be considered. LEAs would be under a duty to make alternative travel arrangements where the nature of a route is such that a child cannot reasonably be expected to walk (accompanied as necessary). LEAs would also be expected to consider the particular circumstances of disabled parents, e.g. where disabled parents could not be expected to accompany children on a walking route.

The LEA's duty to secure suitable arrangements can take account of other free travel that might be available – for example Transport for London (TfL) offers free bus travel to children of school age in the capital. LEAs can expect children to take advantage of this concession, but if a pupil's qualifying school is not reasonably accessible by bus but could be reached by tube (which is not covered by the TfL scheme) the LEA must pay. Similarly, mileage allowances can be offered to parents driving their own children or for travel by bicycle, but parents cannot be required to accept them in lieu of the standard arrangements made by the LEA.

Schedule 8 also amends the statutory 'walking distances' and significantly extends the right to free transport for low-income groups which are defined as children entitled to free school meals and children of parents receiving working tax credit. The Act also strengthens the duty on LEAs to have regard to parents' preferences for children to attend a particular school on the grounds of 'religion or belief'. The statutory 'walking distances' are now:

- 2 miles for children under 8
- 3 miles for children aged 8 and over

- 2 miles for children aged 8, but under 11, from low-income families.

The Act further extends the right to free transport for secondary pupils and aims to overcome transport affordability barriers and to promote fair access to the nearest three qualifying secondary schools. Entitlement to free transport for secondary aged pupils is:

- to one of their three nearest qualifying secondary schools for children aged 11 to 16 from low-income families where they live more than 2 miles, but less than 6 miles from the school

- to the nearest school preferred by the parents on the grounds of 'religion or belief' more than 2 miles but up to a maximum of 15 miles from the child's home.

Section 78: LEAs in England – school travel schemes and Schedule 9: School travel schemes

A new section is added to EA 1996 which, together with s.79, is the legislative vehicle for the introduction of the new Pathfinder school travel schemes.

EA 1996, s.508E LEAs in England: school travel schemes

It allows LEAs to develop school travel schemes concerning children's attendance at school, FE institutions or other relevant places. If the Secretary of State subsequently decides to extend the initial Pathfinder scheme beyond the 20 initially suggested, this section would supersede the requirement on those LEAs to make travel arrangements for eligible children (under s.508B) and their discretionary power to extend them for non-eligible children (under s.508C).

The Secretary of State is required to issue guidance to the Pathfinder LEAs in relation to their functions under Schedule 35C, which may be revised from time to time.

Subsection 78(2) introduces Schedule 9, which inserts Schedule 35C into EA 1996. This sets out detailed requirements for the pilot school travel schemes which include undertaking consultation before submission to the Secretary of State for approval. The LEA Pathfinder schemes will therefore be under the direction of the Secretary of State and the earliest date on which a Pathfinder scheme can come into force is 31 August 2007.

Draft DfES guidance on the Pathfinder schemes indicates that the Secretary of State will not approve Pathfinder schemes which would introduce charges for any pupils who would otherwise receive free home to school transport. It also recognises that there is a strong case for providing additional protection from charges for low-income families with incomes just above the threshold guaranteeing protection from charges (e.g. families receiving less than the maximum level of working tax credit), for large families and those in rural areas involving longer travel distances to school. The draft guidance suggests Pathfinder schemes should exempt from charging the fourth child, and subsequent children, from large families (nationally around two per cent of the pupil population). Graduated charges should also be considered for low-income families not protected from charges, and for the third child of compulsory school age in a family. Pathfinder schemes should explain how LEAs will manage a charging regime cost effectively and also provide evidence as to why they are confident that their schemes will not increase car use. LEA proposals are also expected to be transparent about any differential geographic impact within their schemes, highlighting where net gains and benefits would arise.

Section 79: Piloting of school travel scheme provisions

Section 79 allows the new Pathfinder travel schemes to be piloted in accordance with regulations made by the Secretary of State. The draft DfES guidance on the Pathfinder schemes indicates that the number of approved Pathfinder schemes will be limited to 20 in England. The number of pilots could be expanded, however, through secondary legislation, if justified by demand from LEAs.

The draft prospectus for Pathfinders suggests that successful Pathfinder bids will:

- address the needs of all pupils in the area

- support the enhanced emphasis on parental preference

- promote the health, social and environmental benefits of walking and cycling to and from school and reduce car use

- be underpinned by comprehensive and coherent strategies which set out how the travel needs of all pupils will be met

- will cover walking, cycling and car use as well as bus provision

- demonstrate strong relationships with transport authorities and schools on all aspects of sustainable school travel

- include sound strategies for working with bus operators to secure appropriate provision of commercial and subsidised bus services serving school pupils and other users of public transport, showing how public spend on bus services produces gains for all users.

The DfES will invite Pathfinder bids in 2007 and anticipate that most Pathfinder schemes would start from September 2009, running until the end of July 2012 or possibly later. Each scheme will be evaluated annually, with progress reports disseminated widely to LEAs and schools and an independent evaluation of the pilot overall will be commissioned for publication before 1 January 2012.

Section 80: Power to repeal school travel scheme provisions, etc.

This section requires the Secretary of State to prepare and publish an evaluation of the Pathfinder schemes enabled under s.79 (see above). This section also gives power to the Secretary of State to provide by order (by the affirmative resolution procedures, see s.182) that, subject to the approval of Parliament, the new provisions will cease to have effect, should the Secretary of State decide not to proceed with the Pathfinder schemes. Subsections (3) and (4) respectively provide that the earliest and latest dates on which the new provisions could cease to have effect are 1 August 2012 and 1 August 2015.

Section 81: LEAs in England: provision of transport, etc. for certain adult learners

This inserts a new section into EA 1996.

EA 1996, s.508F LEAs in England: provision of transport etc. for certain adult learners

It covers 'qualifying adult learners' with learning difficulties above compulsory school age attending education or training outside the FE and HE sectors, for whom transport must be provided free of charge and other adult learners who currently benefit from discretionary LEA assistance towards transport arrangements under s.509 of EA 1996. This section ensures that LEAs can continue to make such arrangements.

Section 82: Amendments of s.444 EA 1996 relating to school travel

Parents' possible grounds for defence in law against LEA prosecution for their child's non-attendance at school are amended. This provision, which has been the basis of free transport since the Education Act 1944, is now found in s.444 of EA 1996. A parent has a defence against prosecution for not sending the child to school if he or she can prove that the child's school is not within statutory walking distance and, where the child is not a boarder, no suitable arrangements have been made by the local education authority for the child's transport to and from the school or for enabling the child to become a registered pupil at a school nearer to his home.

New subsections (3A) to (3F) are inserted in s.444 of EA 1996 to clarify the existing law as follows:

- The parent's defence against prosecution for a child's non-attendance is clarified if the parent proves the LEA has failed in its duty to make travel arrangements under new s.508B(1) (inserted by s.77 of E&IA 2006) or, where a school travel scheme is in place, under new s.508E(2)(c) (inserted by s.78 of E&IA 2006).

- LEAs are not under a duty to make travel arrangements to schools in the independent sector (as these are not deemed to be 'qualifying schools') or a 'place other than a school, where the child is receiving education by virtue of arrangements made in pursuance of s.19(1)(of EA 1996)', except where a child with SEN is placed in a non-maintained school catering for pupils with SEN.

- Operation by the LEA of a school travel scheme, under which charges are levied for travel arrangements, does not provide a defence for a parent failing to secure a child's attendance.

Section 83: Learning and Skills Council for England: transport, etc. for persons of sixth form age

This section makes various amendments to ss.509AA, 509AB and 509AC of EA 1996 (as inserted by Schedule 19 of EA 2002) and to s.18 of LSA 2000. From 20 January 2003, LEAs were given responsibility for consulting with their partners locally and preparing and publishing agreed local transport policy statements by 31 May each year. These statements should outline the transport services and support available to full-time students over compulsory school age but under 19, or who are on a course which they started before they reached 19. Statements should include

details of fares/charges and concessions, discounts, etc. that apply. LEAs must continue to make provision for persons receiving full time education at any institution within the FE sector which is no less favourable than that made for pupils of the same age at schools maintained by the LEA (in accordance with Schedule 19 of EA 2002). LEAs are also encouraged to extend provision to part-time students wherever possible and to make provision for students with learning difficulties and disabilities up to at least age 21, although they are also encouraged by DfES and the LSC seriously to consider extending this to age 25.

The changes under this section transfer greater responsibility from the Secretary of State to the Learning and Skills Council for England (the LSC) in relation to the provision of transport by LEAs and their partners for 16–19 year olds. The changes will make the LSC responsible for managing operational arrangements including issuing guidance to LEAs on how they should develop transport policy statements. The LSC will also offer advice to the Secretary of State where there may be a case for him to consider directing LEAs to improve the arrangements set out in their transport policy statements. The measures are intended to ensure that transport services continue to be available, but that they are managed more efficiently in the learner support unit at the LSC. This will allow the DfES to continue the transfer of learner support management to the LSC, as recommended in the Department's efficiency scrutiny.

Section 84: LEAs in England: duty to have regard to religion or belief in exercise of travel functions

In exercising their travel functions, LEAs must have regard to any wish of a parent of a child, student of sixth form age or adult learner, for that person to be provided with education or training at a particular school, institution or other place, where that wish is based on the parent's religion or belief. This is achieved by inserting a new section.

EA 1996: s.509AD LEAs in England: duty to have regard to religion or belief in exercise of travel functions

Subsection (2) provides that the travel functions to which this duty applies are those set out in ss.508A, 508B, 508C, 508E, 508F and 509AA and Schedule 35C of EA 1996 (inserted by ss.76–81 and Schedules 8 and 9 of E&IA 2006). Subsection (3) provides that 'religion' means any religion; 'belief' means any belief and that references to religion or belief include references to a lack of religion or belief. The draft

DfES guidance explains that the definition of 'religion or belief' follows that in the Equality Act 2006 and the duty therefore covers all religions and denominations, as well as philosophical beliefs.

The draft DfES guidance goes into considerable detail attempting to explain the definitions of religion or belief and to address the implications of the Equality Act 2006. The DfES view is that the duty will cover all recognised religions and denominations, as well as philosophical beliefs. Detailed case law, including European case law, is cited in the draft guidance in support of the argument that 'belief' equates to 'conviction' and must be genuinely held, although it should not be incompatible with human dignity or the fundamental rights of the child. The draft guidance acknowledges that parents have no right under the European Convention on Human Rights to have their children educated at a particular faith or secular school. Nevertheless, the DfES suggests that in exercising their transport functions LEAs 'will need to respect parents' religious and philosophical convictions as to the education to be provided for their children in so far as this is compatible with the provision of efficient instruction and training and the avoidance of unreasonable public expenditure'.

It remains to be seen how quickly and to what extent the complex interactions between the Act's requirements and equality and human rights legislation might push LEAs to extend their current discretionary faith transport policies in the future.

Section 85: Further amendments relating to travel to schools, etc. and Schedule 10

This section refers to a number of mainly consequential amendments contained in Schedule 10. The only substantive amendment relates to s.6 of the Transport Act 1985, which provides an exemption from the general requirement for bus services to be registered with the Traffic Commissioner. Currently, seven Traffic Commissioners are appointed by the Secretary of State for Transport and have responsibility in their area for the licensing of the operators of heavy goods vehicles (HGVs) and of buses and coaches (Public Service Vehicles or PSVs), the registration of local bus services and disciplinary action against drivers of HGVs and PSVs.

The amendment means that school bus services operated under the new ss.508B(1), 508C(1) and 508F(1) and the new Schedule 35C to EA 1996, are exempted from the requirement imposed by the Transport Act 1985 to be registered with the Traffic Commissioner.

Food and drink provided on school premises, etc. ss. 86–87

Section 86: Provision of food and drink on school premises, etc.

The existing power to make regulations in connection with nutritional standards for school lunches is extended to cover all food and drink provided on the premises of maintained schools.

SSFA 1998: s.114A: Requirements for food and drink provided on school premises etc.

Subsection (1) of s.86 replaces s.114 of SSFA 1998 with a new cross heading identical to the one above, and a new section s.114A. It also permits the regulations to apply to food or drink provided by LEAs or governing bodies to registered pupils at any place other than the school. It is intended that the regulations will introduce new standards (food based and nutrient based) to increase pupils' access to healthier food/drink options and essential nutrients and reduce the amount of sugar, salt and fats contained in foods/drinks provided to pupils by LEAs and school governing bodies.

Subsection (2) of the new s.114A provides that the regulations may require certain standards to be complied with, that drinking water must be freely available on school premises and that specific types of food and drink may not be provided.

Subsection (3) of the new s.114A exempts food and drink brought on to school premises for personal consumption. This would exempt the content of packed lunches provided by parents, as well as, probably, fast food passed to pupils through school fences during the lunch break (as widely reported in the media late in 2006)! Subsections (4), (5) and (6) place on LEAs and governing bodies a duty to ensure that the standards and other requirements set out in the regulations are met when food or drink is provided on school premises and when those bodies provide it to registered pupils at other places.

Subsection (8) allows regulations to specify:

a) different requirements for particular classes or descriptions of schools or persons

b) periods of the day during which certain requirements apply.

This is intended to give the necessary flexibility to ensure that the standards set are suitable for differing age groups or types of schools. It is also intended to allow appropriate standards to be applied to food and drink provided at after school and breakfast clubs.

Subsection (10) of the new s.114A ensures that references to food or drink provided by LEAs or governing bodies include references to food or drink provided by contractors under arrangements made with LEAs or governing bodies.

The Government confirmed new standards for school food in September 2006 (see DfES Press Notice 2006/0121, 4 September 2006 http://www.dfes.gov.uk/pns/DisplayPN.cgi?pn_id=2006_0121).

These are being implemented as follows:

September 2006	introduction of new 'interim' food-based standards for school lunches and expectation that schools will begin to move towards standards for food provided at other times
September 2007	introduction of food-based standards for all other school food and drink
September 2008	date by which all primary schools must comply with 'final' food-based and nutrient-based standards for lunch
September 2009	date by which all secondary schools must comply with 'final' food-based and nutrient-based standards for lunch.

Section 87: Power to charge for provision of meals, etc.

The current duty on LEAs and governing bodies (under s.512ZA and s.533 of EA 1996) to charge for food and drink provided by them is replaced in each case with a power. This relaxation is intended to help those LEAs and governing bodies who would like to provide pupils with some or all meals/drinks/refreshments free of charge, to do so. This flexibility means that LEAs will no longer need to apply for an order under s.2 of EA 2002 (powers to facilitate innovation) in order to offer some free food/drink to their pupils. This section came into effect on 8 November 2006.

Part 7: Discipline, behaviour and exclusion

The Report from the Practitioners' Group on School Behaviour and Discipline, *Learning Behaviour*, was published in October 2005. The Group, chaired by Sir Alan Steer (Head of Seven Kings High School, in the London Borough of Redbridge) was commissioned to give advice to the DfES on how behaviour in schools could be improved. *The Steer Report* was widely welcomed and acknowledged to be an authoritative statement of appropriate measures to deal with poor discipline in schools. A key message was that schools need to teach values as well as knowledge and skills: 'the quality of learning, teaching and behaviour are inseparable issues and the responsibility of all staff'.

This part of the Act follows many of the key recommendations of the report as they were reflected in the White Paper. It covers governing bodies' and headteachers' responsibilities for establishing and maintaining school behaviour policies, which include reasonable measures to regulate the behaviour of pupils off school premises and when they are not under the control of a member of school staff. It includes a new statutory power on the enforcement of disciplinary penalties which clarifies and strengthens schools' powers, often popularly referred to as 'the power to discipline'. This means schools no longer have to rely on the common law. It also clarifies the law on the use of force where any member of staff needs to restrain a pupil or compel a pupil to comply with a reasonable instruction. Schools will also have greater flexibility to impose sanctions such as detention without parental consent. Schools are also given formal powers to confiscate pupils' property for the first time.

These changes also reflect the wider thrust of government social policy with an emphasis on parental responsibility for the behaviour of their children. Parenting contracts and orders are extended and there is a new requirement on parents to ensure children excluded from school are not found unsupervised in a public place during school hours in the first five days of exclusion. One of the more controversial measures, the imposition of a form of 'house arrest' on excluded pupils, although difficult to enforce, can be seen as a new sanction against both parents and children. Penalty fines can be imposed if excluded pupils are found in public places, creating a new enforcement burden on local agencies.

As with existing legislation exclusions are measured in 'school days'. The Act enables a new requirement to provide suitable education for excluded pupils from

day six of an exclusion rather than day 16 as was previously the case. However, for fixed term exclusions, responsibility for making the provision now rests with the school. This is likely to be highly influential in changing schools' approach to fixed term exclusions of more than five days and in encouraging partnership working between schools, pupil referral units (PRUs) and LEAs to improve behaviour and tackle persistent truancy. It also raises practical issues regarding their potential impact on the capacity of PRUs and other provision for excluded pupils.

Chapter 1 on discipline came into force on 1 April 2007. Most of Chapter 2 on parenting orders and contracts, and exclusions, is expected to come into force in September 2007. Section 109, which resulted from a legal judgment, came into effect by Royal Assent on 8 November 2006.

Chapter 1: School discipline

Chapter 1 effects changes and clarifications of the law governing the legitimate exercise of a school's internal discipline. Many sections contain a subsection to the effect: 'this section is not to be construed as restricting what may lawfully be done apart from this section'. This is to take account of the approach to statutory interpretation which assumes that where public authorities are given explicit powers, anything of a like nature not mentioned is ruled out. The catch-all phrase is therefore included to make sure that nothing within existing established practice, or permitted by another legal route, is inadvertently prohibited.

Certain schools required to have behaviour policy ss.88, 89

Governors collectively and the headteacher have defined roles and responsibilities to establish maintain and implement a behaviour policy for the school.

Section 88: Responsibility of governing body for discipline

Section 88 defines the responsibilities of governing bodies for establishing the principles shaping schools' behaviour policies. It re-enacts subsections (1) to (3) of s.61 of SSFA 1998 with minor changes. Subsection (1) requires governing bodies to ensure that schools pursue policies to promote good behaviour. Subsection (2)

requires them to make and review written statements of general principles to guide headteachers in determining measures to promote good behaviour. Where a governing body wants the behaviour policy to include particular measures or address particular issues they must notify the headteacher. It also enables the governing body to give the headteacher further guidance.

Before making or revising the statement of principles, the governing body must consult the headteacher; parents of pupils registered at the school; all registered pupils and any persons who work at the school that are considered appropriate to consult (e.g. including the kitchen staff and caretaker as well as teachers, classroom assistants and midday supervisors, etc. if the governing body felt that their input would be valuable).

Subsection (4) requires the governing body to have regard to national guidance when carrying out its functions under subsection (2), provided in England by the Secretary of State and by the National Assembly for Wales. Subsection (5) specifies the types of school to which ss.88 and 89 apply. It includes all categories of maintained schools and nursery schools, pupil referral units (PRUs) and non-maintained special schools.

PRUs were not mentioned in the predecessor legislation, although they were covered by separate legislation. Non-maintained special schools are, however, included for the first time. Academies are not mentioned but may be required to comply by the terms of their funding agreements.

Section 89: Determination by headteacher of behaviour policy

Section 89 defines the responsibilities of the headteacher for establishing and maintaining a behaviour policy for the school that promotes self-discipline, respect for others and proper regard for authority. It re-enacts with amendments subsections (4) to (7) of s.61 of SSFA 1998. In addition to the other considerations laid out there, the headteacher must determine the behaviour policy with a view to 'securing that pupils complete any tasks reasonably assigned to them in connection with their education'. The behaviour policy can also include reasonable measures to regulate the behaviour of pupils when they are off the school site or when they are not under the control or charge of a member of the school staff. 'Staff' can include unpaid people designated

by the headteacher for this purpose; so, for example, volunteer helpers on a school trip can be suitably empowered.

Subsection (1) requires the headteacher to determine measures that promote self-discipline and a proper regard for authority, encourage good behaviour and respect for others, prevent all forms of bullying, secure completion of tasks and generally promote an acceptable standard of behaviour by pupils. These measures constitute the school's behaviour policy.

Subsection (2) requires the headteacher to follow the governing body's statement of principles and have regard to any guidance given by the governing body. Subsection (3) requires the headteacher to determine what standards of behaviour should be regarded as acceptable in so far as they are not determined by the governing body. Subsection (4) provides that the measures determined by the headteacher must include the making of rules and provision for disciplinary penalties. Subsection (5) enables the headteacher to determine (to such an extent as is reasonable) measures to regulate the behaviour of pupils when they are not on school premises or under the control or charge of a member of the school staff, e.g. to allow rules governing behaviour on the journey to and from school and during work experience placements. Subsection (6) requires the headteacher to set out the behaviour policy in a written document and publicise it by making it generally known to staff, pupils and parents, in particular, by bringing it to their attention at least once a year.

Enforcement of discipline (including compliance with instructions) ss.90–91

These three sections codify the ability of schools to apply sanctions, 'disciplinary penalties', in general terms and in the specific case of detention. The legitimate use of force for restraint, but not as a form of punishment, and confiscation are dealt with in two further sections under their own cross headings.

Section 90: Meaning of 'disciplinary penalty'

A 'disciplinary penalty' is defined as: 'a penalty imposed on a pupil by any school at which education is provided for him, where his conduct falls below the standard which could reasonably be expected of him' because (for example) he or she fails to follow a school rule or an instruction given by a member of staff. The reference to

'any school at which education is provided for a pupil' is intended to cover both the school a pupil normally attends and any other school that might be attended, for example for a particular course.

'Conduct' includes conduct off school premises and where the pupil is not under the control or charge of staff (so far as that is reasonable) and includes conduct which consists of a failure to comply with a disciplinary penalty previously imposed.

Section 91: Enforcement of disciplinary penalties: general

For the first time the law specifies what schools are allowed to do by way of imposing disciplinary penalties, popularly known as 'the power to discipline'. This section establishes a new statutory framework clarifying, supplementing and strengthening the powers schools previously had, or were presumed to have, under common law. Subsection (1) explains that this section applies to any disciplinary penalties imposed on a pupil other than exclusion. Subsections (2) to (5) specify the conditions that must be met for the imposition of a disciplinary penalty to be lawful. These are where:

- the penalty does not breach any statutory requirement or prohibition. This would preclude, for example, corporal punishment and prevent the imposition of a disciplinary penalty in circumstances which involved any breach of race or sex discrimination legislation

- the penalty is reasonable in all the circumstances. Subsection (6) specifies that a penalty is reasonable if it is 'proportionate' to the infringement and that any special circumstances, including: age, disability, special educational needs or religious requirements affecting the individual concerned have been taken into account

- the decision to impose the penalty is made by a school staff member. Paid members of staff are automatically included unless the headteacher has decided they should not be. Unpaid members of staff (for example parent volunteers) may not impose a penalty unless reasonably authorised by the headteacher to do so

- the decision to impose the penalty was made and any action taken on behalf of the school to implement the decision, was taken on the school premises or elsewhere at a time when the pupil was under the lawful control or charge of a member of staff of the school (for example on an educational visit).

In determining whether the imposition of a penalty is reasonable, relevant personal characteristics of the pupil are those which the person imposing the penalty is, or ought reasonably to be, aware of (s.91(6) (b)). For these purposes disability is as defined in the Disability Discrimination Act 1995.

Subsection (8) states that a headteacher's decisions on whether staff should be able to impose penalties on pupils may be made in relation to individual staff or groups of staff; in relation to an individual pupil or pupils; or in relation to an individual penalty or types of penalty. So a headteacher could, for example, decide that only teachers who are heads of year or heads of department could put pupils in detention or that a volunteer helping to supervise an educational visit should be able to withdraw privileges from pupils who misbehave on the visit.

Subsection (9) makes detention outside normal school hours subject to the additional provisions in s.89. Subsection (10) makes it clear that nothing in this section legitimises corporal punishment. Subsection (11) confirms that nothing in the section restricts other powers that heads and school staff may have. These may include powers conferred on them by the pupil's parent or under the common law when the school acts *in loco parentis*. Subsection (12) defines a 'paid member of staff' as a member of staff who works at the school for pay under a contract of employment or a contract for services. The latter would include supply teachers provided by agencies. Any contract of employment or contract for services need not be made with the governing body or proprietor of the school (so that it includes LEA employed staff that may be working at the school).

Section 92: Enforcement of disciplinary penalties: detention outside normal school hours

The existing law on detention is significantly amended, so that schools have greater powers and flexibility to use this key sanction. In particular, it includes provisions on detentions at weekends, on staff training days without parental consent and the removal of the requirement for 24 hours' notice for lunchtime detentions. Staff in lawful control or charge of pupils can give detentions, not just teachers.

These specific conditions that make the detention of a pupil outside normal school hours lawful, together with the general requirements of s.91 which also apply, replace s.550B of EA 1996 (inserted by s.5 of EA 1997).

Subsection (1) defines detention as a disciplinary penalty that takes place outside normal school hours. Detentions may only be given to pupils below the age of 18, on a 'permitted day of detention' and if the pupil's parent has been given 24 hours' notice (ss.92(2) and 92(3)). These restrictions, however, do not apply if a detention takes place during the lunch break (s.92(4)); but in all cases the headteacher must have made the school's policy on detention outside of school hours known within school and to parents. Subsection (5) adds consideration of suitable travelling arrangements to the other tests of reasonableness prescribed in s.91(3) and (6).

Subsection (6) updates s.572 of EA 1996 which assumed parents' 24 hours' notice would be served in the form of a hard copy letter. Schools can now give a parent the required 24 hours' notice 'by any effective method' which would include text or email.

Subsection (7) makes clear that codification of the law in s.92 does not restrict additional relevant powers that heads and school staff may have, for example by virtue of a pupil's parent having signed a home/school agreement.

A 'permitted day of detention' is defined as:

- a school day, other than one on which the school has given the pupil leave of absence (s.92(8)(a))

- a Saturday or Sunday during the school term, other than weekends preceding or following half-term breaks (s.92(8)(b))

- a non-teaching work day, more commonly known as a 'training day' or 'INSET day', that may fall in or out of the school term other than those excluded in regulations (s.92(8)(c)).

Use of reasonable force

Section 93: Power of members of staff to use force

School staff can use reasonable force to prevent a pupil from committing an offence, causing personal injury, damaging property or doing something that prejudices discipline at the school. Section 550A of EA 1996 (inserted by s.4 of EA 1997) is re-enacted with minor changes enabling a member of staff to use reasonable force to prevent:

- an offence being committed or prevent one continuing (s.93(1)(a))

- personal injury to pupils themselves or others, or damage to property (s.93(1)(b))

- anything which prejudices the maintenance of good order and discipline at the school during lessons or otherwise (s.93(1)(c)).

Thus, reasonable force (such as leading by the arm) might be used to enforce an instruction for a pupil to leave a classroom.

Subsection (2) specifies that the power to use force extends to members of staff at any school at which the pupil is receiving education. Subsection (3) restricts the use of this power to when both the member of staff and the pupil are on school premises or in other situations where the member of staff has lawful control or charge of the pupil involved, e.g. on an educational visit.

Subsection (4) makes it clear that subsection (1) does not legitimise corporal punishment. Subsection (5) clarifies that the power provided by subsection (1) does not remove any other powers that heads and school staff may have, e.g. common law rights of self-defence. Subsection (6) specifies that an 'offence' includes behaviour by younger pupils that would be an offence if they had attained the age of criminal responsibility.

Confiscation from pupils

Section 94: Defence where confiscation lawful

A new specific statutory defence for staff against civil or criminal liability is provided where a lawfully confiscated item is retained or disposed of. The burden of proof rests with the member of staff, to show that the interference with the pupil's human right to property was reasonable and proportionate. Subsection (1) specifies that this section applies where something in the possession of a pupil is seized, retained or disposed of. Subsection (2) protects any person who seizes, retains or disposes of such an item from liability in any proceedings if they can prove that the seizure, retention or disposal was lawful either because it is covered by s.91 of E&IA 2006, or otherwise (see below).

A common-sense approach to what is 'reasonable' is a fair guide to the application of this section. For example it would clearly be unreasonable for a pupil's prescription medicine to be confiscated at a time when it should have been taken. If the item was seized inadvertently, say because the medicine was hidden within another article,

the question would turn on whether, in all the circumstances, the member of staff ought to have known about it.

Subsection (4) is the usual clarification that this section does not prevent anyone using any other defence, e.g. under common law that they would be entitled to use in any civil or criminal action. However, subsection (3), which has similar wording, is a cross reference to parallel legislation. Section 45 of the Violent Crime Reduction Act 2006 inserted a new s.550AA in EA 1996 which provides new powers for school staff to search pupils for weapons.

Interpretation of Chapter 1

Section 95: Interpretation of Chapter 1

This section refers back to s.90 for a definition of 'disciplinary penalty'. It defines 'member of staff' for the purposes of this chapter, as any teacher who works at the school and any other person who, with the authority of the headteacher, has lawful control or charge of pupils at the school, which may include members of the support staff of a school. It would also include unpaid volunteers who are put in charge of pupils, e.g. on an educational visit. It also specifies that: '"possessions", in relation to a pupil, includes any goods over which he appears to have control'.

Repeals

Section 96: Repeals consequential on provisions of Chapter 1

This section repeals the legislation replaced by sections in this chapter; including existing legislation on governing bodies' and headteachers' responsibilities for discipline (s.61 of SSFA 1998), detention and physical intervention (ss.550A & B of EA 1996).

Chapter 2: Parental responsibilities and excluded pupils

The second half of this Part deals with the aspect of school discipline which reaches beyond the walls of the institution: enforcing parental responsibilities, exclusions and attendance.

Parenting contracts and parenting orders ss.97–99

Existing mechanisms for encouraging or requiring parents to take greater responsibility for the behaviour and discipline of their children are modified and extended.

Section 97: Parenting contracts

This amends s.19 of the Anti-social Behaviour Act 2003, which makes provision for schools and LEAs to enter into voluntary 'parenting contracts' with parents in cases of exclusion from school or truancy. It broadens the scope of contracts so that they can be used in cases of misbehaviour of a pupil at the school.

Two new subsections are inserted. Subsection (1A) provides an alternative trigger to enable schools and LEAs to enter into parenting contracts with parents, where they have reason to believe that a pupil has engaged in behaviour which:

- has caused, or is likely to cause, significant disruption to the education of other pupils (s.19(1A)(a)(i))

- has caused, or is likely to cause, significant detriment to the welfare of that pupil or other pupils or to the health or safety of any staff (s.19(1A)(a)(ii))

- forms part of a pattern of behaviour which (if continued) could lead to the pupil being excluded (s.19(1A)(b)).

Subsection (1B) makes clear that such behaviour can take place at school or elsewhere if it is reasonable for the school to regulate it.

Section 98: Parenting orders in cases of exclusion or misbehaviour

As with parenting contracts, the scope of parenting orders under s.20 of the Anti-social Behaviour Act 2003 is extended. Previously LEAs alone could apply to magistrates' courts for parenting orders in respect of excluded pupils. Now orders can be sought by school governors as well and in circumstances where a pupil has seriously misbehaved but not been excluded. The relevant bodies who can apply for orders are LEAs and governing bodies of maintained schools, or proprietors of academies, CTCs, or city colleges for the technology of the arts (CTCAs), at which the person concerned is a pupil or from which he has been excluded.

The subheading in the 2003 Act is amended to add the words 'potential exclusion'. This flags up the key requirement that must be met for an order to be made in respect of non-excluded pupils. Pupils must have behaved in such a way that they could have been excluded and any other conditions specified in regulations are met. However, it is made clear that any policy that the school might have to restrict exclusions or to restrict exclusions in certain circumstances is not relevant in this context; the relevant factor is the seriousness of the misbehaviour. The court can make a parenting order if it is satisfied that behaviour which would warrant exclusion has occurred and that making the order would be desirable in the interests of improving the pupil's behaviour.

In other words this sanction can be applied as an alternative to exclusion but not for lesser breaches of discipline.

Section 99: Parenting contracts and parenting orders: further provisions

This section makes further and consequential changes to the Anti-social Behaviour Act 2003 (ASBA 2003), complementing ss.97 and 98. Section 21 is amended to require a court which is considering whether to grant a parenting order for misbehaviour, to take into account any previous failure by the parent to attend a reintegration interview (see s.102 below) and a new s.22A is inserted.

ASBA 2003, s.22A Parenting contracts and parenting orders: further provisions

This enables the Secretary of State to make regulations covering a number of detailed issues including:

- which LEA should have the power to enter into a parenting contract or apply for an order when the child lives in one authority but attends school in another

- which school should have the power to apply for an order where the pupil has been permanently excluded

- requirements to consult and share information

- how the costs associated with parenting contracts and orders should be met.

Excluded pupils ss.100–108

Section 100: Duty of governing body or proprietor where pupil excluded for fixed period

This section introduces a duty for schools to provide suitable full time education to temporarily excluded pupils. This is a new requirement that education provision for excluded pupils is provided from a day specified in regulation, likely to be day six of a fixed term exclusion, rather than day 16 as is currently the case.

The Secretary of State can prescribe exceptions, make regulations and give guidance relevant to this duty. The use of the phrase 'suitable full-time education' makes it clear that this must be more than sending work for the pupil to do at home.

Such education may be provided on the premises of the excluding school only if it is part of a joint arrangement with at least one other school. So schools cannot meet this requirement simply by running their own internal 'sin-bin'. For the purposes of this section 'governing body' includes the proprietor of an academy, CTC and a CCTA.

Section 101: Duty of local education authority in relation to excluded pupils

Section19 of EA 1996 previously required LEAs to make suitable, but not necessarily full-time, education available for children out of school for any reason. They must now provide permanently excluded pupils with suitable full-time education.

This is the corresponding new requirement on LEAs that education provision for permanently excluded pupils is provided from day six of an exclusion, rather than day 16. LEAs are also required to make suitable full-time education available to pupils excluded for fixed periods from a pupil referral unit. It also provides power for the Secretary of State to prescribe exceptions to this duty and makes clear that pupils excluded from academies and CTCs are covered.

Section 102: Reintegration interviews

The common practice of schools inviting the parents of a temporarily excluded pupil to take part in a reintegration interview can now be made obligatory via regulations to be made by the Secretary of State or the National Assembly for Wales. It should be noted that the obligation is formally imposed on the headteacher to arrange the interview rather than the parent to attend. However, failure to attend can to be taken into account if a parenting order later comes into play (see s.99 above).

Regulations can specify the circumstances in which reintegration interviews must be arranged and the procedures and time limits connected with them. They will apply to maintained schools, academies and CTCs.

Section 103: Duty of parent in relation to excluded pupil

This is the controversial 'house arrest' provision. Where a pupil is excluded for a fixed period or permanently and the parent has been given a s.104 notice, the parent must ensure that the excluded pupil is not present in a public place during normal school hours on the first five school days of the exclusion. If the parent fails in this duty they commit an offence and become liable on summary conviction to a level 3 fine. The parent has a defence if he shows that he had a reasonable justification for the failure. 'Parents' can only be individuals, so a local authority cannot find itself prosecuted as the corporate parent of an excluded looked after child.

LEAs are the only agency that can institute proceedings against the parent.

Section 104: Notice to parent relating to excluded pupil

The form and substance of the notice parents must receive from the school when their child is excluded is set out in primary legislation for the first time. This is largely because a prosecution could follow.

The headteacher must give the parent of an excluded pupil a notice containing information about the exclusion. Regulations can make more detailed provision but the notice must specify:

- when the exclusion starts
- when the parent will be subject to the s.103 duty to ensure that the pupil is not in a public place during school hours
- when alternative full-time education will be provided.

Subsection (3) specifies that house arrest cannot exceed five days. In the case of permanent exclusions, where the LEA must arrange the alternative education, the LEA must also provide information so that the headteacher can include it in the notice to the parent.

Subsection (6) ensures that the notice can be served by any effective method, e.g. by email and that it does not have to be served by one of the methods set out in s.572 of EA 1996. Subsection (7) allows regulations to be made enabling the notice issued to the parent under this section to be combined with the notice the parent receives under s.52(3) of EA 2002 when their child is excluded.

Section 105: Penalty notice in respect of presence of excluded pupil in public place

This section allows for a penalty notice, similar to those that are issued in respect of road traffic violations, to be given to a parent who appears to be guilty of an offence under s.103. The penalty notice will allow a parent to pay a penalty as a way of discharging any liability for the offence of failing to ensure that their child is not present in a public place. Subsection (6) allows for regulations to permit the LEA to retain the revenue they receive from penalty notices to cover the costs of enforcement and requires it to remit any surplus to the Secretary of State. Only authorised persons may issue a penalty notice. These include:

- the police
- local authority officers
- headteachers
- school staff authorised by the head.

Section 106: Penalty notices: supplemental

This section simply provides for the Secretary of State to make regulations and give guidance, about the administration of penalty notices. It enables regulations to specify the form and content of penalty notices; the amount of the penalty, time limits for its payment and to whom it should be paid; how it may be paid and which persons may issue it.

Section 107: Penalty notices: amendments of Police Reform Act 2002

The existing power of police community support officers, or other 'accredited persons', to issue fixed penalty notices to the parents of truants found in a public place is extended to cover those who fail to keep their excluded children at home. This is achieved by amending para.1 Schedule 4 of the Police Reform Act 2002.

Section 108: Removal of excluded pupils to designated premises

The existing power of the police to apprehend truants under s.16 of the Crime and Disorder Act 1998 is amended to allow them to remove excluded pupils from a public place to premises designated by the LEA e.g. the offices of the LEA. It also amends Schedule 4 to the Police Reform Act 2002 to enable community support officers to exercise the new power. The Police and Justice Act 2006 amends the 2002 Act to allow police community support Officers to return truants to designated premises.

School Attendance ss.109–110

Section 109: Failure to secure school attendance

Section 444 of EA 1996, which is amended here, provides that an offence may be committed by a parent whose child fails to attend regularly at a school at which he is a registered pupil. There are two offences:

- the first, under subsection (1), is established if the child is not attending regularly as a matter of fact

- the second and more serious offence under subsection (1A) is committed where the parent knew the child was not attending but failed, 'without reasonable justification', to take steps to remedy the situation.

It was previously assumed that this formulation created a 'reverse burden of proof'. That is to say, where parents are charged with an offence under subsection (1A) the prosecution does not have to prove that the parents knew about the absence and did nothing, but it is for the parents to prove, on the balance of probabilities, that they have a reasonable justification for failing to ensure the child's attendance.

However, a decision of the High Court on 15 March 2006 in *R (on the application of P) v Liverpool City Magistrates* [2006] EWHC 887 (Admin) held that the words 'without reasonable justification' in subsection (1A) of s.444 of EA 1996 created an evidential burden which would allow the parent to offer credible evidence of justification which the prosecution would then have to show to be untrue or unreasonable.

This section therefore reverses the effect of the high court judgment. The words: 'without reasonable justification' are replaced by a new subsection s.444(1B) in EA 1996, which states:

It is a defence for a person charged with an offence under subsection (1A) to prove that he had a reasonable justification for his failure to attend regularly at the school.

The section also makes similar amendments in relation to a defence based on the child's sickness or any other unavoidable cause and alters the wording of the available defence where the child is of no fixed abode and the parent's trade or business requires travel from place to place, but there is no change of substance.

Further amendments ensure that these offences apply to attendance of an excluded pupil at the alternative full-time education that must now be proved under E&IA 2006. This will cover all maintained schools, pupil referral units, academies and CTCs or CCTAs.

Consequential amendments bring the language of ss.444ZA of EA 1996 (inserted by s.116 of EA 2005) and s.16 of the Crime and Disorder Act 1998 into line with the language used in s.444, as amended by this section. These new interpretations do not apply to absences prior to commencement of this section on 8 November 2006.

Section 110: Sums received under s.444A of 1996 Act

This section allows LEAs to use receipts from penalty notices for any of their functions by amending subsection (6) of s.444A of EA 1996. Any sums not so used must be paid to the Secretary of State.

Interpretation of Chapter 2

Section 111: Meaning of 'maintained school' and 'relevant school' in Chapter 2

This section simply defines 'maintained schools' and 'relevant school' for the purposes of Chapter 2 of Part 7.

Part 8: Inspections

Part 8 (ss.112–159) creates a new inspectorate for children's services and learners (outside higher education). Two corporate bodies are created: the Office for Standards in Education, Children's Services and Skills ('the Office') will provide an accountability mechanism for Her Majesty's Chief Inspector of Education, Children's Services and Skills (HMCI). The new inspection arrangements commenced on 1 April 2007. The Government wishes the new body to be known as 'Ofsted', the familiar title of the Office of Her Majesty's Chief Inspector of Schools. To quote the marketing strategy for the changeover: 'a new organisation – a trusted name'. There will be little immediate impact on inspected bodies.

The Government's strategy for the inspection of public services is developing. The existing statutory flexibilities in inspection frameworks have been carried forward which is likely to result in the further development of inspection practice. In particular, the Office and HMCI, in ss.117(1) and 119(1), are required to carry out their work in a way which the old Ofsted did not have to, namely:

- to improve inspected activities
- to assess the extent to which inspected activities are 'user-focused'.

In the longer term, this refocusing of Ofsted towards improvement and the user is likely to lead to changes in the inspection frameworks.

Two sections in Part 8 are not related to the creation of the new inspectorate: s.154 makes a relatively small, but important, change to school inspections and s.156 applies only to Wales.

What will the new Ofsted do?

The new Ofsted brings together all or part of four existing inspectorates as shown in Table 6.

Structure of Part 8

There are seven chapters reflecting the breadth of the new inspectorate's responsibilities.

Table 6 Transfer of Functions into 'New' Ofsted

Existing Inspectorate	Transferring functions	Remaining functions
Her Majesty's Chief Inspector of Schools	Inspection of • maintained schools, academies and non-maintained special schools (EA 2005) • other independent schools (EA 2002) • further education for 16–19 year olds (LSA 2000) • area 14–19 inspections (LSA 2000) • careers/Connexions services (Education and Training Act 1973 and LSA 2000) • initial and in-service teacher education (Education Act 1994) and • local education authorities (EA 1997) Registration and inspection of childminding and daycare (Children Act 1989) and funded nursery education (SSFA 1998) until transfer to childcare (Childcare Act 2006) Lead role in the inspection of children's services and joint area reviews (Children Act 2004)	None
Adult Learning Inspectorate	Further education for persons aged 19 and skills training for person aged over 16 (LAS 2000)	None
Commission for Social Care Inspection	Inspection of local authority social services functions for children under the age of 18 (as listed under the Local Authority Social Services Act 1970) which will include services for children in need including child protection and certain services for person over 18 leaving care (Children Act 1989 as amended) (Health and Social Care (Community Health and Standards) Act 2003) Registration and inspection of the following functions provided by local authorities and voluntary and private sector bodies: • children's homes • residential family centres • fostering agencies • voluntary adoption agencies and • adoption support agencies (Care Standards Act 2000 as amended)	Adult services (except those relating to young people aged 18 and over leaving care which will transfer to Ofsted) CSCI estimates that it will retain over 80 per cent of its existing activites.
Her Majesty's Inspectorate of Court Administration	Children and Family Court Advisory and Support Service (CAFCASS) (Criminal Justice and Courts Services Act 2000 and Courts Act 2003)	All other functions

- **Chapter 1: The Office and the Chief Inspector (ss.112–121)**

  Establishes and specifies the strategic functions of the Office for Standards in Education, Children's Services and Skills, Her Majesty's Chief Inspector of Education, Children's Services and Skills and the Children's Rights Director.

- **Chapter 2: General transfer of functions (s.122)**

  Transfers all the functions of Her Majesty's Chief Inspector of Schools to the new Chief Inspector except where new statutory provision is made in Part 8, for example with the inspection of further education.

- **Chapter 3: Inspection of further education and training, etc. (ss.123–134)**

  Provides a common statutory basis for the inspection of post-16 further education and training. Abolishes the Adult Learning Inspectorate.

- **Chapter 4: Inspection and review of local authorities in England (ss.135–142)**

  Provides a common statutory basis for the inspection of the education and children's services work of local authorities.

- **Chapter 5: Inspection of CAFCASS functions (ss.143–145)**

  Enables the new Ofsted to inspect the Children and Family Court Advisory and Support Service (CAFCASS)

- **Chapter 6: Further provisions relating to the functions of Chief Inspector (ss.146–153)**

  Transfers CSCI's functions for the registration and inspection of children's homes, adoption and fostering services, etc., legislates on how the new Ofsted relates to other public service inspectorates and provides for corporate functions such as the publication of reports.

- **Chapter 7: Miscellaneous and supplementary (ss.154–159)**

  Contains the two sections (154 and 156) not related to the creation of the new inspectorate, provides for payments by local authorities to Ofsted for certain services and introduces minor and consequential amendments and transitional arrangements.

Why change?

The Adult Learning Inspectorate (ALI), formed in 2001, is the oldest of the pre-decessor bodies that make up the new Ofsted. CSCI and HMICA were only formed in 2004 and the statutory basis of the previous incarnation of Ofsted is EA 2005.

Government policy on the reform of public service inspectorates was a key driver for change. After wide consultation, the Prime Minister's Office of Public Services Reform published in July 2003 *The Government's Policy on Inspection of Public Services* which contained ten principles 'based on the Government's understanding of best practice in inspection'. These include:

- the need for inspection to have improvement as a key purpose

- a focus on outcomes

- the level of inspection must be proportionate to risk

- inspection should encourage rigorous self-assessment

- inspection should have a clear focus on the experiences of those for whom the service is provided.

Further details can be found in *Inspecting for Improvement: Developing a Customer Focused Approach* (OPSR, 2003). These principles have fed into the new school inspection arrangements including the pilot launched in September 2006 of light touch inspections for high achieving schools.

The Gershon Review, *Releasing Resources for the Frontline: Independent Review of Public Sector Efficiency*, published as part of the Spending Review 2004 looked at the burden of inspections and the £0.5bn a year spent on public service inspection. This review led to the new shorter school inspection system in EA 2005 and a 30 per cent reduction in expenditure.

The Hampton Review, *Reducing Administrative Burdens: Effective Inspection and Enforcement* (2005) although it was about private sector inspection, was also used to guide the further development of public service inspection.

A public service inspection strategy was published as part of the 2005 Budget Report (p.141). The strategy repeats the need to refocus inspection on what is relevant to users of public services and to reduce the burden of inspections. A new objective of rationalising inspectorates was promulgated 'in order to simplify and manage better

the complex pattern of multiple scrutiny that service providers experience'. Thus the number of public service inspectorates was to be reduced to four covering: criminal justice; education, children's services and skills; health and social care and an inspectorate for local services.

The inspectorate for education, children's services and skills is the only one that has been created so far. The government proposal to merge the five criminal justice inspectorates was defeated in the House of Lords (in the Police and Justice Bill) resulting in the complex arrangements for the inspectorates to work together found in s.149 of the E&IA 2006. The proposal to have a local services inspectorate is found in Part 8 of the Local Government and Public Involvement in Health Bill before Parliament in the 2006–07 session. There is no active proposal to merge the Healthcare Commission and CSCI to form a health and social care inspectorate.

The Government also intends to introduce greater accountability into the inspection arrangements. The new Education, Children's Services and Skills Inspectorate makes Her Majesty's Chief Inspector (HMCI) accountable to a lay board, called 'the Office'. This mirrors the governance arrangements for CSCI. The Chief Inspector will be solely responsible for inspection arrangements and the engagement of staff and will report directly to the Secretary of State on the quality of education, etc. This change also responds to criticisms, dating from the late 1990s, that Ofsted has not been sufficiently accountable.

Every Child Matters

It was perhaps inevitable that with the Every Child Matters programme, which looks to integrate support services for children, there should be demands to integrate inspection arrangements for children's services. There were ten inspectorates and commissions which had a role in assessing the quality of services for children. The Act reduced this to seven by abolishing the Adult Learning Inspectorate, which had responsibility for inspecting skills training for 16 and 17 year olds as well as its adult functions and by removing children's work from the Commission for Social Care Inspection (CSCI) and Her Majesty's Inspectorate of Court Administration (HMCIA).

Consultation and implementation

A comprehensive consultation document *A single Inspectorate for Children and Learners* was produced by the DfES on 29 July 2005 and contains extensive information on how the new inspectorate fits into the Government's strategy for public service inspection. Preparatory work commenced in Summer 2006. Following a public advertisement, Zenna Atkins, an Executive Consultant for Social Solutions Ltd, a specialist consultancy promoting entrepreneurialism and social enterprise, was appointed to chair the shadow Office in September 2006. The Office was formally established on 12 December 2006. The Act provided that Her Majesty's Chief Inspector of Schools (Christine Gilbert) became Her Majesty's Chief Inspector of Education, Children's Services and Skills on the establishment of the new Inspectorate on 1 April 2007.

Chapter 1 – The Office and the Chief Inspector

The Office

Section 112 creates the Office for Standards in Education, Children's Services and Skills. Sections 116 and 117 specify the functions and how the Office is to perform its functions.

Section 112 and Schedule 11: Office for Standards in Education, Children's Services and Skills

This section creates the Office for Standards in Education, Children's Services and Skills and was established on 12 December 2006 by virtue of E&IA 2006 *(Commencement No.1 and Savings Provisions) Order 2006* (SI 2006/105).

The Government announced in *A single Inspectorate for Children and Learners* that it wishes to retain the current popular term 'Ofsted' for the new body. Its official title the Office for Standards in Education, Children's Services and Skills would produce the acronym OfSECSS which Conservative MP Nick Gibb noted in debate has the mnemonic 'off-sex' (Standing Committee E, 11 May 2006, col 901). For convenience, the text will use the term 'Office' (as does the Act) to distinguish it from HM

Chief Inspector (HMCI) although the term 'Ofsted' is used where there is no need to distinguish between the Office and HMCI.

The Office is to carry out its functions on behalf of the Crown, a formulation designed to show that the new body is distinct from the Secretary of State as a member of the Government and is answerable to Parliament directly.

Schedule 11 sets out administrative detail about how members of the Office are appointed and how the Office will work.

The Office will comprise a chairman and between five and ten members appointed by the Secretary of State, and HMCI. The Schedule contains standard rules on the appointment, remuneration, pensions, etc. of Office members except HMCI (see s.115). The Schedule allows the Office to appoint committees to carry out work, regulate its proceedings (including the quorum for meetings), delegate responsibility, etc. Members must not be appointed for a term of more than five years.

On two important issues, staff management (para.6) and contracts, land, property and commendation (para.12), the Office's powers can only be exercised by HMCI. Thus, although the Office will be the employer of all staff, HMCI must exercise the employer's functions and manage the staff, acting on behalf of the Office (with conditions of service being subject to the approval of the Minister for the Civil Service). Similarly, HMCI will enter into contracts on behalf of the Office and will manage all property and accommodation.

The Chief Inspector and other inspectors ss. 113–115

Section 113 creates the office of Her Majesty's Chief Inspector of Standards in Education, Children's Services and Skills. Sections 118 and 119 specify the functions and how the HMCI is to perform his/her functions.

Section 113: Her Majesty's Chief Inspector of Education, Children's Services and Skills

The Queen may appoint a person to the office of Her Majesty's Chief Inspector of Education, Children's Services and Skills (subsection (1)). Of course, the Queen does not have to do the interviewing; Jim Knight (Minister of State, DfES) has

explained that 'There is a longstanding convention that the Secretary of State for Education and Skills, on behalf of the Government, makes a recommendation to Her Majesty on the appointment' (Written Parliamentary Answer, 27 November 2006, col 426W). In any event, subsection (1) requires Her Majesty to act through the Privy Council of which the Secretary of State is a member.

The office of Her Majesty's Chief Inspector of Schools in England is abolished (subsection (8)) by the repeal of s.1 of EA 2005 under Schedule 18 of E&IA 2006, thus bringing to an end a public office which was first created under the Education (Schools) Act 1992. Previously, there was only provision in statute for the appointment of inspectors by Her Majesty (HMI) although one was designated as the Senior Chief HMI. Subsection (9) transfers the HMCI postholder immediately before 1 April 2007 – the appointed day – to the new HMCI post.

As the term 'Chief Inspector' has been used to describe the office holder in legislation, amendments are required to redefine who the Chief Inspector is. For example, para.117 of Schedule 14 replaces the statutory definition of the old HMCI with the new HMCI in CCA 2006.

The Secretary of State determines HMCI's terms of appointment (subsection (5)) but the term of office may be no more than five years. However, an HMCI is not barred from reappointment (subsections (6) and (7)) but may be removed from office by Her Majesty on grounds that he or she is unable or unfit to work.

Section 114: Her Majesty's Inspectors of Education, Children's Services and Skills

Her Majesty, by Order in Council, may appoint Her Majesty's Inspectors of Education, Children's Services and Skills (subsection (1)) to be referred to as 'HMI' (subsection (2)). HMIs will be on staff of the Office and under conditions determined by HMCI (subsections (3) and (4)). On leaving the Office, HMIs will lose their designation. In the past, HMIs have occasionally been allowed to retain their Royal Warrant on transferring to another post in government but this will no longer be possible (subsection (5)). Existing HM Inspectors of Schools in England who are serving on HMCI's staff or on the staff of the Adult Learning Inspectorate (ALI) will transfer to become HMIs (subsections (6) and (7)). Equivalent provision is not made for the staff of the Commission for Social Care Inspection (CSCI) or Her Majesty's

Inspectorate of Court Administration (HMICA) as they do not currently employ HMIs.

Section 115: Further provision about Chief Inspector and other inspectors, etc. and Schedule 12: The Chief Inspector and other inspectors

Section 115 introduces Schedule 12 which is divided into two parts: Part 1 covers HMCI's role and is mainly new material defining the relationship between the Office and HMCI and Part 2 covers the delegation of functions to HMI and additional inspectors which mainly repeats material from Schedule 1 to EA 2005.

Schedule 12, Part 1: The Chief Inspector (paras.1–8)

The Secretary of State determines the remuneration and pension of HMCI (para.1). Paragraphs 4, 5 and 6 are technical provisions covering documents, evidence and ancillary powers.

Paragraphs 2, 3, 7 and 8 are new.

The office of HMCI has previously been vacated twice at short notice (Chris Wood-head in 2001 and David Bell in 2005), requiring the post to be filled without a public advertisement. Paragraph 2 enables the Secretary of State to appoint a person to be HMCI for a period of up to a year and to terminate the appointment when a new HMCI is appointed. Paragraph 3 enables HMCI, when absent or unable to act, to appoint an HMI to perform HMCI's functions. The Chair of the Office has the power to appoint an HMI to perform HMCI's functions if HMCI is incapacitated.

Paragraphs 7 and 8 deal with the relationship between the HMCI and the Office whereby HMCI has statutory independence from the Office but is nevertheless a member of it. References in previous legislation are adjusted to take account of this new arrangement, for example legal proceedings against HMCI will be taken against HMCI and not the Office. The Secretary of State has made an Order (see s.181) which sets out the respective responsibilities of the Office and HMCI for rights and liabilities relating to functions, staff and property. See *The Office for Standards in Education, Children's Services and Skills and her Majesty's Chief Inspector of Education, Children's Services and Skills (Allocation of Rights and Liabilities) Order 2007* (SI 2006/600).

Schedule 12, Part 2 – inspectors, etc. acting on behalf of Chief Inspector (paras.9–12)

Paragraph 9 replaces para.5 of Schedule 1 to EA 2005. HMCI can delegate functions to any HMI, any other member of the Office's staff and any additional inspector (see below). There are exceptions in para.9(3) and (4): HMCI has to authorise personally all findings that a school is in special measures or delegate the responsibility to an HMI who is authorised to carry out this task. Similarly, with the power to enter premises (e.g. s.10, EA 2005 for schools, ss.131 and 132 for further education and skills under E&IA 2006 and s.77 of CCA 2006 for childcare) for the purpose of inspections or otherwise, HMCI must take such decisions personally or authorise somebody to act on her behalf.

Paragraph 10 replaces and expands para.2(3) and (4) of Schedule 1 to EA 2005. Following pressure in the House of Lords during the passage of EA 2005, the Government brought forward amendments to require greater accountability of additional inspectors (see below): HMCI must ensure that additional inspectors must have the 'qualifications, experience and skills' to do the tasks required of them. E&IA 2006 extends this requirement to HMIs and other staff of the Office.

Since the founding of HM Inspectorate of Schools in 1839, there have been additional inspectors who support the work of HMI in a variety of inspection roles such as the inspection of specialist areas. EA 2005 designates as additional inspectors those inspectors provided by private sector 'inspection service providers' (ISPs). These additional inspectors have assisted with secondary, and led primary, school inspections since September 2005. Paragraph 11 confirms this arrangement and that additional inspectors can be directly contracted by HMCI. An additional inspector cannot conduct an inspection unless supervised by an HMI, or has previously conducted an inspection to the satisfaction of an HMI.

Paragraph 12 repeats material from EA 2005 on additional inspectors contracted to ISPs. HMCI must publish the qualifications or experience (or both) required by additional inspectors provided by ISPs and the standards and skills which these additional inspectors are required to meet. HMCI must also publish a list of names supplied by ISPs of all those individuals who may be used as additional inspectors, and republish the list at least every 12 months. The contracts which HMCI has with ISPs must stipulate that additional inspectors must meet the published requirements.

Functions: the Office ss.116–117

Sections 116 and 117 introduce the Office, the new governance arrangement for Ofsted. The new arrangements and in particular the introduction of a Governance Board were the result of pressure from various quarters to make the organisation more accountable.

Section 116: Functions of the Office

The Office determines the strategic priorities, objectives and targets for the HMCI and secures that HMCI's functions (see s.118) are performed efficiently and effectively, or as the consultation document puts it, to 'enable a non-executive chair and board to hold the chief inspector accountable for delivering' her statutory responsibilities (para.2.1.60). The Secretary of State can give additional functions to the Office which are related to HMCI's functions.

The Education and Inspections Act 2006 (Commencement No.1 and Savings Provisions) Order 2006 (SI 2006/2990) commenced the Office's responsibility for setting the priorities, objectives and targets for HMCI on 12 December 2006 along with s.117. *The Office for Standards in Education, Children's Services and Skills (Transitional Provisions) Regulations 2006* (SI 2006/2991) made temporary modifications to s.116 to determine HMCI's strategic priorities before the establishment of the new inspectorate on 1 April 2007.

Section 117: Performance of the Office's functions

The Office has three general functions (subsection (1)) which are also given to HMCI in s.119(1). The Office has to encourage:

- improvement of activities within HMCI's remit

- carrying on of such activities as user-focused activities

- efficient and effective use of resources in carrying on of such activities.

The first two of these are new. In addition, the Office has to have regard to the following (subsection (2)):

- the need to safeguard and promote the rights and welfare of children, that is persons under the age of 18 (a current function of CSCI, see s.76(1)(f) of HSC(CHS)A 2003)

- views expressed by relevant persons about activities within HMCI's remit

- levels of satisfaction with such activities on the part of relevant persons (see below)

- the need to promote the efficient and effective use of resources in the carrying on of such activities

- the need to ensure that action by HMCI in relation to such activities is proportionate to the risks against which it would afford safeguards

- any developments in approaches to inspection or regulatory action

- best practice amongst persons performing functions comparable to those of HMCI.

The Explanatory Notes (para.547) record that 'These are intended, as far as is possible, to reflect the Government's ten principles of public sector inspection' (see page 136).

Subsection (3) repeats the longstanding requirement that HMCI must have regard to 'aspects of government policy as the Secretary of State may direct'. See s.119(3).

Subsections (4) to (6) contain the important definitions of 'relevant persons' and 'activities' in HMCI's remit.

The Office must have regard to the views and levels of satisfaction with the inspected services of 'relevant persons'. These are people benefiting from the services which Ofsted inspects including students and trainees, their parents if under the age of 18 and employers. Employees and those assisting with the provision of services are not mentioned although arguably such persons are included implicitly in the Office's first general duty (see above): if a purpose of inspection is to support improvement then this must be done constructively with those who provide the services.

Subsection (5) makes clear that the definition of the activities that are in HMCI's remit in subsection (6) applies to the whole of Part 8 and to other legislation where HMCI has functions. The activities include the:

- provision of any form of education, training or care

- provision of any form of services or facilities and

- performance of any function.

This means that HMCI cannot inspect educational provision where there is no explicit provision in law. As there is no provision to inspect higher education (except initial teacher training under s.18B of the Education Act 1994), Ofsted cannot inspect universities. Services are also included within HMCI's remit if Ofsted provides a registration service, for example childcare providers under the CCA 2006.

The meaning of 'user-focus' was debated in Parliament: The then Parliamentary Under-Secretary of State for Education and Skills (Phil Hope MP) stated that the term 'user-focus'

> *is a fairly well accepted part of modern management approaches, not just in the public sector but in the private sector ... we send a clear signal to the Office that the views of users matter and should be at the heart of what it does. ... In essence, a user focus means that services reflect the needs of those receiving them, be they children, young people, parents, adult learners or employers. In practice, the views of users are a major source of evidence for inspections. Those views might be learned through speaking to children in children's homes or seeking the views of parents when inspecting schools.*
> House of Commons Official Report, Standing Committee E, Thursday 11 May 2006, cols 911 and 912

Functions: the Chief Inspector ss.118–119

Sections 118 and 119 describe the functions of HMCI.

Section 118: Functions of the Chief Inspector

HMCI (subsection (1)) has a duty to keep the Secretary of State informed about:

- the quality of activities within HMCI's remit and (where appropriate) the standards achieved by those for whose benefit such activities are carried on

- improvements in the quality of such activities and in any such standards

- the extent to which such activities are being carried on as user-focused activities

- the efficient and effective use of resources in the carrying on of such activities and services.

This replaces the separate reporting duties found in s.2 of EA 2005 for schools, s.31 of CCA 2006 for childcare, s.54 (for adult learning) and s.51 (for further education) of L&SA 2000 and s.5B of CSA 2000 (as substituted by HSC(CHS)A 2003) for children's social care. There was no general reporting duty on Ofsted for reporting on local authorities.

The most significant change is with reporting on schools. Section 2(1) of EA 2005 is repealed which required reporting on:

- the quality of the education provided by schools in England

- how far that education meets the needs of their pupils

- the educational standards achieved

- the quality of leadership and management, including whether schools' financial resources are managed efficiently

- the spiritual, moral, social and cultural development of pupils

- the contribution schools make to the well-being of their pupils

- the extent to which schools are developing rigorous internal procedures of self-evaluation

- the behaviour and attendance of pupils.

The remainder of the section mainly repeats statutory provisions that were first enacted in the Education (Schools) Act 1992. HMCI must provide information or advice on any matter in her remit when requested by the Secretary of State (subsection (2)) and can give advice at any time (subsection (3)). Further functions can be assigned by the Secretary of State (subsection (4)). HMCI can use existing powers, with necessary modifications, to carry out his requests for information including powers of entry and inspection of documents (subsections (5) to (8)).

Section 119: Performance of Chief Inspector's functions

Reflecting the same duties that are placed on the Office in s.117, HMCI, in performing her functions, has to encourage:

- improvement of activities within HMCI's remit

- carrying on such activities with a userfocus (see s.118)
- efficient and effective use of resources.

In addition, HMCI must ensure that her functions are carried out efficiently and effectively and with regard to the needs of users of services within her remit (subsection (2)). HMCI must have regard to the same matters as the Office does in performing its functions (subsection (3)) in s.117(2) and (3).

The Children's Rights Director

Section 120: Children's Rights Director

The post of the Children's Rights Director is to be held by an employee of the Office (subsection (1)). The post replaces that of the Children's Rights Director (CRD) in the Commission for Social Care Inspection. The DfES consultation paper *A single Inspectorate for Children and Learners* (DfES, 2005) asked (paras.2.1.40 to 2.1.47) about the future of this post given the creation of the Children's Commissioner under CA 2004 subsequent to the creation of the CRD post under CSA 2000. The Secretary of State, by regulations, can set out the functions of the Children's Rights Director (subsection (2)) but the functions must relate to HMCI's functions on the welfare of children in boarding schools and colleges (s.87 of CA 1989), registration and standards of such institutions (Part 2 of CSA 2000) and the inspection and review of local authority social care functions (subsection (3)). *The Office for Standards in Education, Children's Services and Skills (Children's Rights Director) Regulations 2007* (SI 2007/460) specify the functions. The CRD is required to advise and assist HMCI when she carries out the functions specified in subsection (3) having regard to the need to safeguard and promote the rights and welfare of children and the views expressed by relevant persons (see s.117 above), in particular by ascertaining and reporting the views of children (and, where appropriate, their parents).

A call in the consultation exercise for the CRD post to include other vulnerable children such as excluded children was rejected by the Government on the grounds that the post was for the specific needs of children living away from home. The then Parliamentary Under-Secretary of State for Education and Skills (Phil Hope MP) explained:

> *The essence of the post of Children's Rights Director ... is to be the voice within Ofsted of the most vulnerable children. ... We intend the children's rights director*

to assist and advise the Chief Inspector with his duties to have regard to the need to safeguard and promote the rights and welfare of children when carrying out his functions and in particular to find out what children think about the services they receive. His function is restricted to those children in receipt of social care services – that is a crucial difference between his role in the inspectorate and that of the [Children's] commissioner. He must ensure that the most vulnerable and those most at risk are protected and that those accommodated in schools and further education colleges are given a voice in the new Ofsted.

House of Commons Official Report, Standing Committee E, Thursday 11 May 2006, col 919

Annual reports, etc.

Section 121: Annual report and other reports to Secretary of State

HMCI has to make an annual report to the Secretary of State, who in turn must lay this report before Parliament and HMCI has the power to submit other reports to the Secretary of State as appropriate. This section replaces several sections in existing legislation, for example s.3 of EA 2005.

Chapter 2 – General transfer of functions

Section 122: General transfer of functions to the Chief Inspector

The functions of the HMCI of Schools in any enactment are transferred to the HMCI of Education, Children's Services and Skills except where E&IA 2006 repeals relevant legislation. For example, E&IA 2006 makes new provision for the inspection of further education and training, and the provisions in LSA 2000 are not transferred, and are repealed.

The HMCI/Ofsted functions which transfer are the inspection of maintained schools and academies (in EA 2005), nursery education (in SSFA 1998), child minding and day care (in CA 1989), childcare (in CCA 2006 when the new system is introduced in September 2008), independent schools (in EA 2002), Connexions/careers services (LSA 2000 and the Education and Training Act 1973) and teacher training (in the Education Act 1994). Specific CSCI functions transfer to HMCI under s.148. Sec-

tion 157 and Schedule 14 contain a large number of minor amendments to transfer functions to the new HMCI. *The Education and Inspections Act 2006 (Consequential Amendments) Regulations 2007* (SI 2007/603) amend regulations to transfer mainly CSCI functions to HMCI.

Chapter 3 – Inspection of Further Education and Training, etc.

Chapter 3 (ss.123–134) mainly replicates the existing provisions for inspecting further education, work-based training and adult learning, including area inspections, in Part 3 (ss.52–72) of LSA 2000; the reduction in sections is due to the amalgamation of the Adult Learning Inspectorate functions into those of HMCI.

Education and training to which this chapter applies

Section 123: Education and training to which this chapter applies

The education and training provision to which the chapter applies is (subsection (1)) with the statutory derivation from LSA 2000 in brackets:

(a) secondary education provided in institutions within the further education sector in England , i.e. in FE colleges (s.60(1)(a) LSA 2000)

(b) further education for persons aged 16 or over but under 19 which is provided in such institutions and wholly or partly funded by the Learning and Skills Council for England (s.60(1)(b) LSA 2000)

(c) further education for persons aged 19 or over which is wholly or partly funded by the Council (s.53(1)(a) LSA 2000)

(d) further education for persons aged under 19 which is provided by local education authorities in England (s.60(1)(c) LSA 2000)

(e) further education for persons aged 19 or over which is funded by such authorities (s.53(1)(c) LSA 2000)

(f) training for persons aged 16 or over which is funded by the Secretary of State under s.2 of the Employment and Training Act 1973 (s.53(1)(d) LSA 2000)

(g) training for persons aged 16 or over which takes place wholly or partly at the premises of an employer and which is wholly or partly funded by the Council (s.53(1)(a) LSA 2000).

In addition, the Secretary of State can prescribe, by regulations, other education or training including the training of teachers, lecturers, trainers or other persons providing the education or training listed above (subsection (2)). Subsection (3) allows, by regulations made by the Secretary of State, the provision of information and adult guidance to be inspected. *The Education and Inspections Act 2006 (Prescribed Education and Training etc.) Regulations 2007* (SI 2007/464) prescribe LSC or HEFCE funded training of or for teachers, lecturer, trainers or other persons providing education or training within the s.123 definition. LSC-funded education and training for 16 to 18 year olds which is not in an FE college or a work place is also included as information, advice and guidance falling within s.5 of LSA 2000.

Section (4) defines the 'further education sector' using the definition in s.91 of the Further and Higher Education Act 1992 as the further education corporations, i.e. FE colleges which have their roots in local government, and designated institutions, which will include those colleges established by the churches and other voluntary bodies, but mainly funded out of public money. It does not include private colleges which are funded by fee income or LSC funded provision made by, for example, private companies providing work-based skills.

Inspection ss.124–130

There are three sections on inspection, covering training, work-based learning and adult skills (s.124), FE colleges (s.125) and other education and training outside Ofsted's remit including private colleges and work-based learning not funded by the LSC for which Ofsted can charge (s.126). Section 127 requires inspected institutions to prepare an action plan in response to the inspection report. There are three sections on area inspections of all provision for 15–19 year olds covering inspection (s.128), reporting (s.129) and action planning (s.130).

Section 124: Inspection of education and training to which this chapter applies

Ofsted must inspect education or training which is in the remit specified by the Secretary of State; see s.123(1)(f) and (g). This definition enables education or training to be inspected which is outside FE colleges (see s.125) but publicly funded either by the LSC or local government and covers work-based learning and training provided by employers and also adult education provided by local authorities.

Inspections are to be conducted at intervals specified by the Secretary of State. On completion of an inspection, Ofsted must make a written report and the report must state whether the education or training is of 'a quality adequate to meet the reasonable needs of those receiving it'. Copies of the report must be sent to the provider of the education and training which will include the LEA if the authority is providing funds, for example with adult education provision. The report must go to the Secretary of State and the LSC and may be sent to other persons as Ofsted considers appropriate. The report must be published (see s.151 – this could be by publishing the report on Ofsted's website only). This section is mainly derived from s. 54(3) and s.55 of LSA 2000.

Section 125: Inspection of further education institutions

Ofsted must inspect all 'institutions within the further education sector' at intervals specified by the Secretary of State. See s.123 for the definition of the further education sector. The post-inspection procedure is the same as for s.124 except that the reports do not have to be sent to the LEA, even though the local authority may be funding secondary education provision in the college. This is because s.125 is derived from s.62 of LSA 2000 where there was no such provision. The LSA 2000 wording has been changed to take account of the fact that the Adult Learning Inspectorate (ALI) inspected colleges which provided only adult learning.

Section 126: Other inspections

Ofsted may inspect any education or training as defined in s.124 (subsection (1)). In other words, Ofsted is not limited to being asked by the Secretary of State to undertake an inspection of education or training. A written report may be made but, unlike inspections under ss.124 and 125, Ofsted may, but is not under a duty to, publish the report except that if a report is produced it must be sent to the provider of the educa-

tion and training and the LSC. The report must also go to the local authority if the authority is funding the provision.

Subsection (2) continues the power that ALI had to carry out inspections of further education and training in the private sector at the request of the provider. This includes private further education colleges (funded solely through fee income) or employment related training funded by employers. Ofsted may charge for the inspection. As with subsection (1) inspections, if Ofsted produces a written report, Ofsted may publish the report but is not under a duty to send the report to the LSC. Subsection (2) confirms one of the consultation issues, s.3 of *A single Inspectorate for Children and Learners* (DfES, 2005), namely that the ALI's commissioned support and advice roles will transfer to Ofsted and not the Quality Improvement Agency (QIA).

Section 126 largely repeats legislation from s.56 of LSA 2000. Subsection (7) is new: Ofsted can conduct inspections under subsection (2) outside the United Kingdom.

Section 127: Action plans

Following receipt of a written Ofsted inspection report, all providers must produce a written action plan together with an implementation timetable. This does not apply to inspections commissioned under s.126(2) (see above). The action plan must be published within a period prescribed by regulations made by the Secretary of State and copies sent to prescribed persons. *The Education and Inspections Act 2006 (Prescribed Education and Training etc.) Regulations 2007* (SI 2007/464) prescribes a period of two months for the publication of the action plan, except where the provision is found to be inadequate in which case the report must be published within one month. The report must be sent to Ofsted, LSC, the Quality Improvement Agency and any body providing public funds for education and training at the inspected provision. Copies must be available on request to interested parties.

Subsection (4) allows Ofsted to waive the requirement for an action plan. The Explanatory Notes para.565 give the example that this may happen if the standard of provision is particularly high and appropriate action is already under way and incorporated into existing plans.

Section 127 repeats material currently found in ss.58 and 64 of LSA 2000.

Section 128: Area inspections

Ofsted must, if requested by the Secretary of State, carry out an area inspection. This will cover all relevant provision in an area specified by the Secretary of State, which will 'normally reflect the way in which local education authorities and/or local Learning and Skills Councils are organised territorially' (Explanatory Notes, para.566). The inspection will examine the quality and availability of education or training and the standards achieved by persons aged 15 or over but under 19 (subsection (1)). Effectively this means the 14–19 phase as subsection (8) makes clear that all those who will reach the age of 15 in the current school year, (year 10), will be included in the scope of the inspections.

Ofsted can carry out inspections without being requested to do so (subsection (2)) and may extend the scope of area inspections to consider whether financial resources are being used in an efficient and effective manner in providing education and training for learners. Ofsted can report on whether provision gives value for money (subsections (3) and (4)).

Subsection (5) makes clear that area inspections can include any education or training within Ofsted's remit; that is, inspections can include school-based provision but not associated services which Ofsted inspects such as Connexions/careers services (as they are not education services).

Education and training providers (which will include schools and FE colleges) and local education authorities must supply information required by Ofsted for the area inspection (subsections (6) and (7)).

Section 128 repeats material found in s.65 of LSA 2000.

Section 129: Reports of area inspections

Ofsted must make a written report on completing an area inspection and must publish it (see s.151 below). The report must be sent to the Secretary of State, the LSC and relevant LEAs. Section 129 repeats material found in s.66 of LSA 2000.

Section 130: Action plans following area inspections

The Secretary of State can require either the LSC and/or an LEA to prepare a written action plan, together with a timetable setting out the action to be taken. *The Educa-*

tion and Inspections Act 2006 (Prescribed Education and Training etc) Regulations 2007 (SI 2007/464) require the plan to be published within two months except where the provision is found to be inadequate where the plan must be published within one month. Regulation 9 of the former regulations, *The Post-16 Education and Training Inspection Regulations* (SI 2001/799) required the plan to be published within three months of the Secretary of State asking for it. The person preparing the action plan, whether the LSC or the LEA, must make copies of the plan available to interested parties and send a copy to OfSTED, the QIA, any body providing public funds for the inspected education and training, and each provider of education or training.

Section 130 repeats material found in s.67 of LSA 2000.

Powers of entry, etc. ss.131–132

This group of sections covers Ofsted's power of entry (s.131) and power to inspect documents (s.132). Sections 131 and 132 repeat material found in ss.57 and 63 of LSA 2000.

Section 131: Power of entry

Ofsted has a power of entry to premises used in connection with the provision of further education and training when conducting any inspections except those commissioned by providers (see s.126(2) above). Ofsted must give reasonable notice in writing of an intention to enter an employer's workplace to inspect work-based education and training.

Section 132: Power to inspect documents, etc.

Section 132 complements the power of entry in s.131 by allowing inspectors to require production of documents, including computer records, and to take copies. Inspectors may require the assistance of a person operating a computer to access computer held records. Anybody who obstructs Ofsted in the exercise of the powers in ss.131 and 132 is liable on summary conviction to a fine not exceeding level 4 on the standard scale (£2,500 in April 2007).

Other provisions ss.133–134

This group of sections provides the legislative basis for the Common Inspection Framework (s.133) and abolishes ALI (s.134).

Section 133: Framework for inspections

Ofsted must devise one or more 'frameworks' covering all inspections of further education and training. A 'framework' is a common set of principles governing an inspection. The 'framework' must be published and revised from time to time.

Section 133 provides the legislative framework for the Common Inspection Framework and repeats the legislation found in ss.69 and 70 of LSA 2000. See www.ali.gov.uk/Publications/Publications/Oct+2005/common+Inspection+Framework.htm for the May 2005 Framework which covers all further education and training inspections.

Section 134: Abolition of Adult Learning Inspectorate

The Adult Learning Inspectorate was abolished on the 'appointed day', 1 April 2007.

Chapter 4 – Inspection and review of local authorities in England

The purpose of chapter 4 is to enable the new Ofsted to inspect and review the performance of each local authority's children's services. This is done by repealing, amending and transferring the current legislative functions (HSC(CHS)A 2003) of CSCI with respect to local authority children's social services and likewise with the old Ofsted functions in the heavily amended EA 1997. The problems of splitting CSCI's work and separating the England and Wales legislation on LEA inspection has led to a veritable legislative dog's breakfast. In addition, the legislative vehicle for involving other public sector inspectorates, such as the Healthcare Commission, in inspecting the totality of children's services in an area through the Joint Area Review under the Children Act 2004 remains largely intact.

Although it is very unlikely that this administrative legislation will be challenged in the courts, it is to be hoped that the Government will find Parliamentary time to con-

solidate the legislation to clarify which local authority functions are inspected and reviewed by the new Ofsted and which by the continuing CSCI.

Functions to which this chapter applies

Section 135: Functions to which this chapter applies and related activities

Subsection (1) defines the local authority functions which will be inspected by the 'new' Ofsted as follows:

(a) duties to improve the well-being of and reduce inequalities between, young children; secure early childhood services; secure sufficient childcare for working parents; provide information, advice and assistance, etc. under Part 1 of CCA 2006 (with the repeal of s.14 of that Act)

(b) all functions that the local authority has as a local education authority

(c) the local authority functions as a children's services authority under ss.10, 12 and 17–19 of CA 2004. This covers:

- cooperation to improve well-being

- information databases

- children and young people's plans and

- functions of the Director of Children's Services and the Lead Member for Children's Services

N.B. ss.11, 13–16 of CA 2004 and s.175 of EA 2002 are not included. This is because arrangements to safeguard and promote children's welfare and Local Safeguarding Children Boards will be covered by Joint Area Reviews.

(d) social services functions (as defined in the Local Authority Social Services Act 1970) for persons under 18. This includes those functions under the Children Act 1989 as amended, for: children in need; child protection; provision of children's homes; fostering services, etc.

(e) if paragraph (d) does not catch recent legislation on local authority adoption work, then paragraph (e) will include all local authority work to do with adoption including inter-country adoption

(f) in case anything has been left out, the Secretary of State can make regulations to include additional local authority functions. The power is not limited to services related to children. This matter was raised by the House of Lords Delegated Powers and Regulatory Reform Committee. In response, the Government replied that the use of this power was expected to be similar to the issues covered in paragraph (e) (above) and to provide sufficient flexibility to cover changes to social services functions.

This will ensure that the inspection of relevant local authority social services functions, currently the responsibility of CSCI, is correctly divided between the [new Ofsted] and CSCI to reflect the divisions of these functions into those primarily related to children and services for adults that are closely linked to services to children (the new Ofsted) and those primarily related to adults (CSCI).
House of Lords Delegated Powers and Regulatory Reform Committee, 24th Report of Session 2005–06 (HL 226).

Subsections (2) and (4) cover local authority activities done under the power to promote economic and social well-being in s.2 of the Local Government Act 2000 'which is similar in nature to anything which could be done by the authority' under subsection (1). Regulations under subsection (1)(f) need to mention specific activities if not covered by subsections (1)(a) to (e) if they are to be inspected by Ofsted.

Subsection (3) ensures that specific social services functions are included in Ofsted's remit. For example, adults who have recently left care, or adults who are preparing to, or have become, special guardians (a new provision introduced in 2005 under amendments to CA 1989 made by the Adoption and Children Act 2002). Subsection (5) transfers CSCI's functions for children under HSC(CHS)A 2003 to the new Ofsted.

Inspection and annual reviews ss. 136–138

Provides for Ofsted to inspect and carry out annual reviews of local authorities.

Section 136: Inspection of local authorities in England

This allows Ofsted to inspect the overall performance of a local authority as well as any particular function or functions of a local authority mentioned in s.135. Ofsted must carry out an inspection if requested by the Secretary of State.

Section 137: Reports of inspections under s.136

A written report must be made of an inspection and copies sent to the local authority and the Secretary of State. The local authority has to prepare an action plan in response to the inspection report. Regulations will set the time periods and manner in which the local authority must publish the inspection report and the action plan. Ofsted can publish the inspection report. Regulations may allow the authority to charge for copies of the inspection report and action plan. *The Education and Inspections Act 2006 (Inspection of Local Authorities) Regulations 2007* (SI 2007/462) requires the local authority within 30 working days of receiving the report to publish it by sending copies to a number of bodies including relevant partners as defined by s.10 of CA 2004, partners represented on the Local Safeguarding Children Board (under s.13 of CA 2004), at least one newspaper circulating in the area, and at least one radio station serving the area. The report has to be available free of charge for inspection at offices of the local authority, and copies supplied at a reasonable charge.

Section 138: Annual reviews of local authorities in England

Additionally, Ofsted must do an annual review of the overall performance of each local authority and award a performance rating. The period for the review is the financial year, the 12 month period ending on 31 March. This is similar to the provision in s.79 of HSC(CHS)A 2003. The requirement to carry out an annual review was one of the few issues about which local authority representatives expressed concern; but no parliamentarian chose to raise it in debate.

Powers of entry, etc. ss.139–140

Provides powers of entry by Ofsted to access information for inspection purposes. The powers are similar to those found in ss.88 and 89 of HSC(CHS)A 2003 and s.40 of EA 1997.

Section 139: Power of entry

Authorised Ofsted inspectors are given a power to enter local authority premises in order to carry out inspections and reviews. Domestic premises are excluded unless they are being used as a school. This will presumably prevent Ofsted inspecting the domestic end of home working arrangements.

Section 140: Power to inspect documents, etc.

In order to assist with inspections, Ofsted inspectors have a power to inspect, take copies of and remove documents and other items from premises. Ofsted can require persons to produce documents, such as registration information, insurance certificates, etc. and be given access to and take away, information held on computers. Ofsted can require assistance from anybody in charge of equipment or premises in taking measurements or photographs and collecting information.

Ofsted also has the right to interview in private people working on the premises and any child accommodated on local authority secured premises. The latter is to enable Ofsted to assess welfare issues in children's homes, residential boarding schools, etc. The child has to give consent to be interviewed.

A local authority officer has to be given a reasonable period of time in which to produce information and requests have to be given at 'reasonable times', in order to safeguard local authority staff being asked to do things during the night unless there is a significant concern over the welfare of a child.

Anybody who obstructs Ofsted inspectors in entering premises and inspecting documents, etc. is liable on summary conviction to a fine not exceeding level 4 on the standard scale (£2,500 in April 2007).

Supplementary ss.141–142

Section 141: Power to require information, etc.

Ofsted can at any time ask a local authority, or a body to whom the local authority have outsourced services, to provide information, documents or other items. The information, etc. must relate to a local authority's performance of any functions listed in s.135 and must relate to Ofsted's work in inspecting and reviewing local authorities. Again, any obstruction by a local authority or outsourced body to the exercise of this power can result on summary conviction to a fine not exceeding level 4 on the standard scale.

Section 142: Interpretation, etc.

Contains various definitions. It is made clear that Ofsted can inspect and review any relevant function that a local authority has outsourced. The Secretary of State is given a power to amend any requirement of Chapter 4 in relation to the Isles of Scilly.

Chapter 5 – Inspection of CAFCASS functions

The Children and Family Court Advisory and Support Service (CAFCASS) was established in 2001 by the Criminal Justice and Court Services Act 2000 to bring together support for vulnerable children in family proceedings including the local authority Family Court Welfare Service, the work of the guardians ad litem and the reporting officers of the children's division of the Official Solicitor. Responsibility for CAFCASS transferred to the DfES in 2004, at the same time as the new court inspection service, Her Majesty's Inspectorate of Court Administration, was established and made responsible for inspecting CAFCASS. This work transferred to Ofsted on 1 April 2007.

Section 143: Inspection of CAFCASS functions

Requires Ofsted to inspect the performance of CAFCASS. Reports must be sent to the Secretary of State, to CAFCASS and be published.

Section 144: Power of entry

Similar powers of entry are granted to Ofsted to inspect CAFCASS's work as are given to Ofsted under s.139 to inspect local authorities.

Section 145: Power to inspect documents, etc.

Again, similar powers to inspect documents, etc. are granted to Ofsted as they have under s.140 for the inspection and review of local authorities. There are two noteworthy differences. For CAFCASS, if computers, apparatus or material, etc. are kept on domestic premises, i.e. used for home working, Ofsted can take possession and retain them for as long as they are needed; but must return them thereafter. There is no penalty for obstructing Ofsted.

Chapter 6 – Further provisions relating to functions of Chief Inspector

Functions ss.146–149

Section 146: Inspection of secure training centres

The four Secure Training Centres (STCs) in England are purpose-built centres for young offenders and those on remand, from the ages of 12 to17. Although the institutions are managed in the private sector, places are commissioned and monitored by the Home Office's Youth Justice Board. Currently the institutions are jointly inspected by CSCI and Ofsted with the agreement of the Home Secretary. Section 146 allows this practice to continue, by repealing s.112 of the HSC(CHS)A 2003, thus enabling Ofsted to carry out inspections alone.

Section 147: Inspection of premises in connection with adoption and fostering functions

Ofsted can inspect 'relevant functions' of local authorities which are defined in s.43 of CSA 2000 as those relating to adoption (under the Adoption and Children Act 2002) and fostering (under CA 1989). Currently, s.45(4) of CSA allows CSCI to inspect premises where the local authority carries out such functions in accordance with regulations made by the Secretary of State. Section 147 re-enacts the provision. *Her Majesty's Chief Inspector of Education, Children's Services and Skills (Fees and Frequency of Inspections) (Children's Homes etc) Regulations 2007* (SI 2007/694) require local authorities to be inspected at least once in every three-year period.

See s.155 (below) for Ofsted's power to charge for this service.

Section 148: Transfer of certain CSCI functions to the Chief Inspector

The CSCI functions found in Part 2 of CSA 2000 relating to registration and inspection of private, local authority and voluntary services for children are transferred to Ofsted under this section. They are:

(a) children's homes

(b) residential family centres

(c) fostering agencies

(d) voluntary adoption agencies

(e) adoption support agencies.

Paragraphs 39–50 of Schedule 14 make consequential amendments to CSA 2000. See para.39 for the key provision which splits CSCI's functions. Paragraph 53 deals with the fees payable for registration and inspection. Many of the amendments are to add the words: 'or the CIECSS' (as this part of the Act refers to the Chief Inspector for Education, Children's Services and Skills) after the existing reference to 'CSCI'. This approach, rather than separating children's functions from other functions complicates and muddies the legislation and increases the scope for doubt, mistake and error. For example, s.5B of CSA 2000 leaves CSCI having a particular regard to the 'need to safeguard and promote the rights and welfare of children'. Purists may say that the catch-all nature of s.148 will mean this responsibility transfers to Ofsted. On the other hand, given that the adults who use the services inspected by CSCI will often live in close proximity to children, there is something to be said for CSCI having regard to the welfare of children as well. Either way, leaving legislation in this state is unhelpful.

The section also provides for the transfer to Ofsted of CSCI's functions under s.65 of the CA 1989 (disqualification from carrying on a children's home) and ss.87 to 87D of the Act (welfare of children in boarding schools and colleges). See paras.12 and 16 of Schedule 14 for consequential amendments.

Section 149: Interaction with other authorities and Schedule 13: Interaction with other authorities

Section 149 brings Schedule 13 into effect. This complex legislation supports the Government's policy on reducing the burden of public service inspection (see page 136) by getting the public service inspectorates to work together so that, for example, when inspecting a local authority for a Joint Area Review (JAR) there is a coordinated approach. The Government intends to put duties similar to those placed on Ofsted in Schedule 13 on the other public service inspectorates as the opportunity arises. For example, Part 4 of the Police and Justice Act 2006 puts similar duties on the five criminal justice inspectorates.

Ofsted can, under para.3, delegate any of its inspection functions to a public authority. Although a 'public authority' is a broad term, which includes school governing bodies and local authorities, the likelihood is that this will be used only to delegate functions to another inspectorate in order to reduce burdens and improve efficiency in performing inspections. Paragraph 4 requires Ofsted to adopt an inspection programme and an inspection framework after consultation with the other inspectorates and other bodies. Although the concept of an 'inspection framework' is not new, this is the first time it has been mentioned in legislation. It is now necessary to do so to support cooperation with the inspectorates, promote efficient working and prevent duplicate inspections. Under para.5, if Ofsted believes that another inspection would impose an unreasonable burden on an institution (which could include a local authority) which Ofsted inspects, then Ofsted must say so and this intervention can forestall the other body's inspection. However, there is an appeal mechanism to the Secretary of State. The remaining paragraphs enable cooperation and joint action with the other inspectorates. Assistance can be provided to other public authorities and inspections can be carried out also in Wales and Northern Ireland.

General provisions ss. 150–153

The provisions in these four sections apply to all of Ofsted's work, replacing separate provisions located elsewhere, for example EA 2005 for schools, CCA 2006 for childcare.

Section 150: Evidence of authority

Any person carrying out an inspection activity on behalf of Ofsted must be able to produce an authenticated document showing that he or she has the authority to carry out the inspection.

Section 151: Publication of inspection reports

All Ofsted reports are privileged. That is to say it is not possible to make a case in law that an Ofsted report has defamed a teacher, local authority officer, etc., unless the report can be shown to have been made with malice. Ofsted can publish reports in any manner including solely by electronic means; that is, publication is achieved even if a document appears only on the Ofsted website.

Section 152: Combined reports

Ofsted can combine one or more inspection reports into a single document, for example a thematic report drawn from inspecting a number of institutions, or a report on all the schools in a 'hard' federation. The existing powers are extended to enable a single report to include reporting by another inspectorate, for example the Healthcare Commission on the health and social care needs of vulnerable children in a locality.

Section 153: Use of information

Information acquired by Ofsted in pursuit of one of its functions can be used for any others.

Chapter 7 – Miscellaneous and supplementary

Miscellaneous ss.154–156

Section 154: Duty to report on contribution of certain schools to community cohesion

Section 5(5) of EA 2005 requires school inspectors to report on:

(a) the quality of the education provided

(b) how far that education meets the needs of the range of pupils

(c) educational standards achieved

(d) the quality of leadership and management, including whether the school's financial resources are managed effectively

(e) the spiritual, moral, social and cultural development of pupils

(f) the contribution made by the school to the well-being of those pupils (where well-being refers to the Every Child Matters five outcomes in CCA 2004).

This section, which was a late government amendment in response to concerns about the admission arrangements of faith schools, adds a seventh area of reporting, namely:

(g) the contribution made by the school to community cohesion.

See ss.33 and 38 above, for an amendment to school governing body duties in respect of community cohesion and the meaning of community cohesion.

Section 155: Payment of annual fee to the Chief Inspector by local authorities

Ofsted has to be paid an annual fee for the registration and inspection of local authority adoption and fostering services undertaken under s.147 (above).

This clarifies the arrangement for payment following the repeal of the former specific provision in s.51 of CSA 2000 in 2004. The provision differs from the repealed s.51 in that, although the Secretary of State's power to make regulations requiring a local authority to pay is retained, Ofsted is given the power, in the absence of regulations, to introduce a scheme for payments. Local authorities will now have to pay fees on the same basis as independent providers of adoption and fostering services. The fees are set out in *Her Majesty's Chief Inspector of Education, Children's Services and Skills (Fees and Frequency of Inspections) (Children's Homes etc.) Regulations 2007* (SI 2007/694).

Section 156: Removal of HMICA's duty to inspect performance of Assembly's functions relating to family proceedings

CAFCASS was established as an England and Wales body. However, following transfer of CAFCASS to the DfES in 2004, s.35 of CA 2004 transferred the CAF-CASS functions in Wales to the Assembly to be exercised by Welsh family proceedings officers. Under s.38 of CA 2004, Ofsted had to comply with a request to inspect the Assembly's performance of these functions. Section 156 (of the E&IA 2006) repeals s.38.

Supplementary

Section 157: Minor and consequential amendments and Schedule 14: Minor and consequential amendments relating to Part 8

This section brings Schedule 14 into effect. These minor and consequential amendments relate mostly to transferring functions from the other inspectorates to ensure that any ragged edges left by the division are tidied up and that CSCI, in particular, can fulfil its continuing functions.

Section 158: Transitional provisions and Schedule 15: Transitional provisions and savings relating to Part 8

This section brings Schedule 14 into effect. It provides for staff and property transfers to the new Ofsted and the continuity of inspections during the transition to the new arrangements. A time scale is set for the first annual report of the new HMCI.

Section 159: Interpretation of Part 8

None of these definitions is significant, although it is noteworthy that it contains another definition of the 150 local authorities which have education and social care responsibilities: a 'local authority in England'. This omits the 238 shire districts, all of which would consider themselves to be a local authority in England. Confusingly, the definition of an 'English local authority' in s.106 of CCA 2006 excludes the shire districts, but they are included in the definition of an 'English local authority' in s.100 of the Local Government Act 2003. See s.162 below.

Part 9: Miscellaneous

As the heading implies, this covers a range of topics requiring legislation, but which do not fit in with any of the themes covered earlier.

In this part of the Act cross headings often only introduce one or two sections. In several places therefore there is little if any difference between the cross heading and the title of the section itself. Although this introduces an element of duplication, we have maintained our convention of following the structure of the Act by including both the heading and the section title.

Investigation of complaints by Chief Inspector

Section 160: Power of Chief Inspector to investigate complaints by parents about schools

This implements the commitment in the White Paper (para.5.16, p.68) to give Ofsted a new power to investigate complaints made by parents. The White Paper indicated that parental complaints could lead to an immediate inspection, which in turn could trigger intervention. The new provisions do not go as far as to require Ofsted to consider the possibility of an inspection taking place as a result of a parental objection; although Ofsted's s.8 of EA 2005 power to inspect any school could be used, if deemed appropriate.

It operates by inserting three new sections after s.11 in EA 2005 which implemented the recent changes in the law with regard to inspection (see the *Plain Guide to the Education Act, 2005* NFER 2005). It inserts a new cross heading and sections as follows:

Investigation of complaints

EA 2005, s.11A: Power of Chief Inspector to investigate complaints about schools

The Chief Inspector can investigate written complaints from parents about any publicly funded school including CTCs. Registered parents of registered pupils at the school will qualify to make a complaint if they have exhausted all other complaints procedures. This came into force on 28 March 2007. Information made available

during debate on the Bill indicated that regulations would define matters for legitimate complaint which would include:

- the quality of education provided in the school

- the extent to which it meets the needs of its pupils

- standards of attainment achieved

- the quality of leadership and management, including financial management

- spiritual, moral, social and cultural development of pupils

- the contribution made by the school to its pupils' 'well-being' – the five outcomes.

EA 2005, s.11B: Investigations under s.11A

Ofsted can demand relevant information from the governing body of the school and hold a meeting with parents to explore the nature of complaints. The school must be notified and has to cooperate in the organisation of any such meeting. If it is a maintained school, the LEA is also required to cooperate with the investigation and may attend any meetings held as a result.

EA 2005, s.11C: Reports of investigations

This provides a permissive power for Ofsted to publish a report, although the receipt of a complaint does not create a duty to do this unless Ofsted considers it appropriate. Whenever a report is produced, it must be sent to the governing body (or the LEA where the school does not have a delegated budget), who can be required to distribute it to parents.

Powers to facilitate innovation

Section 161: Powers to facilitate innovation and Schedule 16: Powers to facilitate innovation

This amends the arrangements, initially introduced by s.2 of EA 2002, to allow schools to apply for a relaxation of any statutory provision to undertake experimental or innovatory activities designed to improve the quality of education. These are now adjusted to take account of the new framework of institutional arrangements introduced by E&IA 2006. Further education college governing bodies are now included as a body which can apply for a suspension of a statutory requirement.

An application could be made to permit FE colleges to participate in the creation of a foundation school. See the FE White Paper *Further Education: Raising Skills, Improving Life Chances* (Cm 6768, March 2006), para 61. This may no longer be necessary once the proposals in the Further Education and Training Bill, before Parliament in the 2006-07 session, give FE governing bodies additional powers to be involved in corporate bodies. Foundations associated with trust schools can also apply for exemption from statutory provisions, but they have to obtain the agreement of the relevant headteacher and governing body of any schools concerned. If the governors of a trust school seek a power of innovation they must consult the foundation. Headteachers in their own right are given the right to apply for a suspension of a statutory provision.

The initial provision was time-limited to four years from its commencement by virtue of s.2(7) and s.2(8) of EA 2002. Since that was 1 October 2002 the capacity to take advantage of this concession expired shortly before E&IA 2006 was passed and s.161 came into force. Paragraph 2 of Schedule 16 removes those sections from the earlier Act, thereby making these arrangements permanent.

November 2006 DfES guidance on the power to innovate can be found at www.innovation-unit.co.uk/images/stories/files/pdf/pti_guidance2006.pdf.

References to 'local education authority' or 'children services authority'

Section 162: Power to repeal references to 'local education authority' and 'children's services authority', etc.

Six subsections spread over two pages are in pursuit of the Government's policy of doing away with the terms 'local education authority' and 'children's services authority' on the grounds that they are 'becoming increasingly redundant and confusing as local authorities integrate education and children's social services functions'. A policy statement issued during debate on the Bill suggested that the use of the term 'children's services authority' was a transitional arrangement because the integration of separate education and children's services departments was expected to take place over a four-year period up to 2008. The expectation is that the generic term 'local authority' will reflect the fact that local government now operates in an integrated way across all its relevant functions. The fact that only a minority of the

500 plus local authorities in England actually have education and social services functions is not seen as an obstacle to this approach, although it is recognised that the actual changes to the wording of legislation will have to take account of this reality in order to avoid creating new confusion (see s.159 above). This section came into force on 8 January 2007, but has not yet been used by the Secretary of State or the National Assembly for Wales.

Provision of advice by Adjudicator

Section 163: Provision of advice by Adjudicator

Section 25 (Adjudicators) of the SSFA 1998 is amended to enable the Secretary of State to require the Office of the Schools Adjudicator (OSA) to provide advice on any matters relating to school admissions. It gives the OSA power to demand information from any schools about which the Secretary of State requires advice and schools have a duty to provide it.

This section is widely drawn, in that the Secretary of State can ask for advice about any schools that are in receipt of public funds. There is, however, an overlap with powers the OSA has, under Part 2 of E&IA 2006, to demand information from community, foundation and voluntary schools in the exercise of its own functions.

The significance of this section is that the School Admissions Code says in its introduction (para.10 (a) and footnote 4, p.9) that the Code applies to academies. However, the Code is enforced via the funding agreement (which in law is a contractual arrangement) by the Secretary of State, rather than by direct application of the legislation. In practice, the Secretary of State will use the OSA as the agent for investigating complaints and deciding how, and to what extent, the Code should be enforced rather than relying on DfES officials. This section gives him the necessary legal powers to operate in that way.

Interestingly, this legal power includes CTCs, even though the School Admissions Code appears not to. References to CTCs may quickly become an historical relic since it is expected most will convert to academy status by 2010.

This section came into force on 8 January 2007.

Information about children receiving publicly-funded education

Section 164: Information about children receiving funded education outside school

This refers to children of compulsory school age receiving education under arrangements made by a local education authority otherwise than at a school, for example in a hospital tuition unit, home tuition, FE college or from institutions that are not formally registered as schools. A new section is added to the EA 1996.

EA 1996, s.537B: Provision of information about children receiving funded education outside school

This mirrors the previous section (s.537A Provision of information about individual pupils) which is the statutory basis for the individual pupil record which feeds individual pupil information into the Annual Schools Census, formerly the Pupil Level Annual Schools Census (PLASC). Prior to the implementation of s.537B, data on children receiving funded education outside school were collected in aggregate form only on 'Form 8b'. Section 537B gives local authorities the statutory basis to collect data at individual pupil level and use the information to return timely and robust data to the DfES for planning and funding purposes. The DfES had planned to introduce this new provision for the 2007–08 financial year although this may be delayed.

This section, along with the new provision in ss.99 and 100 of the CCA 2006 will mean that local authorities will collect individual level information about children participating in all local authority secured provision.

Further education ss.165–166

The two sections under this heading have little in common except that they arise from the increasing expectation of collaboration across institutional and sector boundaries on the 14–19 agenda. The presence of increasing numbers of 14–16 year olds in FE institutions not only makes the formality of collaboration between schools and FE colleges more appropriate; but also perhaps makes it more likely that staff may need to use legitimate force to maintain discipline.

Section 165: Power of members of staff of further education institutions to use force

This parallels s.93 (which applies to schools – see page 122) and enables a member of college staff to use reasonable force to prevent a student from committing an offence, causing personal injury, damaging property or doing something that prejudices discipline. It inserts a new section into the Further and Higher Education Act 1992.

FHEA 1992, s. 85C Power of members of staff to use force

Subsection (1) enables a member of staff to use reasonable force to prevent, or prevent the continuation of:

- an offence being committed (s.85C(1)(a))

- personal injury to the students themselves or others, or damage to property (s. 85C (1)(b))

- anything which prejudices the maintenance of good order and discipline at the college or other institution (s.85C (1)(c)).

Subsection (2) specifies that the power to use force extends only to circumstances where both the member of staff and the student are on the premises of the institution or in other situations where the member of staff is in lawful charge of the students (for example, on a field trip). Subsection (3) makes it clear that subsection (1) does not legitimise corporal punishment. Subsection (4) clarifies that the power provided by subsection (1) is in addition to any other powers that staff may have, e.g. common law rights of self-defence. Subsection (5) defines 'member of staff' as anyone who works at the institution whether or not as its employee.

Section 166: Collaboration arrangements: maintained schools and further education bodies

A regulation making power is created to allow further education institutions to collaborate with each other and with maintained schools. Draft regulations, *The Education (Collaboration Arrangements: Maintained Schools and Further Education Bodies) (England) Regulations 2007,* were issued for consultation on 13 November 2006. They make detailed provision allowing one or more school governing bodies to arrange with one or more further education bodies for their functions to be discharged jointly. Schools and colleges can delegate the exercise of those functions through a

joint committee and the regulations prescribe the establishment, membership and proceedings of such committees, as they go about this form of 'collaboration'.

This parallels the provision of s.26 of EA 2002 which allows schools to collaborate in what is loosely termed a 'soft federation'. These arrangements are straightforward and are, self-evidently, designed to facilitate the promotion of the 14–19 agenda. The DfES intend to implement this new provision in May 2007.

Early years provision ss.167–168

The two sections grouped here make minor adjustments to arrangements for nursery schools which were previously deemed to be directly managed by the LEA, but are now are increasingly being treated like any other maintained school.

Section 167: Consultation with young pupils

Section 176 of EA 2002 introduced a general requirement for LEAs and governing bodies to consult pupils in connection with any decisions that might affect them. Although the requirement is that pupils' views must be considered in the light of their 'age and understanding', pre-school children were, at that time, considered to be too young to be included. That philosophy has now changed and this effectively extends the duty of consultation to cover all children over the age of three. DfES intends to commence this section in September 2007. Interestingly, Schedule 2, paragraph 42, of CCA 2006 amends s.176 of EA 2002 to exclude children aged below Year 1, that is those who are still in early years education, from consultation. It is assumed this earlier change is superseded and will not be commenced.

Section 168: Maintained nursery schools: amendment of sections 496 and 497 of EA 1996

This again adjusts an innovation in EA 2002, requiring nursery schools to have their own governing body. The relevant sections of EA 1996 are further amended to make the governing bodies of nursery schools subject to the possibility of direction by the Secretary of State, or the National Assembly for Wales under ss.496 and 497. Such directions can be made if governors are exercising their powers unreasonably or are failing properly to fulfil their functions. This puts them on an equal footing with other school governing bodies.

Independent schools ss.169–172

EA 2002 introduced new requirements concerning the registration and inspection of independent schools. It set out the circumstances in which unsatisfactory operation of such institutions could be identified and, acted upon; ultimately they could be forced to close by removal of their registration. These arrangements operated in parallel with general child protection arrangements which automatically covered anyone working in such institutions with regular contact with children.

Sections 169 to 172, which occupy some four pages of the Act, are all about extending the rigour of the child protection regime as it applies to people who own or operate private schools. It allows directions to prohibit inappropriate people from involvement with such institutions, even if they do not have direct contact with children. The complexity arises from the need to dovetail with the existing body of law and the variety of agencies involved in this important and sensitive area; coupled with the need to have regard to the human rights of those who might be accused of inappropriate behaviour and thereby prohibited from working. As well as introducing additional requirements with regard to individuals, the managers and proprietors of private schools can also be prosecuted if they connive with offenders or negligently allow them to operate.

Section 169: Prohibition on participation in management of independent school

After s.167 of EA 2002 a new cross heading and four new sections are inserted as follows.

Prohibition on participation in management of Independent schools

EA 2002, s.167A: Prohibition on participation in management of Independent schools

This allows the registration authority for independent schools – the Secretary of State in England and the National Assembly for Wales – to prohibit an unsuitable person from taking part in the management of an independent school. It is also

possible for any other public authority to be 'prescribed' for the exercise of this power which can be varied or revoked after it has been used.

Regulations can prescribe the grounds upon which a person may be deemed unsuitable and the procedures for giving directions and the basis on which anyone subject to direction may seek to have it varied or revoked.

EA 2002, s.167B: Directions under s.167A: appeals

Individuals subject to this procedure have a right of appeal to the Care Standards Tribunal established under s.9 of the Protection of Children Act 1999. Regulations can prescribe the powers available to the Tribunal and the circumstances in which it might allow an appeal. Appeals cannot be entertained, however, if the appellant's case would be inconsistent with previous conviction for an offence.

EA 2002, s.167C: Directions under s.167A: information

This ensures that there is proper provision for the exchange of information between relevant bodies that might be involved in such cases. These include the Secretary of State or the National Assembly in Wales and any authorities that hold information relating to the protection of vulnerable persons under the Protection of Children Act 1999, CSA 2000 and EA 2002. There is also provision for the exchange of information to include the registration authorities for independent schools in England or Wales.

EA 2002, s.167D: Directions under s.167A: notification

Similarly, where directions are made or revoked, all the public bodies with an interest have to be notified.

Section 170: Prohibition on participation in management: supplementary

This extends the impact of the changes to allow the fact of directions having been made against an individual, in certain circumstances, to lead to an independent school being removed from the register.

There is a consequential amendment to s 113BA of the Police Act 1997 to allow information about any directions under the sections to tie in with the work of the Criminal Records Bureau and be included in enhanced criminal record certificates.

The Protection of Children Act 1999 is also amended to allow the Care Standards Tribunal to deal with any appeals arising under these sections.

Section 171: Prohibition on participation in management: transitional provisions

This section provides for investigations or appeals which are under way when these sections come into force, to be concluded under the old arrangements so that those cases do not fail as a result of the changes in statutory provisions.

Section 172: Offences relating to independent schools

This introduces three new sections, in Part 10 of EA 2002 (independent schools) as follows.

EA 2002, s.168A: Proceedings for offences

The consent of the registration authority (the Secretary of State or the National Assembly for Wales) is required before proceedings can be brought against an individual for an offence.

This requirement previously appeared in s.159 of EA 2002. Section 172(3) of E&IA 2006 removes it.

EA 2002, s.168B: Offences by bodies corporate and EA 2002, s.168C: Offences by unincorporated bodies

These two new sections, taken together, provide that where there has been negligence, consent or connivance in the commission of an offence, proceedings can be brought against:

- any individuals who might have been personally involved
- the institution as a collective entity.

Penalties and sanctions can therefore be applied both to the institution and anyone who has personal responsibility; without prejudice to other people who, despite having a managerial role with the institution, may be personally innocent. This applies irrespective of the general position that might otherwise have pertained, which could mean treating unincorporated bodies as if they were a body corporate.

Section 172(4) confirms that this new arrangement does not have retrospective effect for offences committed before the two sections come into force.

Special educational needs ss.173–174

These two sections make changes to the requirement for schools to have a special educational needs coordinator and the time limits, which apply to the making or maintenance of Statements of Special Education Need by local education authorities.

Section 173: Special Educational Needs Coordinators

This section was introduced in response to concerns expressed by the House of Commons Education and Skills Select Committee, which reported on Special Educational Needs on 6 July 2006, about the status and training of SEN coordinators in schools. It is expected this new provision will come into force in September 2007.

The Special Educational Needs Code of Practice 2001, in its description of this role, indicated that it would normally be undertaken by a teacher. Since then, however, as the Government has acknowledged, there has been a huge increase in the number and range of support staff working in schools, whilst this role has become increasingly complex and onerous in a significant number of schools. Section 173 reflects the Government's agreement with the Select Committee that this is a key role for which responsibility should be exercised by a teacher who is a member of the senior leadership team in each school.

The DfES is also committed to developing an accreditation system for SEN coordinators. This is likely to cover such core aspects of the role as implementing SEN policies, securing help for individual pupils from external agencies and specialist knowledge of key aspects of special educational needs. The Government has indicated that it will require all new SEN coordinators to undertake nationally accredited training which will link to a new statement about the key components of the role and the knowledge, skills and experience required of those leading and developing

special needs and disability-related provision in schools. Section 173 gives the Secretary of State the power to make associated Regulations which will cover these concerns.

Section 174: Time limits relating to statements of special educational needs

This Section amends Schedules 26 and 27 of EA 1996 in order to provide the vires in primary legislation for the existing provisions in *The Education (Special Educational Needs) (England) (Consolidation) Regulations 2001*. The new, technical provisions set out in *The Education (Special Educational Needs) (England) (Consolidation) (Amendment) Regulations 2006* (SI 2006/3346), are intended to clarify where necessary what is required in relation to prescribed time limits for LEAs on giving written notice to parents of proposals to amend or cease to maintain a child's Statement of SEN. The Amendment Regulations came into force on 1 March 2007

In responding to concerns set out in the Education and Skills Committee's Report on Special Educational Needs (July 2006), the Government confirmed that parents should be confident that when their child's needs have been the subject of a statutory assessment, any Statement of SEN is issued within a clear and reasonable timescale. The DfES has committed itself to establishing a new Local Authority Performance Indicator of 26 weeks for the production of final Statements which will complement the current indicator for producing proposed Statements within 18 weeks. The Secretary of State has indicated that he takes very seriously any failure to meet the statutory timescales, but has also accepted that there have been significant year on year improvements in local authority performance.

Other miscellaneous provisions ss.175–177

This heading exists to signal the end of the previous group of sections related to special education needs, rather than denote any connections between the remaining three sections in this Part.

Section 175: Miscellaneous amendments relating to Wales and Schedule 17: Miscellaneous amendments relating to Wales

The sole function of this section is to bring Schedule 17 into force. This lists a small number of minor amendments, consequential on the separation of arrangements for England and Wales which, as noted above (see page xii), is a major feature of this legislation.

Section 176: Support schemes relating to education and training for persons aged 10–15

This inserts a new section in LSA 2000, before s.12 under the cross heading 'Other functions' which precedes it, as follows.

LSA 2000, s.11A: Support schemes relating to education and training for persons aged 10–15

This enables the LSC to develop and fund schemes designed for secondary aged pupils. The power is expressed generally but it is intended to cover certain existing schemes as well as providing for new ones to be developed in the future.

In particular, it allows for the LSC to take over full responsibility for the 'Care to Learn' scheme, which gives financial support to teenage parents who want to continue education or training and need help with the cost of childcare. This scheme is currently operated by the LSC for 16–19 year olds but is run directly by DFES for younger people.

It is also envisaged that, as a result of the 14–19 agenda, there will be increasing numbers of students under 16 who are following a mixture of academic education and vocational training and possibly moving across institutional boundaries as a result of increased collaboration. This provision will allow the LSC to fund such activities; for example by supporting transport for those who need to travel to take up appropriate opportunities.

Section 177: University bodies: amendments of s.29 of Leasehold Reform Act 1967

The Leasehold Reform Act 1967 enables tenants of houses held on long leases and low rents to acquire the freehold or on extended lease. Section 29 of that Act allows universities to prevent that happening by imposing restrictive covenants on the grounds that they need to reserve the land for possible future development. This section amends the 1967 Act to remove a previous requirement for institutions to obtain the consent of the Secretary of State or the National Assembly for Wales before exercising this right.

Part 10: General

This final Part of the Act contains standard provisions about the use of the Secretary of State's, and the National Assembly for Wales', powers to make subordinate legislation and general provision on the interpretation, repeals, commencement (that is, when it comes into force) and the geographical extent of the Act's effect.

Section 178: Framework power relating to Wales

The purpose of this section is to give effect of the principles articulated in the government White Paper, *Better Governance for Wales* (Cm 6582), published on 15 June 2005. See page xii. This set out proposals for extending the devolution settlement by allowing the Welsh Assembly maximum discretion in making its own provisions using secondary legislative powers whenever new legislation is made that otherwise would have effect in Wales.

Subsection (1) therefore sets out a long list of matters, largely equating to the content of E&IA 2006, upon which the Assembly may make regulations. This covers:

- categories of maintained schools
- establishment, discontinuance and alteration of maintained schools
- school admissions
- the curriculum in maintained schools
- attendance, discipline and exclusion
- entitlement to education and training and services to encourage, support or assist young people with regards to education and training
- travel of persons receiving education and training
- food and drink provided for children.

Section 179: Restriction on framework power conferred by s.178

This limits the scope of the previous section by making clear that the Assembly cannot:

- make any provision imposing or increasing taxation

- make retrospective regulations

- sub-delegate its power to legislate to any other body

- create new criminal offences (except with regard to school attendance and behaviour and parents' activities in those connections)

- make provisions which extend beyond England and Wales

- make any provision which applies to England without the consent of the Secretary of State.

Section 180: Functions to be exercisable by the National Assembly for Wales

Most of the functions of the Secretary of State under education legislation have, so far as they relate to Wales, been transferred to the National Assembly by order in Council made under s.22 of the Government of Wales Act 1998. The notable exception is teachers' pay and conditions. However, detailed amendments have not always been made to reflect that and therefore some legislation continues to refer to the Secretary of State, even though those references should be read, in relation to Wales, as references to the National Assembly for Wales. This section is a device to ensure that all powers that the Government wishes to transfer to the Assembly are deemed to have been so transferred.

Section 181: Orders and regulations: general provisions

This is a standard provision concerning the making of secondary legislation, orders and regulations, by statutory instrument. This confirms the discretionary power of the Secretary of State to make different provisions for different circumstances or geographical areas, to make provision generally or by reference to specific cases and to make incidental, supplementary transitional or saving provisions by this mechanism.

Section 182: Parliamentary control orders and regulations

The process of issuing statutory instruments has a Parliamentary dimension but it is largely administrative. The regulations contained in the statutory instrument are

'ordered to be printed', become available on the HMSO website and come into force on a specified date when they have met the appropriate Parliamentary requirement. Most statutory instruments therefore contain three dates: when they are 'made', 'laid before Parliament' and 'come into force'. In most cases, this will be as a result of the 'negative resolution procedure' which minimises the extent of Parliamentary scrutiny. Once any such regulation has been laid before Parliament it can only be annulled, if a negative resolution is tabled and achieves a majority in either house of Parliament. This very rarely happens although debates are sometimes held. Commencement orders made under s.188 do not have to be laid before Parliament.

The 'affirmative resolution procedure' is rare, but does allow greater Parliamentary scrutiny because both houses of Parliament are required to record a positive vote in favour before the measure can come into effect. In either case, however, the decision that can be made by MPs or peers is simply to accept or reject the measure. Statutory instruments under E&IA 2006 cannot be amended.

This section confirms that all the statutory instruments containing regulations and orders made by the Secretary of State will be subject to the negative resolution procedure, except for a limited number of sections applying to:

- the designation of a primary school as a rural primary school (ss.15 and 16)
- commencement orders (s.188(3))
- the power to repeal school travel schemes (s.80)
- changing the references to LEA, local education authority or children services authority (s.162)
- regulations under s.183, which amend or repeal other legislation.

The designation of a primary school as a rural primary school and commencement orders are not subject to any direct Parliamentary scrutiny. The other three issues require an affirmative resolution.

Section 183: Power to make consequential and transitional provision, etc.

This gives the Secretary of State a general power to make 'supplementary, incidental, consequential, transitional or saving' provisions that he considers necessary or expedient in consequence of, or to give full effect to, any provisions in the Act.

Where such regulations amend or repeal an Act of Parliament, the statutory instrument containing the regulations must be approved by the affirmative resolution procedure(see s.182 above).

Section 184: Repeals and Schedule 18: Repeals

This section brings into effect Schedule 18, which is a list of previous legislation that is repealed because it is rendered redundant by the new legislation or is a spent enactment.

Section 185: Financial provisions

This is a standard section allowing public money to be spent by Ministers of the Crown as a result of the legislation. Ofsted is specifically mentioned in this section because of its special status as a non-ministerial department of government.

Section 186: Abbreviations of Acts

This confirms the use of the four previous Education Acts most frequently cited, 1996, 2002, 2005 and the School Standards and Framework Act 1998 to be identified by their initials. We have adopted similar conventions in this guide (see p. xviii and the Glossary on p. 189).

Section 187: General interpretation

Another standard section, confirming the interpretation of various terms in a way which is consistent with previous legislation.

Section 188: Commencement

Defines when the provisions of the Act will come into force. These fall into three groups. A small number of sections came into force on enactment, 6 November 2006. These are ss.86 and 87, 109 (except subsection 8) 111, anything in part 8 (inspections), which confers the power to make regulations; 161, 180–183, that part of 184 that activates part 1 of Schedule 16; 185–187 and 189–191.

A second raft of sections came into force two months after the Act was passed (8 January 2007). These are: ss.6, 52, 58, 162, 168, 172, 174, 177–179, Schedule 1 and Part 2 of Schedule 18 and s.184, so far as it relates to that Part.

The remainder of the Act comes into force as a result of commencement orders. There is a degree of discretion in the hands of Ministers to decide when this will happen. DfES have issued a handy chart entitled *Education and Inspections Act 2006: Wall Planner* which is available free from the Department indicating the expected timetable for various aspects of the Act to come into force, including consultation and implementation dates for associated regulations and guidance. Commencement dates from this Wall Planner have been used in this guide.

Section 189: The appropriate authority by whom commencement order is made

This indicates who will be responsible for making commencement orders, which is expressed in detail, but amounts to the Secretary of State for those aspects of the Act which apply to England and the National Assembly as it applies to Wales.

Section 190: Extent

This indicates that for the most part, the Act applies to England and Wales, although as we have seen, much of it has a very limited effect on Wales. However, ss.162, 181, 182 and 185–191 also extend to Scotland and Northern Ireland.

Section 191: Short title

This indicates that the Act should be cited as 'the Education and Inspections Act 2006' and confirms that it should be construed as a single entity with the Education Act 1996, which was the last relevant consolidation Act.

References

Audit Commission (2006). *Higher Standards, Better Schools for All: More Choice for Parents and Pupils* [Department for Education and Skills Consultation Response January 2006) [online]. Available: http://www.audit-commission.gov.uk/Products/ NATIONAL-REPORT/FC8B4B31-C278-4987-8EFA-DA0F2C20A6DB/ ACResponseHigherStandardsBetterSchoolsforAll.pdf [29 March, 2007].

Brettingham, M. (2006). 'Hare Krishna school angers Hindus', *Times Educational Supplement*, **4714**, 8 December, 3.

Communities and Local Government (2004). *Community Cohesion Education Standards for Schools* [online]. Available: http://www.communities.gov.uk/pub/613/ CommunityCohesionEducationStandardsforSchools_id1502613.pdf [5 April, 2007].

Curtis, P. (2005). 'MPs to publish alternative white paper', *Guardian Unlimited*, 14 December [online]. Available: http://education.guardian.co.uk/admissions/story/ 0,,1667203,00.html [29 March, 2007].

Department for Education and Employment (2004). *The Protection of School Playing Fields and Land for Academies* [online]. Available: http://publications.teachernet. gov.uk/eOrderingDownload/1017-2004DOC-EN-01.doc [3 April, 2007].

Department for Education and Skills (2001). *Special Educational Needs Code of Practice* [online]. Available: http://www.teachernet.gov.uk/_doc/3724/SENCodeOf-Practice.pdf [5 April, 2007].

Department for Education and Skills (2005a). *A Single Inspectorate for Children and Learners: the Government's Response to Consultation* [online]. Available: http://www.dfes.gov.uk/consultations/downloadableDocs/SingleInspect4Children.p df [29 March, 2007].

Department for Education and Skills (2005b). *Youth Matters* (Cm 6629). London: The Stationery Office.

Department for Education and Skills (2006a). *Johnson Announces Multi-Million Pound Package to Improve School Food and Fight Childhood Obesity* (DfES Press Notice 2006/0121) [online]. Available: http://www.dfes.gov.uk/pns/DisplayPN.cgi? pn_id=2006_0121 [5 April, 2007].

Department for Education and Skills (2006b). *A Short Guide to the Education and Inspections Act 2006* [online]. Available: http://www.dfes.gov.uk/publications/educationandinspectionsact/docs/Guide%20to%20the%20Education%20and%20Inspections%20Act.pdf [29 March, 2007].

Department for Education and Skills (2006). *Youth Matters: Next Steps. Something to Do, Somewhere to Go, Someone to Talk To* [online]. Available: http://www.dfes.gov.uk/publications [13 March, 2006].

Fowler, J. and Waterman, C. (2004). *Plain Guide to the Education Act 2005*. Slough: NFER.

Fowler, J. and Waterman, C. (2005). *Digest of the Education Act 2005*. Slough: NFER.

Gershon, P. (2004). *Releasing Resources to the Front Line: Independent Review of Public Sector Efficiency* [online]. Available: http://www.hm-treasury.gov.uk/media/B2C/11/efficiency_review120704.pdf [29 March, 2007].

Great Britain. Parliament. House of Commons (2005). *Better Governance for Wales* (Cm 6582). London: The Stationery Office.

Great Britain. Parliament. House of Commons (2005). *Higher Standards, Better Schools for All: More Choice for Parents and Pupils* (Cm. 6677). London: The Stationery Office.

Great Britain. Parliament. House of Commons (2005). *14-19 Education and Skills* (Cm 6476). London: The Stationery Office.

Great Britain. Parliament. House of Commons (2006). *Further Education: Raising Skills, Improving Life Chances* (Cm 6768). London: The Stationery Office.

Great Britain.Parliament.House of Commons.Education and Skills Committee (2006). *Special Educational Needs: Third Report of Session 2005–06. Report, Together with Formal Minutes* (HC 478-1). London: The Stationery Office.

HM Treasury (2003). *Every Child Matters* (Cm. 5860). London: The Stationery Office.

Hampton, P., (2005). *Reducing Administrative Burdens: Effective Inspection and Enforcement* [online]. Available: http://www.hm-treasury.gov.uk/media/A63/EF/bud05hamptonv1.pdf [29 March, 2007].

McAuliffe, A.-M., Linsey, A. and Fowler, J. (2006). *Childcare Act 2006: the Essential Guide*. Slough/London: National Foundation for Educational Research/National Children's Bureau.

Miller, F. and Benn, M. (no date). *A Comprehensive Future: Quality and Equality for all Children*. Compass.

Morris, E., Denham, J., Whitehead, A., Raynsford, N., Chaytor, D., Eagle, A. and Salter, M. (2005). *Shaping the Education Bill: Reaching for Consensus* [online] Available: www.ioe.ac.uk/IS/WebsiteDocs/ShapingtheEducationWPFinalDraft.doc. [2 April, 2007].

Office of Public Services Reform (2003a). *The Government's Policy on Inspection of Public Services* [online]. Available: http://archive.cabinetoffice.gov.uk/opsr/documents/pdf/policy.pdf [4 April, 2007].

Office of Public Services Reform (2003b). *Inspecting for Improvement: Developing a Customer Focused Approach* [online]. Available: http://archive.cabinetoffice.gov.uk/opsr/documents/pdf/inspecting.pdf [4 April, 2007].

Practitioners' Group On School Behaviour and Discipline (2005). *Learning Behaviour: the Report of the Practitioners' Group on School Behaviour and Discipline* (Steer Report). [online]. Available: http://publications.teachernet.gov.uk/eOrdering-Download/STEER-FINAL.pdf [11 April, 2005].

The Sutton Trust (2006). *The Social Composition of Top Comprehensive Schools: Rates of Eligibility for Free School Meals at the 200 Highest Performing Comprehensive Schools* [online]. Available: http://www.suttontrust.com/reports/FreeSchoolMeals.pdf [5 April, 2007].

Whitbourn, S., Morris, R., Parker, A., McDonogh, A., Fowler, J., Mitchell, K. and Poole, K. (2004). *What Is the LEA For? An Analysis of the Functions and Roles of the Local Education Authority*. Slough: EMIE at the NFER.

Glossary

ACC	Association of County Councils
ALI	Adult Learning Inspectorate
APA	Annual Performance Assessment
AWP	Alternative White Paper
CAFCASS	Children and Family Court Advisory and Support Service
CCTA	City college for the technology of the arts
CIECSS	Chief Inspector for Education, Children's Services and Skills
CIO	Charitable Incorporated Organisation
CSCI	Commission for Social Care Inspection
CTC	City Technology College
DfES	Department for Education and Skills
ECM	Every Child Matters
HEFCE	Higher Education Funding Council for England
HMCI	Her Majesty's Chief Inspector of Education, Children's Services and Skills or Her Majesty's Chief Inspector of Schools (if reference is to before 1 April 2007)
HMICA	Her Majesty's Inspectorate of Court Administration
IEB	Interim Executive Board
ILEA	Inner London Education Authority
ISP	Inspection Service Provider
JAR	Joint Area Review
LEA	Local Education Authority
LSC	Learning and Skills Council
NRwS	New Relationship with Schools
OSA	Office of the Schools Adjudicator
PFI	Private Finance Initiative
PRU	Pupil Referral Unit
QIA	Quality and Improvement Agency
RIA	Regulatory Impact Assessment

SIP	School Improvement Partner
SOC	School Organisation Committee
TfL	Transport for London
WAG	Welsh Assembly Government

Acts

ASB 2003	Anti-social Behaviour Act 2003
CA 1989	Children Act 1989
CA 2004	Children Act 2004
CCA 2006	Childcare Act 2006
CSA 2000	Care Standards Act 2000
EA 1996	Education Act 1996
EA 1997	Education Act 1997
EA 2002	Education Act 2002
EA 2005	Education Act 2005
E&IA 2006	Education and Inspections Act 2006
FHEA 1992	Further and Higher Education Act 1992
GoWA	Government of Wales Act
HSC(CHS)A 2003	Health and Social Care (Community Health and Standards) Act 2003
LSA 2000	Learning and Skills Act 2000
SSFA 1998	School Standards and Framework Act 1998

Index

Entries in *italics* denote publications/initiatives.